Principles of Fire Investigation

First published in 1985
by the
Institution of Fire Engineers
148 New Walk, Leicester LE1 7QB
Reprinted 1992, 1995, 1996

Printed in Great Britain by
BPC Wheatons Ltd

The subject of investigating causes of fire may involve professional staff from a wide spectrum, each concerned with their own discipline and with a different viewpoint, but sharing a common objective of accurate definition.

On occasions careful and informed observation will quickly identify the answer but there are many and varied instances where identification is extremely difficult, requiring a long, methodical and patient investigation, introducing scientific analysis and assistance. Sometimes evidence can be totally destroyed or deliberately misleading. 'Principles of Fire Investigation' provides assistance to those concerned with this subject in acquiring a disciplined approach, skills needed for successful fire scene investigation together with practical hints, detailed facts and specialist knowledge, to give specific attention in a clear concise way which not only helps to avoid ambiguity but makes interesting reading. The information presented is born from years of practical experience, real life examples and situations, quoted alongside scientific fact. It is an important and authoritative publication on the subject and will greatly enhance the quality of fire investigation in the United Kingdom.

Sir Peter Darby CBE, C.ST.J., QFSM, FIFire E, CBIM

CONTENTS

Appendices

AUTHORS' NOTE

This book is intended for those whose duties include the investigation of fires, particularly fire officers, police officers and forensic scientists.

Whilst some topics can be dealt with simply, if this book is to have anything more than superficial value, certain aspects of the subject must be covered in more detail. Elementary and more advanced material are therefore included in the text. For this reason it is recommended that although the reader can select sections or individual chapters as his needs dictate, he must not select too narrow a field of knowledge to the exclusion of other material.

Stringent precautions have been taken to ensure accuracy. It is however certain that no two fires behave in exactly the same manner, and it is possible to find particular circumstances in which many normally accepted patterns of behaviour do not apply.

In addition, the science of fire investigation is undergoing a period of rapid expansion and what might be termed an information explosion. Many beliefs commonly accepted in the past have now been superseded and it is important for the investigator to realise that future developments may modify concepts presented in this volume.

The authors are Home Office forensic scientists; it must be emphasised, however, that views expressed in this book are essentially our own and do not necessarily reflect those of the Home Office.

We are pleased to acknowledge the very generous help and encouragement given to us by many colleagues; firemen, policemen, scientists and others, listed below, and in particular we thank our wives Carole Ide and Jacqueline Cooke for their patient assistance in preparing this volume.

R. H. Ide, R. A. Cooke

ACKNOWLEDGEMENTS

Mr S. A. Ames
Mr A. G. Badger
Mr P. A. Barker
Mr K. G. Barnett
Dr R. A. Batten
Mrs P. Beever
Mr A. J. Bolister
Dr R. K. Bramley
Mr G. M. Charlton
Dr P. D. B. Clarke
Mr P. B. Claxton
Mr P. G. W. Cobb
Mr D. A. Collins
Mr R. W. Collins
Dr D. Cooke
Mr M. J. Cooke
Mr G. Cox
Mr S. D. Cupples
Dr A. S. Curry
DCO D. T. Davis
Mr G. Devonport
Mr A. J. Downey
Dr D. D. Drysdale
Dr R. J. Dudley
Mr J. Duke
DCO W. W. Dunlop
DCI G. Dunwoody
CFO T. F. Elton
Dr K. Feenan
Mrs S. Fleet
Mr B. German
DCO H. Haddock
Dr P. W. Hall
SDO R. Hart

Mr D. J. Hanks
Dr T. Hayes
A Fmr G. S. Hibbard
CFO K. Horan
DO L. Howcroft
Mr P. E. H. Ide
Miss W. H. Ide
Mr L. T. Jones
Mrs G. S. Kemp
Mr F. A. S. Lewis
CFO A. N. Lightbody
Dr J. B. F. Lloyd
Mr D. S. Loxley
Dr E. W. Marchant
Mr B. Morgan
DO C. Moseley
Miss M. Pereira
Mr K. N. Palmer
Dr M. A. Payne
Dr B. Rees
Mr B. R. G. Roberts
CFO D. F. Robins
Dr T. Rothwell
DS R. H. Sands
Dr A. W. Scaplehorn
DCI A. Scrafton
Mr P. A. D. Sheen
Mrs M. A. Taylor
Mr C. P. White
DC M. W. Whittaker
Dr N. T. Weston
SO W. T. Winmill
Dr C. Wood
Dr D. Woolley

Principles of Fire Investigation

Chapter 1

Effects of Structures and their Contents

When a fire starts to burn in a building, its early stages may well resemble any bonfire ignited in the open air. Heat is transmitted away from the burning material and the rate of fire growth is largely dependent on the type, quantity and arrangement of the fuel.

Unlike a fire in the open air however, a stage is reached in a building when the surrounding structure exerts its own influence on the fire growth. This could take the form of restricting the amount of air which can feed the flames. Insufficient air will slow down fire growth, or may even cause the fire to go out of its own accord. More frequently however, enough air is present to maintain burning, and the flames radiate heat to surrounding surfaces as well as back to the fuel. Convected heat from hot smoke and gases also helps to raise the temperature in the room. Eventually a point is reached at which all the combustible materials nearby will become hot enough to ignite on their own, and the room will become totally involved in fire. This stage is known as 'flashover', or possibly more correctly as 'flameover'. The former is the more usual term and will be used in this book.

Obviously the time taken to reach this stage depends on many factors. Researchers in fire sciences have examined how the burning materials interact with their surroundings, and many of the results are well established enough to be used in fire prevention planning. They also have definite relevance in fire investigation studies, although the situations found in a real fire will rarely match the controlled conditions of a scientific experiment.

This chapter will look at the behaviour of some of the basic materials which are encountered in fires, and consider their significance to the fire investigator. Other more specialised aspects of fire and fire development will be examined in subsequent chapters.

The contents
Because in most cases a fire in a building starts in the contents, it

3

is more convenient first to examine their fire properties and then to proceed to those of the building itself.

Traditional Furniture

The change in furniture design and manufacture from the mid-1960's, has meant that traditionally held concepts of fire development in any place where soft furniture exists in any quantity have radically changed. It must be remembered that the premises where these can be found are not just homes, but can include hospitals, furniture stores or warehouses.

The traditional type of upholstered furniture was largely made of natural materials, such as leather, woollen or cotton exterior coverings, kapok or feather filled cushions, upholstered chairs comprising coiled springs with coire fibre, animal hair and interlining materials. All these were supported on robust, hardwood frames.

Such furniture is relatively difficult to ignite to flaming combustion although it is well capable of developing smouldering ignition. Smouldering can be induced by the insertion of, say, a glowing cigarette end in the division between the seat and the backrest or arms. If this smouldering is sustained, it can, after a period of perhaps one and a half hours or so, burst into flames. The development of flaming from smouldering combustion is not clearly understood, but may be a combination of the raising of intermediate products of combustion to their spontaneous ignition temperatures and the raising of the temperature of the mass by self-induced ventilation. The geometry of the smouldering material appears to be quite important and experiments have also shown that mass and time of development are interdependent, particularly with fibrous materials. Fires caused by the smouldering ignition of traditional furniture frequently show a distinctive damage pattern, where localised charring caused by the smouldering furniture will develop into a regularly shaped hole in the floor corresponding in size and in shape to the base of the item. The general appearance of the room may also give a clear indication of smouldering ignition with a very slow rate of temperature rise (see Chapter 14).

Apart from the damage patterns to the room, the furniture remains themselves can illustrate the probable mode of fire development. Indications that the furniture was ignited from within or from an externally developing fire can generally be seen by the directional effects of charring.

Considerable care in reconstruction may be necessary before this can be determined. The char patterns themselves (bearing in mind the *caveat* entered into char pattern interpretation in Chapter 7) may give some indication of the slowness of the fire development (see Plate 7I).

An internal development of smouldering in traditional furniture, which involves sustained temperatures of about 600°–650°C, will affect the temper of coiled springs causing them to collapse and flatten. Excessive flattening of springs may indicate sustained smouldering (see Plate 14B). Care must be taken not to confuse this with the normal flattening through wear and tear which can usually be seen in localised positions, for instance, in seat centres. Coiled springs in furniture exposed to fire from an external source, seldom show this de-tempering effect unless the total fire duration is such that the entire piece has disintegrated.

The development of fire in traditional furniture from an applied flame, frequently does not produce persistent flaming ignition. Following the initial flame (even if moderate quantities of a fire accelerant have been used) the burning can either self-extinguish or settle down to a smouldering development. This might, given available time and oxygen within the room then follow a smouldering and back to flaming combustion sequence. Palmer and Taylor[1][2] have demonstrated this in controlled tests.

Modern Furnishings:—Polyurethane Foam

Flexible polyurethane foam which, from an upholsterer's point of view, provides cheap, comfortable and easily produced soft furniture has, from its introduction, been involved in extraordinarily rapidly developing fires which have been frequently responsible for multiple fatalities. This upholstery material is present in virtually every home and in many other occupancies. Many domestic fires which spread beyond the item of origin involve such furniture in some way. Much has been written about it and in its own way it has collected its own folklore.

Disposing of the myths first; the foam will not 'explode' spontaneously, it may smoulder under special conditions but, although it will produce cyanide in the form of HCN when it burns, it does not appear to produce sufficient to be the cause of death[3,4]. It will, however, produce more than enough carbon monoxide in an average fire to achieve this.

5

Currently, in the United Kingdom, the sale of domestic furniture is covered by regulations requiring the customer to be warned if the furniture is capable of being ignited by a small flame source or by a cigarette, an obvious indication of the interrelationships of covering, interlining and foam base. Indeed, the choice of covering is, probably, the most important ignition parameter.[5]

An easily ignitable combination is polypropylene fabric with a polyester interlining on the polyurethane foam. This type of furniture is capable of achieving full flashover conditions in domestic circumstances within four to five minutes of ignition from a small flame source, such as a match. Fire development as rapid as this occurred in the Woolworth's (Manchester) fire in 1979, where stacking of the furniture added to the hazard. Acrylic coverings have been found to propagate flame to a similar extent. Unsupported P.V.C. imitation leather is a particularly bad covering for this type of furniture owing to its properties of shrinking away from the flame and exposing continuously fresh quantities of foam to the advancing flame front.

Materials such as nylon, which can be found as an 'uncut mocquette', can form an intumescent char on the surface which may slow down the flame development to such an extent that the part of the piece of furniture which was first ignited may, on occasions, be noted.

Cotton or other cellulosic coverings can smoulder readily after the application of a flame. Such smouldering generally involves a large surface area and, from this, the large heat transfer to the foam can cause the foam to smoulder, a condition not thought to be possible at one time. Similarly, sustained close contact with an incandescent object, such as an electric fire, can induce smouldering.

It is clear that one of the first things the investigator must do is to find out what sort of furniture was present before the fire, so that the possible ignition characteristics can be reviewed against the general scene observations. With polyurethane foam furnishings this may not be so easy as a fully developed compartment fire may have existed within four or five minutes (or even less) of ignition. Given even normally fast response times of the fire brigade once the fire is reported, it may be twice that time before the fire is extinguished. Scraps of covering may be found in concealed joints on the burnt furniture but, frequently, only the characteristic springs of polyurethane upholstered furniture (see Plate 14C) are all that remain, together with some wood. Under conditions such as these, the radius of error in determining the seat of fire (see Chapter 8, Excavation) may be as large as the room itself and the more lengthy processes of trial excavations will be needed to interpret the pattern of burning.

In the smouldering mode, however, polyurethane foams produce a highly characteristic char which looks like a fragile black froth and which often shows a grainy appearance. While it is normally held that smouldering requires a large area heat source, such as a cotton waste pad or electric radiator, it has been found possible to cause smouldering occasionally directly from a cigarette end.

Unless salvage operations are carried out very carefully in the room where such smouldering has taken place it may not be possible to find traces of the charred foam although one may be able to find the localised internal charring to furniture frames or charring patterns on floor boards, etc., which are characteristic of such origins.

Spontaneous heating to ignition of polyurethane foam slabs may just be possible from radiant heat sources[1] provided that the slabs are greater than 20 cm (8 inches) thick. These are seldom found domestically.

Other Forms of Polyurethane Foam
'Reepol', a multi-coloured, hard compressed foam formed from reclaimed foam cuttings and low density chopped foam used as infill for cushions, pillows, etc., are examples of other furnishing foam applications. These are as flammable as the foam upholstery and could provide the necessary flame source for fires in domestic situations where little fire load from modern furniture exists. Being of a totally combustible nature they may burn away leaving virtually no trace, particularly if the materials on which they were placed also burn extensively. Burning on a floor would generally produce a detectable residual char pattern with, possibly, the remains of the lower surface of the material still recognisable.

Modern Furnishings—Latex Foam
This material, found in some furniture and occasionally in mattresses, is usually cream or grey in colour and exists in slab

7

form pierced by transverse holes about one centimetre in diameter to provide ventilation and to control the resilience. It may be a natural product (polyisoprene) or a synthetic rubber (styrene-butadiene). Either can develop smouldering from a small ignition source, such as a cigarette end, and if ignited directly by a flame, will burn fiercely with much black smoke and high thermal output.

In the smouldering mode, latex foam can produce the so-called 'cold smoke', a white, condensed smoke or vapour probably containing styrene vapour, butadiene and intermediate pyrolysis products. Subsequent ventilation of a compartment containing this 'smoke' and the smouldering latex foam has, in instances, caused explosions[6].

The resultant char from smouldering latex foam is denser than that produced by polyurethane foam and is easily distinguished from it.

Carpets
Horizontal surface spread of flame at floor level has never traditionally been a major form of fire propagation. A standard wool/nylon Wilton or Axminster carpet woven onto a fabric base can resist severe exposure to burning and will not spread fire beyond an immediate area of primary ignition. Even when stored in rolls, either stacked as an upright 'chimney' form or on horizontal roller racks, these carpets contribute little to general fire spread. Of more concern to the fire investigator, however, are the newer designs of synthetic floor coverings comprising acrylic, modacrylic and polypropylene piles generally bonded via a polypropylene 'hessian' type backing onto a foam base. These carpets possess totally different fire characteristics from traditional carpets.

Acrylic and modacrylic rugs
Frequently of 'shag' pile with up to one inch long pile threads, these rugs, if made from acrylic fibres alone or in combination with cotton fibres constitute a high fire hazard when exposed to ignition sources. In one fire it was estimated that horizontal fire development from a point source ignition achieved 40 m² in ten minutes[7]. Current United Kingdom requirements are that modacrylic fibres should be added to reduce the surface spread of flame. Acrylic carpets with less than 50% modacrylic fibres must be

suspected to be capable of potentially high surface spread of flame[8]. Direct ignition of such carpets by dropped cigarettes appears to be improbable. Numerous experiments have failed to produce anything more than a charred scar immediately beneath the cigarette tip.

Polyolefine fibres (polyethylene and polypropylene) are very easily ignitable and can, on their own, support combustion very readily. The major hazard from modern carpets is, however, the latex foam backing which exists on the vast majority of cheaper carpets. Carpets made in this manner, are, particularly if they possess acrylic, cellulosic or polyolefine pile, capable of transmitting flame horizontally from an incandescent or flaming source. Additionally, in a room fire, a laid foam-backed carpet can, with pre-heating, ignite over its whole surface[9]. This may produce an anomalous burning pattern in which the normal appreciably lower temperature at floor level (which enables the plotting of a seat of fire to be tackled by directional signs) to be drastically raised. This creates an inversion of some fire damage patterns and can produce low-level burning *under* chairs, beds, etc., where, normally, protection would exist.

In storage, these carpets are readily ignitable. Reports exist of the ignition of foam backed carpeting in rolls from contact with a naked light bulb. Ignition from a flame is very easy and fire development is extremely rapid. Some preliminary experiments (Rogers 1976)[10] indicate that even, in a sprinklered building, fires in racked carpets may not be controllable unless special measures are taken. The rapidity of flame spread and thermal output of well developed fires in carpet storage areas is likely to present extreme difficulties for the investigator.

Fire Load Density
Fire loading in rooms and compartments is, for practical reasons, expressed as a fire load density of kilogrammes per square metre (kg/m^2) wood equivalent. This enables fires in buildings to be compared with experimental fires. In experimental fires, cribs of wood of varying dimensions are used to establish the relationships between fire load and building geometry. In fires in different occupancies, the materials involved will vary considerably in the heat of combustion available for any given mass. Examples of the varying quantities of heats of combustion can be found in Appendix B2. Of even more importance is the rate at which the

heat of combustion is released; consequently the temperature developed in a compartment will vary according to both the rate of release and the total fire load.

Typical fire load densities for office rooms[11] have been computed at about 20–25 kg/m^2, and for domestic rooms at between the range of 16–22 kg/m^2 whether traditionally furnished or not[4].

The building

As fire progresses from its fuel dependent to its ventilation dependent stage, (e.g. after flashover), different parameters apply to influence its behaviour.

Indeed, whether flashover occurs or not, depends on not only the fire load but on the thermal characteristics of the room. For instance, a room in which the wall and ceiling surfaces can absorb much heat may considerably retard flashover.

A ventilation dependent fire will, at first, burn smokily in many cases, giving a reducing atmosphere. Windows and doors will fail progressively and thus increase the ventilation. This will affect the severity of the fire in two basic ways. One is the relationship known as Law's Law[11,12]. The other, dealt with later, refers to the rate of burning due to ventilation.

Law's law

This is expressed as: $t_f = K \cdot \dfrac{L}{\sqrt{A_w \cdot A_t}}$

where t_f = a measure of the severity of the fire involving the compartment, expressed in minutes of exposure.

    L = The total fire load (in kilogrammes of wood equivalent).

    A_w = Window area (m^2).

    A_t = Sum of the wall and ceiling area, excluding A_w (m^2).

    K = A constant factor determined by experiment and is taken to be approximately unity.

This relationship is used to predict the required fire resistance of a compartment, knowing its probable contents in terms of fire load, and is based on experimental data accumulated from the burning of cribs of wood in rooms with varying geometry of walls and windows. The fire load in this calculation is expressed in kilogrammes of timber, or its equivalent (in terms of heat of combustion) of other combustible fuel. Law's law does not apply to the initial fuel dependent stage of the fire.

Applying Law's law to a room furnished to domestic standards, as indicated above, one could calculate the total fire load of a 3 m by 4 m by 3 m high room to be about 240 kg wood equivalent, and A_t to be 51 m^2. If the windows are 3 m^2, then t_f (the measure of exposure time) is 19.4 minutes.

The significance of this result is that, on average, such a room would need at least twenty minutes fire resistance (calculated to British Standards) to contain the fire. Smoke and toxic products are not considered. Most domestic rooms have doors which have considerably lower fire resistance than this (for example a typical 'egg box' filled flush door may have an actual fire resistance of about 10–15 minutes). It is inevitable that a fully developed fire of this nature will spread beyond the room of origin even if the door is shut.

In reverse, it is possible to estimate the probable initial fire loading of a room after a fire, if one can determine the degree of fire resistance that has been overcome. Thus, a statement by an occupier to the effect that a burnt out room had contained nothing of significance was, in a recent case, successfully challenged. Calculations had suggested that the flammable contents of the room had been at least to domestic furnishing levels of about 20 kg per square metre. The occupier retracted his original statement and admitted storing highly combustible materials (of which very little physical evidence remained) in the room in question.

Ventilation

The rate at which a fire burns, as opposed to its duration, varies, for any particular fuel, as the available ventilation. This is both a function of the area of the window (or whatever aperture is supplying the ventilation) and by its shape. This relationship is expressed as:— R is proportional to $A_w\sqrt{H}$[12].

Where R is the rate of combustion (in abitrary units).

A$_w$ is the area of the window aperture, in square metres.

H is the height of the window, in metres.

In general this would not be used in a quantitative manner by the investigator, a qualitative approach is probably as much as is needed. The implication of the expression is that rates of burning in a room are heavily influenced by the sizes and shapes of windows and doors.

Attempts to utilise this formula in real fires are probably invalid in many cases because the ventilation in an ordinary room will certainly progressively increase as windows fail at certain stages. This is one reason for the 'stepwise' rate of increase in burning rates when ventilation induced flashover conditions are approached. These have frequently been noted by witnesses and occasionally interpreted as 'explosive' fire development.

Taking into account the effects of both fire load density and ventilation, it is obvious that the non-uniform distribution of fuel in a room and the non-uniform ventilation will produce equally non-uniform effects on the structure. Areas of rapid fuel combustion will give higher temperatures and, consequently, higher radiation values. The subsequent damage to the building structure is governed by its intrinsic resistance to fire and heat. Two aspects of this which concern the investigator need to be considered here; fire resistance (defined in the United Kingdom by BSS 476) and the presence of combustible linings.

Fire Resistance

In the United Kingdom, the fire performance of building materials is governed by standards which cover such aspects as, 'Fire Propagation Tests For Materials' (BSS 476 part 6: 1968), 'Surface Spread of Flame' (BSS 476 part 7: 1971) and Specification for Fire Resistance of Elements of Building Construction (BSS 476 part 8:) Similar standards exist in other countries, for example, A.S.T.M. E 119 in the United States of America.

The investigator should be aware of the importance of these tests, demanded for building codes and legislative requirements, and of their limitations where test results are considered against actual fire spread and damage.

Insofar as fire resistance is concerned, certain elements of structure are required to have certain minimum performance standards. The so called 'half-hour door' is a frequently encountered object in commercial properties, where means of escape routes have been regulated. This is a door, more properly designated in the United Kingdom by two numbers (e.g. 20 : 30) which would indicate that, in the furnace for which the fire resistance is tested, the integrity (that is the time at which no flame transmission is possible from one side of the door to the other) is at least twenty minutes, and the stability (that is, the time at which the door physically breaks down) is at least thirty minutes. The reader should study the conditions in the appropriate national standard tests. One very important point is that the quoted values are only consistent for consistent design and are valid only for conditions which parallel the rate of temperature rise in the standard test furnace. This is definitely not to be found in many room fires. For instance, a smouldering fire will have a very much lower rate of temperature rise than a rapid, accelerated arson.

Low fire loads and low ventilation will also have limiting effects on temperature rises. Clearly then, the test rating will never give any adequate method of timing how long it took a fire to penetrate an element of structure, unless the fire is known to have developed in the way the furnace temperature rises. Additionally, the quoted values are generally sequential in half-hour steps (e.g. $\frac{1}{2}$ hour, 1 hour, etc.) so that one finds that the values represent minimum steps provided that the structure is not breached as, for example, a door being left open.

In short, elements of structure of known fire resistances cannot, apart from exceptional circumstances, be relied upon to provide exact times of fire involvement. Used carefully, they may possibly provide some minimum or comparative times of exposure.

Wall and Ceiling Linings

(a) *Plywood, Hardboard and Laminates.* These materials are frequently found as linings covering interior walls and placed onto wooden battens. Unless the battens are arranged so that adequate vertical fire stopping exists, the exposure of these to flame will result in an extremely rapid fire spread which, if extensive use has been made of these, may cause total involvement of the structure. In house fires the extensive use of plywood wall linings has resulted in fire venting through the roof within a few minutes of the original item catching fire. The burning of laminates, particularly wood laminates on blockboard, can also give the misleading appearance of a fine 'crocodiling' effect, believed by some to be associated with rapid ignition (see Chapter 7, Locating Seats of Fire).

(b) *Polystyrene.* It has been known for many years that unusually rapid surface spread of flame has resulted from the ignition of painted polystyrene ceiling tiles. Along corridors the velocity of flame propagation may even exceed that of a running person. Tiles on their own, stuck with the correct adhesive applied over their whole contacting surface, present little problem; exposure to heat causes shrinkage but little flame is developed due to heat being transferred away from the plastic by the substrate. This is an example of the effects of thermal conductivity, density and specific heat capacity described in Chapter 17.

A painted outer surface is, in effect, analogous to a dried, combustible film exposed, on both sides, to flame by virtue of the foam shrinking. The whole surface will rapidly ignite causing burning material to drop down. A fire helped by this mechanism will frequently show rapid and random-seated low-level propagation. A less recognised problem is that of polystyrene wall veneer over which wallpaper is pasted. Surface spread of flame of an extremely rapid nature up walls has been noted in fires, giving an impression of extreme heat over a wall with complete loss of wallpaper. Wallpaper pasted directly to the plaster usually merely carbonises on the wall surface.

(c) *Other Materials.* Imitation wooden panelling or beams made of plastic foam mouldings and found possibly, in 'Mock Tudor' conversions can substantially aid fire development. Prior to the fire these can give the visual impression of solid wood. After a fire they will probably have completely disappeared. The investigator must then make positive steps to check for the existence of such items prior to the fire and then consider what effects they may have had.

Rigid polyurethane ceilings are allowed under current United Kingdom building regulations on the top floors of buildings. Thus, they can be found in first floor bedrooms of some modern houses or as the entire ceiling of a bungalow. They have been found as false ceiling linings in single storey warehouses or even as false ceilings lowering the height of rooms in house conversions. Even with a plaster skim, their fire resistance is negligible and flame penetration can occur almost instantaneously. Some flame propagation may also occur, causing, again, an appearance of random, simultaneous seats of fire. In domestic premises with pitched roofs, the fire development may be completely novel to the investigator used to more traditional houses. A bedroom fire may cause immediate venting from the room into the roof space without any smoke development beyond the room of origin. Deflection of the flame by the pitched roof may then cause re-entry at ceiling level into an adjacent room, thus giving the appearance of two separated fires and strong suspicions of arson. Furthermore, prefabricated roof trusses held together with nail-plates and overlaid by bitumenous felt can, under these circumstances, fail very rapidly[14]. The teeth of the nail-plate (typically about 3 mm long) will rapidly heat up because of the high thermal conductivity of steel. They can then char free from the wood in a very short time.

References

(1) K. N. Palmer and W. Taylor. Fire Hazards of Plastics in Furniture and Furnishings: Ignition Studies. 1974 CP 18/74 BRE.

(2) K. N. Palmer, W. Taylor and K. T. Paul. Fire Hazards of Plastics: Characteristics of the Burning. 1975 CP 3/75 BRE.

(3) R. A. Anderson, I. Thompson, L. R. Calder and W. A. Harland. Elucidation of the Role of Smoke and Toxic Gases in Fatalities Occurring in Fires in Buildings. 1979 DOE Note 44/79.

(4) K. N. Palmer, W. Taylor and K. T. Paul. Fire Hazards of Plastics: Fires in Furnished Rooms. 1976 CP 21/76 BRE.

(5) D. Wooley, S. A. Ames, A. I. Pitt and K. Buckland. The Ignition and Burning of Fabric Covered Foams. 1978 CP 30/78.

(6) D. Wooley and S. A. Ames. The Explosion Risk of Stored Foam Rubber. 1975 CP 36/75 BRE.

(7) Fires in Acrylic Carpeting. Fire Journal 1968 March Vol. 13.

(8) Studies of the Flammability of Carpets. Fire Prevention 122, 14. Fire Prevention Association.

(9) Tu. King-Mon and S. Davis. Flame Spread of Carpet Systems Involved in Room Fires. 1976 United States Department of Commerce.

(10) S. P. Rogers. Preliminary Experimentation on the Sprinkler Protection of Carpets in Storage. Fire Research Note 1061. 1976 Fire Research Station.

(11) M. Law. Relationship Between Fire Grading and Contents. 1971 JFRO Research Note 877/1971.

(12) S. Coward. A Simulation Method for Estimating the Distribution of Fire Severities in Office Rooms. 1975 CP 31/75. Building Research Establishment.

(13) P. H. Thomas. Fires in Model Rooms. 1974 CP 32/74 BRE.

(14) A. Silcock, N. P. Savage and D. Robinson. Fires in Dwellings—An Investigation of Actual Fires. Part 1. 1977 CP 51/77 BRE.

Chapter 2

Effects of Occupancy

In the previous chapter, a generalised view of buildings and their contents was taken. There are, however, many types of occupancy which, because of their peculiarities of structure or contents, present specific points of interest to the fire investigator. Industrial premises have problems of processes, power sources and highly specialised risks, the details of many of which are inappropriate for discussion in this book. The investigator needs to be aware of the many possibilities of causes of fire in, for instance, factories and, in view of the increasing degree of automation, making for less personal supervision of large areas, cannot always rely on accurate eye-witness accounts of a process fire. Institutional buildings such as schools, hospitals, nursing homes, etc., have their own characteristic fire patterns. Some of these will be looked at in this chapter.

Factories
Because of insurance pressures and safety requirements, many industrial properties possess automatic fire protection in the form of sprinklers, other fire-fighting systems or heat or smoke detectors. These can be of great use in estimating the time and location of an outbreak of fire.

Sprinklers
Because of their action in both heat sensing and fire-fighting, sprinklers can give the investigator some indications of the temperatures, position and, of course, the time of the fire. The mode by which they operated can also give some indications of the type of fire.

Sprinkler heads are of two main types, the fusible strut which, on melting, releases water, and the liquid filled bulb which, on reaching a predetermined temperature, bursts to produce the same effect.

There are also 'wet' sprinkler systems, in which the system is charged with water up to the sprinkler heads and 'dry' systems (used where frost may freeze water pipes) in which the water is

16

held back from the risk area until the head operates. 'Wet' systems tend to operate faster than dry ones but the following remarks may be considered general.

The majority of sprinklers operate in the 57–68°C range. Specialised risks, such as those involving high workshop temperature fluctuations, may require higher operating temperatures.

When a sprinkler operates, provided that the system is correctly designed for the risk, an immediate check is put upon fire development. In these cases few heads will operate (perhaps only one or two) and the original area of fire will be obvious. Cases where sprinklers have failed to check a fire, have, on investigation, been found to occur generally because the risk was beyond the design capability. A frequent example of this is when the building has undergone a change of use. The system may also be of an outdated design or the sprinkler may have failed to work correctly. This last can invariably be traced to human agency, the reasons ranging from shutting down the entire system to painting over fusible struts, thus raising the operating temperature. The blocking of a sprinkler head by rust in an old system may well affect one or two heads but should not affect others. The apparent lack of any sprinkler operation warrants a very careful enquiry as to the reason.

In its operation as a heat detector, a sprinkler head has potential in indicating to fair limits the time of origin, bearing in mind the factors which may modify performance. Rogers (1976)[1] indicates from experiments with sprinkler protection of carpet roll storage that with synthetic pile, foam-backed carpeting, which will develop bulk burning fairly quickly and which has a high calorific value sprinkler operation can be expected to start in about three and a half to five minutes after ignition.

Because of thermal lag, a fast fire will achieve a higher local temperature around the head before it operates, than a slow fire. Radiated heat alone may cause slower operation than convected heat. However, a flaming fire beneath a sprinkler head in which the flames actually reach the head can cause operation within about half a minute.

Nash and Young[2] indicate that, within the range of rates of temperature rise found in many fires (from 1°C/min to 100°C/min), there seems to be a limiting time of about four minutes below which, for convected heat alone, sprinkler operation will probably not occur.

As a very rough guide, a room involved in flashover in about six minutes (for example from a plastic foam ignition) may have a rate of temperature rise at ceiling level of more than 100°C per minute. So in fast fires sprinkler operation may occur within about three to four minutes.

Modification of Fire Damage

The designed intention of a sprinkler system is to put the fire out but frequently, due to the stacking of goods etc., protected areas can persist in burning because they do not receive enough water to extinguish them. Fires may thus spread but at a slower rate and via low routes. Even when deliberate fires have been set using petrol, sprinkler operation has slowed down the development and preserved much original evidence. Due to the curtain of water which is produced by an operating sprinkler head, a well defined limit may on occasions be set for the fire damage beyond which lesser burning than might normally be expected for the overall size of fire may exist. A study of the array of activated sprinkler heads against building geometry can be instructive.

Smoke can be entrained by sprinkler water spray which can cause it to be cooler and thus to reach lower levels than in unsprinklered fires. This may cause considerable modification of the smoke record when compared with an unsprinklered fire.

Other Fixed Fire-Fighting Installations

These can be modified forms of sprinklers, including drenchers for walls or external installations, automatic foam discharge devices or total flooding systems utilising carbon dioxide or one of the halogenated hydrocarbons, such as BCF.

These may be heat operated, sometimes several heads being linked to one sensor, and the drenching flow is designed for complete saturation of a specific item of machinery or other object. In these cases the situation will not arise, as with the normal sprinkler system, of merely one or two heads operating; all will simultaneously operate. In other systems the drenchers may be hand operated; their operating time then depends on when action was taken after the fire was discovered.

Total flooding systems may be found in special enclosed risks, such as computer suites or special test rooms. The obvious danger of these systems where, if they operated while a person was inside the area they could produce a fatality, means that they may operate on a 'double shot' system with two detectors linked in series. Only when both operate does the flooding system work. Because no liquids are used the fire damage should be preserved dry and intact giving the investigator a very advantageous situation.

Heat Detectors

These are found more frequently as a rate-of-rise of temperature detector. Maximum limiting temperatures can be preset on these detectors, irrespective of how slow the rise in temperature is. In this way smouldering fires can sometimes be coped with, albeit in a very insensitive manner relative to smoke detectors. Fixed temperature heat detectors may be found in specially protected areas, the operating temperature being adjusted to conditions as, for example, in areas where wide and rapid fluctuations in temperature occur.

The use of heat detectors in fire investigation parallels that of sprinklers. The time of response can be considered against the possible type of burning. So, for example, in a fire which started as a flaming combustion, a correctly installed heat detector can be expected to operate after about one-and-a-half to two minutes.

In one case of a fire in a furniture store, an assistant warehouseman claimed he had been working alone in the fire area for about five to ten minutes before he became aware of the alarm ringing. Immediately after this he claimed he had seen flames 'flash over' from nearby electrical wiring. An examination of the scene showed clearly that a chair had been the original seat of fire and that the initial flame development on spreading to some stacked polyurethane foam upholstered furniture would have been fast. A heat detector was situated in the immediate area. It was obvious that his story was inconsistent with the known performance of the detector and that he must have been in the room when the fire was first ignited. After further questioning he confessed that he had lit the fire in the chair so as to get his name in the papers.

Smoke Detectors

In virtually every fire, smoke is produced in the very early stages, sometimes well before any appreciable heat is developed. Smoke may be produced in copious quantities in fires containing aromatic hydrocarbon fuels, (petrol, polystyrene, etc.), or it may be thin and attenuated as in the early stages of a smouldering cellulosic fire.

There are two basic types of smoke detector; the optical, measuring light scatter or sometimes smoke density and the ionising chamber utilising a small radioactive source. The performance of these differs somewhat regarding the type of smoke to which they are exposed. Smoke from plastics, particularly PVC, may not be detected very easily by the ionising chamber type of detector but the optical type possesses good sensitivity to this. Cellulosic smoke reverses the situation.

The smoke detector may be expected to give fair to excellent pre-flaming response to a smouldering fire, depending somewhat on the initial fuel present and the type of detector.

Further specialised forms of detectors, such as infra-red or ultra-violet 'flame flicker' detectors are usually found only in very specialised open space risks (e.g., aircraft hangers or high cost storage). The performance of these is usually so well tailored to the risk that they should respond rapidly to fire. In at least one case, however, a very serious fire occurred where an infra-red detector had been installed. During the investigation which ensued, sabotage was considered because the detector had not responded. It was found that the installation had been faulty so that the electrical fault which caused the fire had also stopped the detector from functioning or even signalling a fault condition.

Building Modifications

There is a great flexibility in industrial building usage. Firms are formed or go out of business and whole industrial patterns may change. The buildings, in many instances, endure and may eventually be used for purposes quite different from their original design.

There are two basic building modifications which concern the fire investigator. These are (a) when the original building is added to and (b) when the original building use is altered.

(a) *Additions to the Original Building*. Anomalous fire spread patterns can be set up very easily where an interconnecting range of buildings, added to over many years, exists. Such building ranges can have widely varying constructions and may, as in Plate 2A, consist of a single-storey, stone-built, North-light roofed

Plate 2A. Complex roof structures can affect the apparent pattern of burning. Separate seats of fire exist in the foreground and in the background. The roof damage in the middle left has been caused by heat spread along the apex terminating at the gable end. (Photo: Courtesy of West Yorkshire Metropolitan Police).

building opening into a steel-framed, single-span roofed warehouse with, beyond, a further portal-framed area. In such cases preferential fire spread in the North-light roof area may be parallel to the roof lines, whereas in the portal framed area (generally an undivided area) fire spread (according to the contents and their disposition) may be roughly equal in each direction. The resistance to fire of differing sections will vary widely and the collapse of an unprotected light steel-trussed roof in a modern shed may occur within minutes of a fire developing, whereas a wooden joisted warehouse floor may resist collapse for considerably longer.

(b) *Change of Use of Building.* Here, the classical instance is that of the large textile mill which, having out-lived its original function, has been converted into multi-occupancy storage or light industry. Two points should be remembered. The first is that years of textile or other industrial use may have effectively

21

saturated areas of the floor with oils making them highly combustible. Ambiguous burning patterns may well be observed as a result of this. The second point is that internal modifications, possibly breaching originally fire resistant partitions, may have taken place. Frequently these premises were originally sprinklered (the sprinkler system was developed specifically because of fire hazards in cotton mills). Generally in 're-used' buildings, particularly multi-occupancies, such sprinklers are inoperative or, at the best, just not maintained. Thus, the remains of a sprinkler system in a fire damaged room does not necessarily mean that any effective sprinkler control of the fire was possible.

Chemical Works
Large chemical manufacturing complexes present many problems in identifying the cause of fire, and the investigator must work very closely with a responsible works chemist or engineer. Many chemical problems only show themselves in the manufacturing scale, pilot plants failing to reveal a fundamental hazard. Further, the interaction of plant design and the chemical reactions required for the manufacturing process may be at the limits of the available technology. An example of this is the recently recognised hydrogen and magnesium embrittlement of stainless steel at high temperatures and various types of corrosion of reaction vessels by by-products of the main reactions.

Much chemical plant is constantly monitored, particularly in petro-chemical complexes and deviations from normal process conditions should be detectable and recorded before problems arise. There are some basic factors to consider in the investigation of fires or explosions in these industries which may lead to problems of identification of the cause.

(a) *Runaway Reactions.* Uncontrolled reactions as a result of process failures will generally affect one specific reaction vessel or production line. However, catastrophic failure of one section may physically affect other parts of the plant causing separate fires, or may, by affecting control circuitry, cause 'knock-on' effects in further remote plant. The investigator may be faced with numerous damaged sites all interlinked and will have to decide on the sequence of failure. Most plant of this type will possess flow charts. These will be invaluable as a first step in applying elimination logic.

22

(b) *Lagging Fires.* Pipelines carrying hot liquid or vapours will generally be lagged to reduce heat losses. The leakage of oils or other flammable liquids onto the hot lagging can cause ignition of these flammable contaminants at much lower temperatures than the standard accepted spontaneous ignition temperatures. These ignition temperatures are also dependent on the lagging thickness and, to a lesser extent, on the materials used[3]

EFFECT OF LAGGING ON LOW VISCOSITY TRANSFORMER OIL[3]

Lagging material	Thickness (cm)	Ignition temperature
Mineral wool (resin bonded)	5.1	212–218°C
Asbestos	5.1	187–195°C
Calcium silicate	2.54	ca 222°C

The values quoted above are specimen results only. The complexities of a system involving pipe temperature, lagging thickness and characteristics of oil contamination makes it virtually impossible to predict whether or not spontaneous ignition will occur. Observations at the scene of hot spots burnt within the lagging should be checked by experiment.

(c) *Effects of Scale.* As has already been mentioned, reactions on the industrial production scale may not proceed at the same rate or in the same controlled manner as in a laboratory or pilot experiment. Examples which have occurred include the spontaneous ignition of large piles of oxidisable materials which were innocuous in small quantities and the behaviour of large, unconfined, vapour cloud ignitions which in theory would not so much detonate as deflagrate.

The investigator is then faced with the problem of proving an assertion which may involve re-running the plant or, possibly, a section of the plant at full size and capacity in the hope that it will fail again. This was done in the investigation into the Flixborough disaster to demonstrate that unsupported double 'concertina' type expansion joints could 'squirm' and rupture. Such experiments carry obvious risks and before committing oneself to the high financial outlay that this approach demands it must be certain that it is the key to the investigation.

(d) *Inefficient Processes*. Many processes, particularly those involving continuous flow, have a low inherent efficiency. Process control could also be ineffective. Reactants may not be used up or products may not be as pure as theory suggests. This possibility may give rise to unexpected reactions in a supposedly pure and perhaps harmless substance.

In one case, a powder tanker discharged its load of powdered calcium hydroxide (not considered to be a fire risk). When the tank was empty, the driver forced the delivery valve to close it and was killed when the valve and rear of the tank blew out in a violent explosion.

An investigation revealed that the calcium hydroxide was actually 'carbide sludge'—the waste product of acetylene production from wet calcium carbide—and that plant inefficiency had allowed free calcium carbide, which was evolving acetylene gas, into the tanker. Acetylene and air mixtures are explosive under wide ranges of concentration and are extremely spark and shock sensitive. The delivery valve had been jammed by metal fragments and had undoubtedly sparked.

Altered conditions in a process may yield unexpected results as seen in another case in which a food product was being ground under cryogenic conditions using liquid nitrogen (boiling point $-195.8°C$). Due to an 'improvement' in the process the nitrogen boiled off leaving the organic material still below the boiling point of oxygen ($-183°C$). Atmospheric oxygen condensed onto it and the friction of grinding caused a violent explosion which killed two men.

When a reaction is incomplete in a continuous process the reactants may be recycled after the successive separation of products. The analysis of materials from the scene may reveal the section first involved by the relative proportions of the reactants and the products. In the Flixborough explosion, the relative proportions of cyclohexane and cyclohexanone (the product) in the lungs of one of the deceased indicated that he had inhaled escaped vapour from one particular part of the process before the explosion must have occurred.

Hospitals and Residential Homes

Relatively few fires grow to any large size in hospitals in the United Kingdom because of the general day and night supervision which exists and the presence of smoke or heat detectors. The potential life risk which exists in all residential institutional classes of buildings means that there will be considerable pressure on the management and staff to investigate all fires exhaustively, even small ones such as those in waste bins.

Bearing in mind these situations, most fires will present little problem of locating the seat or determining the time of origin but, because of their frequently very small nature and the urgency of removing debris from, say sterile areas by hospital staff the actual igniting agent may be hard to determine.

In mental hospitals or old persons wards direct ignition of bedding is a frequent occurrence. Some of this is 'deliberate'—if people in such wards can be said to possess any true intent— much is due to carelessness in using smoking materials.

Two main factors affect the investigator's approach to determine the cause of a fire in a hospital.

(a) *Witnesses*. Patients who are sedated, geriatric or mentally unbalanced naturally do not make the best witnesses. Frequently those patients, who, by their behaviour, may well constitute the greatest fire hazard will be kept in one group and by force of circumstance may be given only superficial supervision by one overworked nurse. The nursing staff who may, if they witness the outbreak, be able to provide a rational and accurate account, will most likely be more concerned with evacuation and saving life.

(b) *Accurate Timing*. This can be achieved in many cases. The presence of people will ensure a rapid response and, where detectors are installed, these may actuate shortly afterwards. In many instances, though, the fire may be put out before the detector raises the alarm. Most hospital fire routines ensure an automatic call to the Fire Brigade or a fire alarm call point, in which case the time will be logged.

Schools

There is hardly a typical school. Buildings may vary from small 19th century (or earlier) brick-built single-storey structures via ranges of buildings encompassing all periods, including portable classrooms to modern, flat-roofed comprehensive schools capable of housing possibly 2,000 pupils.

In recent years schools have predominated in the statistics of malicious fires of public buildings and, as a cause of fire when that fire has been discovered burning in the early hours of the morning, arson may well be uppermost in the investigators mind.

(a) *Open Spaces*. Most modern schools have large central halls in which flashover may be difficult to achieve even when high fire loads are combined with lengthy burning periods. Many of these open spaces are multi-purpose, however, combining staging, seating, curtains, etc., so that the total fire load density may be considerable and continuous fuel beds may permit wide-ranging surface burning.

(b) *Contents*. Apart from the usual desks, books and general cellulosic fire risks most schools now provide stacking chairs for concerts, meetings and other extra-mural use. These may be polypropylene shells mounted on a steel framework. When stacked, these chairs are easily ignited by a small flame and will burn with a very high calorific output with much molten plastic burning at floor level. It can be difficult to decide whether such a burnt stack of chairs constitutes an original seat of fire.

(c) *Roofs*. In common with many modern, flat roofed buildings schools may be equipped with flat, open-trussed roofs with a suspended under-ceiling or a similar equivalent. Two features of these are (i) that there is frequently a bitumenised coating on the upper surface and (ii) there is often no fire barrier inside the open roof void. The fire performance of these roofs is generally poor, and once a fire in a room has penetrated into the roof void, considerable lateral spread commences. This, because of the low fire resistance of the roof-trusses causes fire both to drop into rooms remote from the original seat of fire and allows entire sections of roof to collapse over the original fire making excavation very difficult. The bitumenous covering burns very fiercely and can cause cascading liquid fires to pour down in areas remote from the original source. The result can be a fire with apparently numerous seats even when the cause was accidental.

The fire performance of a series of modern school buildings has been well analysed by Silcock and Tucker[4].

Ship Fires

Although ships and boats form a very individual subject with respect to their fire prevention and fire fighting difficulties,[5] they are in their own way a specialised form of building.

26

Wooden hulled and wooden decked ships will not be discussed because frequently a well developed fire in them will cause a total burnout above the waterline or deck area in which determination of the cause and origin of the fire by physical means is virtually impossible.

The usual commercial ship is steel hulled and multi-compartmented and for the purposes of fire investigation, represents a three dimensional structure in which fire propagation is considerably aided by conduction across metal bulkheads whereas ventilation, when compared with a conventional building will frequently be very limited.

Consequently, fires in ships frequently fail to show the rapid, intense fire development found in, say, a domestic living room; neither do they always present a clear-cut seat location when a smouldering fire has occurred because of heat transmission to opposite faces of metal partitions.

The following are some basic points concerning ship fire investigation, the full expansion of which is beyond the scope of this book. Particular specialist problems exist when different types of vessels are considered; for example, container ships have considerably different aspects from bulk carriers or mixed cargo vessels, and tankers are totally different from passenger ships, although parts, such as crews quarters, may parallel each other.

(a) *Duration of Fire*. If a ship has caught fire at sea the total duration of fire, particularly if it is a cargo hold fire, may be days or even weeks. Clearly, such fires are never properly ventilated in the same sense as fires can be in buildings and holds may have been partly or even wholly flooded during the period. The general fire damage will bear little resemblance to a building fire. Temperature gradients may be impossible to detect because of the 'oven' effect of a long lasting, closely confined fire. The flooding of a hold will frequently cause dislodgement of the cargo so the general aids to locating the seat of fire may not be applicable.

In compensation for this, heat effects on metal partitions and the bulk-heads may be very apparent. Consequently, the ships manifest showing the position of the cargo can be of great importance.

(b) *Heat Transmission*. The high coefficient of thermal conductivity of bulkheads means that fire can be propagated on

27

the opposite face to the original fire. Multiple apparent seats of fire may then be seen. Protracted fire fighting may cause loss of fine detail which can make the problem of establishing the progression or the sequence of fire spread rather difficult.

(c) *Combustible Linings.* Ships usually have linings to cover the metalwork below decks particularly if they operate in cold waters. Examples of this may be found in rigid polyurethane foam thermal insulation found in some fishing boats or freezer ships.

Surface spread of flame upwards via companionways and deck hatches can be extremely rapid and, as is usual in vertical fire orientations, an opportunity exists for fire to drop as well as rise. The true seat of fire may then not be at the lowest point of burning.

(d) *Ducts.* Fire spread by ventilation ducts can 'leapfrog' decks or cabins and can simulate multiple seats. Care is needed to trace the possible pathways of fire spread by these routes.

(e) *Wind Effects.* On open decks and, possibly, on lower decks fire and smoke-spread patterns will normally be biased towards the stern if the ship is under way for a major part of the burning stage of a fire. This may provide additional information to the investigator if an exact point is in dispute. Owing to the protracted nature of many ship fires, if the vessel is not kept head to wind and way is lost these patterns may become misleading.

(f) *Housekeeping.* A well managed ship, particularly if she is carrying a hazardous cargo (such as bulk fuel) will have critical areas clean and free from unnecessary materials. Shaft tunnels, paint lockers and similar areas may well be used for casual storage of many materials, some of which may not be acknowledged by the crew in the investigation. Much patience will be needed to trace these if they are thought to be significant, particularly if a language difficulty exists.

Most ships are diesel engined and will carry numerous containers of the fuel for purposes other than propulsion. Smells of supposed accelerants will probably abound and the presence of fuels will be almost inevitable. Certainly, the current sensitivity of hydrocarbon detection means that positive results in a chemical analysis will be almost automatic. The investigator must rely heavily on fire seat detection logic using patterns of burning.

(g) *Fire Detection and Fire Fighting Systems.* Continual monitoring of holds, engine rooms and cabins is generally practiced in ships. The form of monitoring may be smoke detection by tubes sampling air and transmitting it to a central detection unit (probably on the bridge). In passenger ships individual smoke detectors can be found in each cabin. In these cases relatively early indications of fire should be possible. Within holds it may, however, not be possible to act effectively because of the disposition of the contents.

Fire fighting systems are built into most ships and vary from auxiliary engine driven deck hydrants through carbon dioxide injection to inert gas generators (usually a diesel engine exhaust gas).

The quantity of inert gas carried is theoretically calculated to treat a hold containing cargo and even if it fails to extinguish the fire will at least quieten it down. Water (provided its use will not be commercially disastrous) may be used to make certain the fire is controlled thus leading to the problems set out above.

References

(1) S. P. Rogers. F.R.N. 1061. 1976 Fire Research Station.
(2) P. Nash and R. A. Young. Performance of the Sprinkler in Detecting Fire. CP 29/75. 1975 Building Research Establishment.
(3) P. C. Bowes. Fires in Oil Soaked Lagging. CP 35/74. 1974 Building Research Establishment.
(4) A. Silcock and D. M. Tucker. Fires in Schools. An Investigation of Actual Fire Development. CP 4/76. 1976 Building Research Establishment.
(5) F. Rushbrook. Fire Aboard!

Chapter 3

Effects of Fire Fighting

Little has been written on the effect that fire fighting can have upon the final appearance of the burnt structure. Fire fighting must necessarily be intrepid, and in order to save as much of the building as possible, doors, windows and other items may be deliberately damaged. In some instances it would be true to say that the fire fighting measures had as much effect on the final appearance of the building as the fire itself. Since the fire investigator is seeking to reconstruct the early events in the fire, he should understand not only the principles of fire spread, but also the common techniques of fire fighting.

First aid fire fighting
In the minutes which will precede the arrival of the Fire Brigade, neighbours and passers-by may attempt to rescue trapped occupants and to extinguish the fire. Such amateur fire fighters often show extreme courage but seldom have any knowledge of fire fighting. If, as is sometimes the case, would-be rescuers are not traced after the fire, it will be difficult to establish whether damaged doors or windows were forced by them or by an arsonist. However, there are likely to be many eye witnesses who will express opinions as to which doors were forced and what fire fighting measures were used. Their evidence should be treated with caution since they are likely to have been excited and confused.

The normal behaviour of a person who discovers a fire, whether he is an occupant or a passer-by, is to raise the alarm, rescue trapped persons and to attempt to extinguish the flames. The two latter actions may require that doors or windows must be forced. Since amateur fire fighters are not equipped or trained to force entry into buildings, they commonly force doors by body pressure and break windows with their bare hands. Many would-be rescuers enter the building standing upright and are quickly forced back by the heat and smoke. In some cases rescuers and escaping occupants run through flames and suffer terrible burns. Under these circumstances the burnt person may attempt to extinguish the flames with towels, curtains or similar items, or may tear off and scatter his burning clothing.

Such behaviour, together with the moving of burning items of furniture, may result in apparent multiple seats of fire. It is particularly common to find burnt fabric in a kitchen or bathroom totally separated from the main seat of a fatal fire.

Other evidence of fire fighting attempts may be the presence of a container such as a saucepan near to the seat of the fire. In industrial fires, discharged fire extinguishers and unwound hose reels may tell the same story.

Amateur fire fighting attempts are normally made by the legitimate occupants of a building or by well intentioned passers-by, but it is by no means uncommon for the arsonist himself to attempt to extinguish a fire which he had just ignited.

Brigade fire fighting

The delay period before the arrival of the first fire appliance will normally be in the region of a few minutes, except in some rural areas where the fire stations must necessarily be more separated.

On arrival, the first priority of the firemen will be the rescue of any persons trapped in the building. The majority of the available resources will be dedicated to this end, even if it means that the unoccupied part of the building will suffer more fire damage.

Forcing entry

Anyone who has observed the rate of development of a fire in a room will understand that a delay of seconds may make a considerable difference to the size of the fire. For this reason firemen force entry in the quickest manner consistent with safety. A damaged door is of little consequence compared with the value of the whole building or a human life.

Doors

Fire Brigade recommended methods of effecting entry through locked doors include kicking out the bottom panel, hitting the door beneath the lock with a large axe and levering it with crowbars.[1]

Forcing a door by body pressure (a technique favoured by criminals) is not recommended because of the danger that the fireman may overbalance into the burning room. However, it is evident that some firemen use this technique.

31

In general, the Fire Brigade use fast but normally noisy techniques to break doors, whilst criminal intruders often use quiet and probably slower methods.

If the door is forced in an area affected by smoke, the broken surfaces will indicate whether the door was forced before or after the fire. Clean broken surfaces on an otherwise smoke-stained door, indicate that this damage was caused by the Fire Brigade. Smoke-stained broken surfaces may indicate that the damage occurred prior to the fire.

Locks

Both the Fire Service and the criminal fraternity recognise that locks can be weak links in the security of a building.

Recommended Fire Brigade techniques include:—

(a) Forcing the bolt of a mortice lock out of the lock plate using a heavy wedge and a large axe.

(b) Cutting out the portion of the door which includes the lock.

(c) Cutting a hole near to the lock so that a hand can be inserted to turn a key left on the inside of the door.

(d) Cutting through the lock bolt with a hacksaw.

Padlocks

Many fire appliances carry bolt cutters which can be used to cut the hasps of padlocks. Other techniques include twisting the lock from its staple using the point of a fireman's axe.

Windows

Many criminals enter buildings by breaking windows. In general, criminals normally break ground floor windows, reach through the broken glass and release the catch to open the window. Most criminals are extremely reluctant to climb through the broken window pane.

The Manual of Firemanship recommends breaking windows as a cheap and quick method of forcing entry into a burning building. Since speed rather than silence is the overiding consideration in fire fighting, firemen may smash all of the glass from a window and enter through the frame. However, many operational firemen prefer to force doors rather than break windows because of such considerations as the handling of hoses, difficulty of entry in bulky breathing apparatus sets and ease of retreat in an emergency. From a logistics point of view also, doors have an advantage in that they normally give access to thoroughfares in buildings whilst windows normally give access only to rooms.

Fire fighting
There is no one standard method of fighting fires, and decisions made on the fire ground by the officer in command will take into account the particular circumstances prevailing. However, in most present day fires, considerable volumes of toxic smoke are normally encountered. For this reason it is likely that the first firemen to enter a smoke-logged building will be wearing breathing apparatus (B.A.). It is difficult to see much detail in a smoke filled room, but when wearing B.A. visibility is further impaired. Firemen in B.A. are trained to feel their way around the walls of rooms using the backs of their hands. They may have to pay out life lines in order to find their way back and they must remain with their partner. Heavily encumbered with B.A. sets, blinded by smoke, partially deafened by the hiss of compressed gas, unfamiliar with the building that they are searching, firemen have been known to climb into wardrobes thinking that they were entering another room. Under such difficult conditions firemen search for the seat of the fire, guided mainly by the radiated heat.

It is not surprising that the first firemen to enter a burning building may not be able to give detailed information about the positions of doors and the exact location of the seat of the fire. The first firemen to enter the building are likely to be carrying a hose reel and they will be directing this at what they believe to be the seat of the fire. As more men and equipment become available to the officer in charge, he will deploy them in such a way as to prevent the fire from spreading to undamaged parts of the building.

When water hits hot material at the seat of the fire, it is converted to steam, absorbing heat in the process. Water which is entirely converted to steam is being used in the most effective way to absorb the heat of the fire. However, when water is converted to steam, it undergoes a sudden considerable increase in volume (about 1300 times). This sudden expansion can have the effect of forcing the fire to travel in the direction away from the jets. Clearly, if the fire fighting is carried out in an ill-considered manner, far from decreasing the damage, the fire spread may be

Plate 3A.   A fireman in breathing apparatus at the entrance to a smoke-filled room.

*   In fires involving modern synthetic materials, visibility inside the building may be so limited that firemen must rely almost entirely upon their sense of touch. Photograph courtesy The County Fire Officer Cheshire Fire Brigade.*

34

greater. A resolute man with a jet can drive a fire all around a building, causing untold damage.

From the point of view of the subsequent investigation, one of the features of particular interest is the effect of fire fighting jets on furniture and light items in the building. Items can be knocked over and displaced considerable distances across the room. Even hose reel jets can have this effect, but the greatest disturbance will be caused by jets from branches and from monitors. Fire debris may also be displaced and may for example be found underneath unburnt carpets and behind undamaged skirting boards.

Fire fighting jets also crack and break windows, and strip heated plaster from walls. If the main fuse has not already failed, then it is likely to blow directly water reaches exposed conductors. Damage caused in these ways may be of value in reconstructing the events during the fire, and establishing how the fire had been fought. (see Chapter 9, Deductive evidence at fire scenes).

Venting
It is normally the practice during fire fighting to ventilate the building to remove the smoke. This procedure increases the chance of survival of any trapped person, reduces smoke damage and improves visibility, thus greatly enhancing the efficiency of fire fighting measures.

When the decision is made to ventilate, doors and windows may be opened in various parts of the building. For certain aerodynamic considerations, more openings are required at a high than at a low level. Windows are opened by B.A. men from inside the building when possible, but it may often be necessary for the windows to be broken. The windows are sometimes broken from inside by the B.A. men or they may be broken from the outside by the use of jets of water. In either case windows broken for this reason can normally be distinguished from windows broken prior to the fire by criminals.

Regions last extinguished
Certain parts of the building are likely to be less accessible to fire fighters than others. These regions will be extinguished last and will consequently burn for a longer period than most of the other parts of the building. It may also happen that all fire fighting efforts are being directed towards a more worthwhile goal, such as the saving of life or protection of an undamaged or valuable part

of the building.

If the sequence of fire fighting operations is not taken into account when the fire is investigated, these regions last extinguished may be thought incorrectly, to have been the original seats of fire.

When the main fire has been extinguished, certain regions of smouldering may remain. These 'bull's eyes' can also give the appearance of seats of fire and should be taken into consideration. Smouldering 'bull's eyes' in structural timbers produce characteristic deep hollows in the charred timber.

Turning over debris

It is clearly important for fire fighters to ensure that the fire has been completely extinguished. Pockets of burning may remain beneath piles of debris, and in spaces above ceilings and behind panelling. It is therefore normal policy for fire fighters to move anything which could conceal a pocket of burning. Ceilings and panels are torn down until an area is reached where it is evident that there can be no more burning material concealed. Debris is turned over to establish whether any burning material remains. Clearly there is little danger of pockets of burning under shallow layers of sodden debris, but at large fire scenes where debris may lie in heaps several feet deep, the danger is greater.

Debris may also be removed completely from the building. Much evidence can be lost by the indiscriminate disturbance of debris, but it is possible for debris to be turned over in a restrained manner which causes little evidence of value to be lost. In particular, the debris at the seat of the fire will provide most evidence regarding the cause. The bottom few inches of debris are likely to include the remains of the material or items which first ignited.

Other places where smouldering may continue after the extinguishment of the main fire, are amidst the contents of cupboards and drawers. Metal filing cabinets remain intact during the fire but their contents often ignite. Firemen must therefore force the drawers open to extinguish the contents. In a subsequent investigation, it may be necessary to establish whether the drawers had been forced before the fire or afterwards. Drawers forced by criminals are often left open and it may be possible to establish, from the smoke staining or characteristic heat distortion, whether the drawers had been open throughout the fire.

Sprinklers
Many industrial premises are fitted with sprinklers. These operate when fires occur and frequently extinguish or at least control the fire, preventing it from spreading.

Fires extinguished by sprinklers are normally simple to investigate and can provide useful background information into the causes of a sample of fires. Even in the rare event when a fire is not controlled by the sprinklers, information may be available from the sequence of operation of the sprinkler systems which may give some indication where the fire started.

Information from fire crews
It is evident that much information of importance to the investigation may depend upon the observation and actions of the firemen who actually fought the fire. The whole investigation is in fact, likely to have been initiated because of the suspicions of the first officer to arrive. Although the officer in charge of the attendance at a fire will have much to occupy his mind, it is desirable that he should consider any factors or observations likely to give an indication as to the cause of the fire. In any subsequent investigation the following information is likely to be required from members of the fire crew:—

1 What had been the time of the call, the time of attendance and the time that the fire was brought under control?
2 Had the premises been secure at the time of arrival?
3 What had been the apparent location of the seat or seats of fire on arrival?
4 Had there been any abnormalities in the behaviour of the fire?
5 Had there been any abnormalities in the behaviour of any witnesses?
6 What had been the original positions of any items moved during the fire fighting?
7 In what order had the different regions of the premises been extinguished?

Even when the cause of the fire is apparently obvious, it is important for the officer in charge of the fire fighting team to keep an open mind and to consider all possible causes.

Reference
(1) Manual of Firemanship, Book 11, Part 2.

Chapter 4

Management of Fire Investigation

It is obvious that fires should, in some way or other, be investigated. The causes of fires will need to be known for the determination of liability and for the development of future fire prevention policies. The reasons for fire growth and development will need to be sought so that fire protection policies can be reviewed and their effectiveness measured. Furthermore, compilation of the methods by which the fire was discovered, notified, fought and extinguished will suggest policies aimed to reduce fire loss and to protect life and property. These, and other aspects are discussed in Chapter 6, Information Gathering.

The primary objective of this book is to suggest techniques for the effective investigation of the causes of fires but it is clear that other considerations, such as those listed above, should be capable of being examined confidently.

Few fires can be investigated totally by one person alone; team work of some sort should exist and, as is the case in the United Kingdom, when no statutory duty for fire investigation in general is laid upon any particular authority, the maintenance of a team competent to carry out this function presents difficulties. Fire presents a complex set of interdisciplinary problems ranging from the science and technology of the scene through laboratory testing to legal aspects of liability. The management of an investigation, covering all of these aspects tends to cut across established police or fire service practices.

In the analysis of an accidental fire, the investigator may well find himself working alone unless the incident was noteworthy by reason of size or value. Some point will arise when his results will be subject to scrutiny, as, for example, when insurance interests seek to establish liability. Here the fire service officer may find himself working with, or providing information to a private investigator. Thus, no less than in an arson investigation, is the correct approach needed to get the best of results.

The main problem is to identify when more resources than are available to the first-line investigating officer are needed to establish the correct cause of fire.

From the initial reporting and extinguishing of a fire, the investigation process in the United Kingdom has, in the past, proceeded largely in the following way.

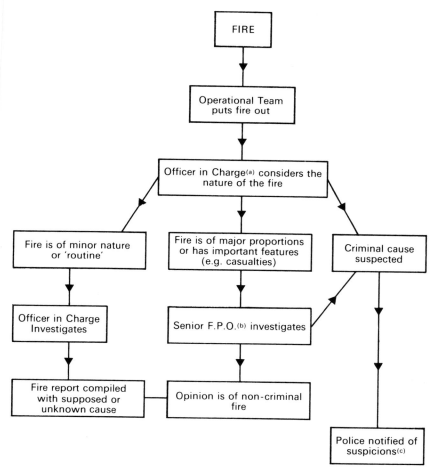

Notes
(a) Officer in Charge may be a Sub-Officer with no training and little experience of fire investigation.
(b) Senior Officer may not have direct knowledge of the operational fire fighting involved.
(c) Police may be informed of suspicions but may not receive a statement of evidence.

Figure 4.1. Communication Pathways.

What can be seen is that this system of investigation is 'response' orientated, i.e., a large, important fire is likely to receive the most attention. Indeed, where standing orders exist for fire brigade investigation, secondary, senior officer investigation will, most likely, be required for fires of over a particular set value of loss, fires involving more than a specific number of fire appliances, or fires involving, say, brigade personnel injury or civilian deaths. Thus, the 'important' fires receive the most investigatory effort. It must be said, however, that as most fires have accidental causes recorded, such 'in-house' organisation maintains the fire service involvement in fire investigation.

In North America, Fire Marshals may act in the dual roles of inspecting fire prevention officers, and fire investigating, law enforcement officers. Their existence is due to the fragmented and voluntary nature of fire departments in rural communities where local expertise in fire prevention and fire investigation may be uncertain. Drawn from the police forces and being experienced law enforcement officers, they possess powers of arrest and interrogation and receive technical training in fire sciences. Compared with their British counterparts they would seem to have a distinct advantage in that they can control an investigation from the technical and interview side, can subpoena witnesses and can initiate an investigation on their own behalf. It is hard to measure their efficiency in actual problem solving or arson detection, but the existence of an agency holding a defined responsibility would seem to be desirable if fires are to be investigated properly. However, there is evidence to suggest that their response to fires is orientated in a manner very closely related to that in the United Kingdom, so that important fires (by public and press standards) tend to receive more than their fair share of attention. In areas such as New York City, the problem of arson is so great that Fire Marshals may actually act as 'Arson Control' Officers.

In the United Kingdom, the lack of any one organisation having a statutory duty to investigate fires *per se*, (not suspected arson, which becomes a criminal investigation nor fire fatalities which become the subject of a Coroner's inquest), means that inter-service co-operation or, better still, inter-service co-ordination becomes a necessity.

Fire investigation, therefore, becomes a matter of organisation and training. How investigations are organised is not, as yet, standardised in this country. Individual investigations can be organised; this occurs after a problem is recognised. How to recognise the problem requires training, how to deal with it effectively requires organisation and training.

The organisation of fire investigation
There is little doubt that *ad hoc* investigation by any officer as he comes across a fire causes information to be missed. Partly, this may be due to a lack of specific training but even a trained man has to be able to operate within an effective framework of responsibilities.

The organisation of effective fire service fire investigation has been attempted in two basically different ways in the United Kingdom. The first, traditional approach has been discussed above. Several brigades have now developed a cadre of experienced investigators (usually of senior rank) who stand by with a specific responsibility to investigate fires referred to them. Such a group may eventually become a team. In a large, well concentrated brigade area (Metropolitan or city areas for instance) a team such as this can conceivably be economically justified and may be able to maintain its own service requirements; transport, photographic and search equipment, etc. It has never been envisaged that such a team could investigate every fire in its operational area in depth. It can only respond to a request by the operational officer in charge when he feels it to be needed.

At some point the brigade investigator, particularly if he is a junior officer working in the traditional way, must decide if he is to carry on and uncover further evidence or whether to stop and hand over to another. The reasons for this may be that he either lacks the necessary knowledge or lacks the resources because of the new scope of the enquiry. Thus the enquiry may pass to another entity such as the police.

What is needed then, is a structure in which the fire service, through good training can recognise fire causes more surely and then, on the occasions where suspicion of crime exists, can communicate that suspicion to the police and be assured that action will be taken.

Remedies for the lack of knowledge are available in training. Because it is very difficult for a person to realise precisely what he does *not* know, a full training programme must be available for all

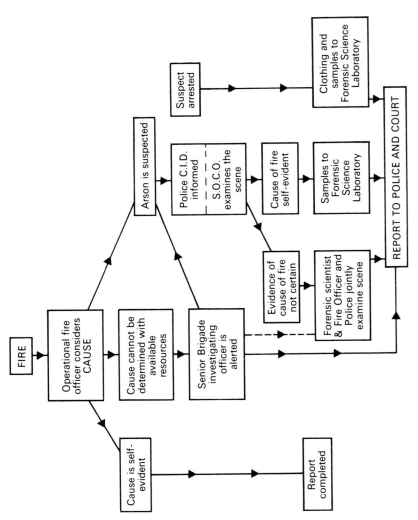

Figure 4.2. Alternative Fire Investigation Procedures.

who are to be given the responsibility of investigating fires. Turning over an investigation to another because of a lack of resources is a much more identifiable situation and one which may well be laid down in standard procedures. The fire service in the United Kingdom seldom have the resources for scientific evaluation of the cause of fire directly available to them. These may need to be the analytical capabilities for determining the ease of ignitability of articles, detecting fire accelerants in fire debris or detecting trace contact materials on a suspect. The police, in the latter instances will usually turn to the appropriate Forensic Science Laboratories. These possess scientific staff skilled in conducting these examinations and in relating their significance to the actual scene of the fire itself.

Such forensic science activity, which may cover evidence of fact and opinion relating to the scene and to the suspect, and which extends to the giving of expert testimony in court, complements the evidence which can be produced by the fire officer.

The general organisation of a fire investigation has been re-examined by several people and one possible approach which utilises effective areas within each service is shown in Fig. 4.2.

The pathways produced by this approach are not 'response' orientated by fire size or apparent importance but are 'cause' orientated. In this way, small fires get the same potential investigation as large ones; this being very important because of the fact that small fires have greater evidential possibilities than large ones.

If a suspicion of arson exists, the police S.O.C.O. (Scenes of Crime Officer or Scientific Aids Officer) now becomes an important link in the chain of the investigation. His role is to link the fire service, the C.I.D. and the forensic science investigation and make a decision, based on his training, as to whether the evidential material at a scene is self-explanatory and, possibly, only needs to be sampled or, whether the presence of a scientist who specialises in fire investigation could further develop the evidential possibilities. It is his job also to advise C.I.D. officers on these technical options; in fire investigations his decisions would be made in conjunction with advice given by the appropriate fire officer and forensic scientist.

The basis for success in this multidisciplinary approach is training so that each party recognises the role of the other and realises the strengths and weaknesses of their roles.

Training

It is not enough merely to train people to investigate fires. Before any training can begin it must be recognised that a successful investigator must be motivated, technically competent and possess the necessary enquiring mind for such a job.

Over recent years much effort has been put into training for all participants in an attempt to place this complex subject in the recognisable specialist category it deserves rather than, as has been in the past, a side-line to an otherwise slightly related job. It must be recognised that the ability to know how to fight fires or even the knowledge of how to prevent them does not necessarily confer a competence to investigate. Likewise, the police officer who can investigate crimes must rely on competent technical support for the special type of evidence that an arson investigation produces. A scientist, even a forensic scientist who has experience of difficult analyses and resulting opinions of their evidential value, also needs educating in the field of fire and fire scene investigation.

Fire Officers

As the service which has direct involvement with fire fighting it is logical and correct that the first stages in any fire investigation should be performed by the officer in charge of the attendance. His ability to discharge this function will rest on what freedom of operation he has and, if he is a junior officer in charge of, say, an initial attendance of one or two appliances, his other operational responsibilities may severely limit his effectiveness in investigation. Nevertheless, he is the man who must identify correctly the possibilities of the cause of the fire, and take steps to preserve evidence which may be needed at a later stage.

At junior officer level it is important that his minimum knowledge encompasses an awareness of causes of fire and the methods by which fire causes are determined. As his experience develops he will be able to apply extended techniques suitable for the more complex issues which would warrant a more senior level of investigation.

Police

The training of police Scenes of Crime Officers (S.O.C.O.) follows somewhat different lines. The S.O.C.O. is not an investigating officer as such; his duty is to provide a technical input at the scene of a crime by taking fingerprints, photographs and collecting relevant samples for future forensic science examinations and comparisons. In the situation where a fire is considered to be suspicious because the fire officer has formed such an opinion, that suspicion may fall short of legally acceptable proof. The S.O.C.O. in conjunction with the fire officer and the police investigating officer can make a decision as to whether the cause of the fire is self evident, whether the cause may become evident by the analysis of debris at a forensic science laboratory or whether the presence of the scientist at the scene could be necessary to help to determine the cause. He is not a fire expert and should never be put in the position where he tries to give expert testimony on that subject in Court, but with the appropriate training his expertise in fire scene management can be enhanced.

The form of training considered to be of value for the S.O.C.O. is as follows:—

(a) *Causes of fire.* He must be able to appreciate how fires can be caused and what likely fire spread patterns can be expected, considering different causes and different occupancies.

(b) *Location of the Seat of Fire.* Frequently, the S.O.C.O. can find himself alone at a scene when he has to make a decision regarding the area where the fire started. General instruction in deciding where a fire originated from is given together with help in deciding when he must refer such a search to a further examiner (e.g. referral back to the fire officer or a forensic scientist).

(c) *Sampling Procedures.* Sampling fire debris requires special techniques to avoid spoilage (e.g. the use of nylon bags to retain hydrocarbons). Contamination prevention also needs to be taught.

(d) *Terminology.* The S.O.C.O. must be able to talk to and understand fire brigade and forensic science officers. Knowledge of technical terms reduces the possibility of misunderstanding.

Forensic Scientists
Scientists may find themselves involved in a fire investigation either at the laboratory bench, where the analysis of materials is needed, or at the scene. By the nature of things a forensic scientist

will frequently become involved after the suspicion of arson or a fire fatality has been identified by the fire officer.

His involvement is useless, however, if he fails to understand the special problems of a fire scene. His training will necessarily include knowledge considered to be basic to any fireman.

Few scientists have practical experience of fire fighting and the general problems of fire ground operations. The background knowledge gained from close contact with brigade activities provides an invaluable aid to any scientific assessment.

In summary then, if all the personnel involved in a fire investigation liaise effectively and know each others roles, the end result should bear scrutiny and provide a true answer with the minimum of wasted effort.

Chapter 5

Safety Aspects

There is a slight but real danger that you, the investigator, could be killed or seriously injured whilst examining a fire-damaged building. Police officers, forensic scientists and other investigators may not be fully aware of the hazards to which they are subjecting themselves. Fire officers are all too familiar with the dangers to which they are subjected during the fighting of the fire, but there is a risk that even they could underestimate the dangers in a cold building. This chapter lists some potential hazards, and suggests precautions which may be taken to lessen the danger to a more acceptable level.

Collapse of parts of the building
Buildings most commonly collapse whilst the fire is still burning or during the early stages of cooling, but it is not unknown for them to fall a considerable time after the fire has been extinguished. It is therefore dangerous to take the complacent attitude that because the building did not collapse during the fire, it will not do so after extinguishment. A fire-damaged building may have suffered serious structural weakening which could make it liable to fall at any moment. Before carrying out any investigation, it is important therefore, to appraise the damage, and possibly liaise with other qualified personnel, in order to assess whether it is safe to enter.

Since buildings can collapse outwards, even this initial safety study can involve an element of risk. The safest place to stand is normally somewhere on or near a diagonal line out from a corner of the building.

Examination of walls
Damaged walls can remain standing in apparent defiance of all of the laws of physics. Although the building may exhibit many of the features of damage listed below, it does not necessarily mean that it will collapse immediately. However, the following features are indications of serious structural weaknesses:—

(a) *Severe cracks.* Most walls in fire-damaged buildings are

47

likely to be cracked to some extent, but severe cracking will seriously weaken a wall. Horizontal and diagonal cracks are more serious than vertical ones. Serious cracks should be observed at intervals of time in order to establish whether they are increasing in length or width.

(b) *Distortion.* The effect of the heat of the fire on one surface of a wall is to cause differential expansion which results in the wall bending or bulging. This effect is at its worst at the time when the fire is at its fiercest, or shortly afterwards. If a bulging wall survives the fire there is a good possibility that it may slightly correct itself on contraction. However changing circumstances such as subsequent disturbance to the wall or an associated part of the building, or the springing up of a wind, may cause the wall to collapse suddenly. When the cause of the distortion has been

Plate 5A. The collapse of parts of a building can leave surviving brickwork in a dangerous condition leaning, cracked and unsupported. Contraction or movement of steel joists can cause substantial masses of brickwork to collapse suddenly. Photograph Cheshire Fire Brigade.

such as white phosphorus, then re-ignitions are not only possible but probable if any of the material remains after the fire.

When a fire has been started by one of several incendiary devices, it may be that some of the devices could operate some hours or even days after the others. Since such devices would be planted with a view to causing rapid fire development, the investigator could suddenly find himself faced with a large and rapidly growing fire in a part of the building which had not previously been involved.

It has been the practice of certain terrorist organisations to place secondary or 'follow-up' bombs in places where investigators and fire fighters might be expected to gather. Devices of this type, timed to explode minutes or hours after the initial incendiary or explosive device, have been placed near to view points where senior officers might meet to discuss the situation. Secondary explosive devices operated by timers, anti-tamper switches, control wires and radio-control have been used. The devices may be small enough to be disguised as a packet of cigarettes or they could comprise many pounds of explosive concealed in a drain, post box or car.

Accidental post-fire explosions can be a result of interference with critical control processes in industry as a result of the fire. Normally, under these circumstances the plant manager is well aware of the danger and it is possible to evacuate the area before the explosion occurs.

Precautions
Policy
It is important for the investigation team to agree at an early stage which parts of the building are safe and which are not. If necessary it is better to abandon the investigation than to endanger lives by venturing into a building in imminent danger of collapse. The decision should be made using the best information available and the advice of works managers, engineers and Brigade Safety Officers should be sought where possible.

Once a decision has been made that parts of the building are too dangerous to approach, the policy should be adhered to unless further information becomes available. It is easy for a group of investigators, reassured by each other's presence, to become over confident about structural damage that they had previously regarded as unsafe.

Protective clothing

All who enter seriously damaged buildings should wear protective clothing. This should include a helmet, overalls, armoured boots and gloves. Helmets should be worn in buildings where structural steelwork and pipes have distorted even if there are no precariously balanced items at a high level.

Overalls, although primarily intended to protect the clothing in the dirty environment of a fire scene can also, if waterproof, provide weather protection and partial protection against toxic and corrosive chemicals. It is desirable that the overalls should be brightly coloured in order that all investigators are conspicuous.

The partial burning and collapse of wooden structural members exposes many nails. In the wet environment of a fire scene, it is easy for a protruding nail to penetrate the sole of a shoe or boot. For this reason armoured boots, preferably with flexible steel sole inserts, should be worn. Most armoured boots do not offer total sole protection and it is not uncommon for nails to penetrate an unprotected area, inflicting memorable wounds. Although the nails involved have been subjected to very high temperatures, it is not reasonable to suppose that they are still sterile at the time of the injury, and the boot through which they have passed will most certainly not be sterile. It is therefore, important to observe normal anti-infection procedures after receiving an injury of this type, and if necessary to receive anti-tetanus injections.

Other sharp items, particularly glass fragments, are normally present in fire debris and heavy duty gloves are desirable. It is not advisable however, to wear gloves of this type when climbing ladders, or undertaking other operations which require a strong reliable grip.

General approach

Careless behaviour on the part of investigators, demolition workers or salvage experts can result in danger to others working at the scene. All have a responsibility towards the safety of others. Debris dislodged at a high level could injure those below. Before any operation is undertaken which could affect the stability of the structure of the building, or could cause debris to fall, warnings should be given to all those in the vicinity, particularly those below.

It is important that all workers at the scene should be aware of the approximate locations of the other workers. Conspicuously coloured overalls help to ensure that if a worker suffers a fall or some other accident, others at the scene will be quickly aware of his problem and be able to render assistance.

Experienced firemen develop the equivalent of a sailor's 'weather eye'. Without consciously doing so they learn to recognise the almost imperceptible signs which indicate imminent danger. The creaking of timber, or a particular sponginess of the floor may indicate instability. Slight movements of walls may actually be visible or may attract attention by causing small falls of debris or dust.

Although the investigator's attention will be concentrated on the cause and spread of the fire, it is important that he or she should keep all senses alert to the possibility of danger.

Further reading
(1) J. K. Basson. Fire Engineers Journal 1977 p. 37.
(2) D. R. Richards. Fire Engineers Journal 1976 p. 21.
(3) G. H. Almond. Fire Engineers Journal 1974 p. 26.
(4) Manual of Firemanship Book II part 1.
(5) A. Everton, J. Holyoak and D. K. Allen. Fire Safety and the Law. Victor Green.

Chapter 6

Information Gathering

The whole purpose of investigating any incident is, obviously, to obtain information about it; for example, what caused it, how it developed and when it occurred. There will be several interested parties and the collected information is likely to be used in different ways by each of them. For instance, the first question the police will probably ask concerning the fire is, 'Is it a crime?'. If the answer is 'No', (barring those fires involving fatalities which the police will investigate on behalf of the Coroner), little investigative work will follow. If it is 'Yes' then a series of actions will be taken, some of which will be highly dependent on the information obtained from the fire.

The information the fire service needs is primarily, 'How was it caused and what contributed to its development?' followed by 'How well was it fought?', the details varying, depending on whether or not a standard fire report alone or supplementary reports need to be completed. For insurance interests, the two main questions after the cause has been determined may well be, 'How much loss is there?' and, 'Who, if anyone, is liable for damages?'. So it can be seen that a fire investigation could mean many things to different people and that prime requirements may differ from the point of view of who is to use the investigation report. Although all parties will want to know how it started the secondary questions will vary.

The investigator should then recognise the fact that his results may be of use, indeed, may be possibly vital, to many different interested parties. Additionally, if he has channelled his mind only into the point of view of his immediate and obvious interest, he runs the danger of finding out too late that his investigation results rest on incomplete information if the enquiry takes an unexpected turn. He also lays himself open to the charge of a biased or sloppy investigation. After *one* person has disturbed the scene it can never be reconstructed completely and to discard or destroy evidence without adequate record because it was not of immediate importance or was not required by him is an unforgivable sin in the eyes of the unfortunate who tries to follow his investigation. From time to time this does happen and can only be recognised as having happened when the *second* person investigating finds that the information he requires is missing and can never be retrieved.

We can consider what the main interested parties (the fire service, the police and the insurers) want to know about a fire.

The fire service

It is not the intention of this book to discuss in any detail the information required on the standard fire report form (such as the United Kingdom Form F.D.R.I.) as all fire officers should be aware of this. In general, irrespective of where the incident occurs, the fire officer will have recorded relevant times, such as when the fire call was received, when the response was made and the amount of equipment used, when the fire was put out and what he thinks was the cause. He may also record the materials involved and what part they appeared to play in the fire. All these facts and opinions are collected nationally but nevertheless are gathered by the fire officer as part of his general interest in fire and its causes. Indeed, the keen and professional fire officer will have noted far more information than the statistical minimum requirements.

National statistics are required to examine trends in fire hazards from both the ignition and growth of fire in materials. These are constantly analysed with a view to legislative requirements including building regulations, consumer protection, etc. These are of public and political interest, particularly when loss of life is concerned, and as relatively few fires involve fatalities some of those statistics are very sensitive to small changes. Thus, accuracy of reporting is essential, otherwise the whole basis of legislative fire prevention may rest upon false foundations. Causes of ignition are required to be assessed. Here, a tendency to guess rather than to investigate must be avoided. It is well known that at the end of a watch there is a temptation to clear away reports as rapidly as possible; this must not be done at the expense of accuracy for the reasons which have been mentioned above. The problem in the past has been that for statistical recording, the phrase 'supposed cause of fire' may have implied that accuracy in this area is of secondary importance.

Basically, the fire service is concerned with aspects of performance; performance of materials and performance of men and equipment. Through constant measurement of these by

INTERESTS IN FIRE INVESTIGATION

Information required	Fire service	Police suspecting crime	Police acting for coroner	Insurance
Time of origin	In step values 0–5, 5–30, 30 min.	As accurately as possible to review alibi (frequently minutes accuracy vital).	Accurate as possible to compare with movements of deceased.	May be necessary to prove liability etc.
Cause	Most likely cause for report form and statistics. Operational officers will require knowledge for future use.	*Determination* of arson with admissible evidence for court. If not arson, actual cause has low priority.	Cause needs to be known to aid coroner's verdict.	Knowledge of cause is vital to determine liability.
Reasons for spread (a) Materials first ignited.	For statistical and F.P. use. Little precision in identifying them.	Materials ignited could be found as trace contact with suspect.	May be a notifiable hazard and may be publicised.	May be breach of insurance conditions. May be need to reassess insurance surveys.
(b) Performance of fixed installations.	For statistical and F.P. use. Precisely identified when found.	May indicate time of outbreak.	Of interest where involvement of deceased is concerned.	Periodic review of surveys, premium setting, etc.
(c) Contribution of contents and structure to fire.	For statistical and F.P. use. Variation in effective identification of materials.	Of little interest except where evidence is destroyed.	May be a notifiable hazard and may be publicised.	As in (a) and (b).
(d) Effectiveness of fire fighting methods.	Operational research reports leading to review of training.	Of little interest.	Only of interest if methods contributed to fatality.	Does not affect loss calculations. Breach of Statutory Duty may influence claims.
Evidential materials at scene.	Of passing interest*. Will refer to police.	Vital to preserve and sample.	Vital to preserve and sample.	Vital to preserve and sample. Physical count may be needed to quantify loss.

Information required	Fire service	Police suspecting crime	Police acting for coroner	Insurance
Samples from suspect.	Rarely encountered.	Vital for linking evidence from scene to accused.	Will be informed but case will probably be referred to Criminal Court.	Rarely encountered.
Cost of fire.	Indirectly considered.	Specimen value needed in framing the charge.	Of little direct interest.	Immediate interest in adjusted loss, consequential loss.

* i.e. no requirement to preserve or sample but awareness is important for liaison with police.

statistical analysis, fire fighting and fire prevention techniques are kept under review.

The Police

There are two basic fields where police forces would investigate fires, using either their own resources or by utilising the expertise of, say, Home Office forensic scientists. These are:—

(i) fires where a suspicion of arson exists and
(ii) fires involving death or very serious injury.

Major incidents involving fire or explosion often involve some police investigation or involvement (with regard to their public order responsibilities) until other agencies can take over. These could be factory inspectors or other statutory bodies.

Here there is a major overlap and, unfortunately, sometimes a conflict with fire service interests. Precisely because the police involvement many only become apparent or necessary after the fire service have commenced their investigation, it is at this point that a lack of awareness of the other parties' requirements provokes criticism and allegations of poor investigative techniques.

As an example of what may happen, a fire may have been recorded as of 'unknown' cause and the fire report requirements may have caused the brigade investigating officer to note merely

that:—
- (i) the fire had been burning for between five and thirty minutes before discovery,
- (ii) it was confined to the room of origin and involved an area of five square metres,
- (iii) the first ignited materials were probably papers, the fire spreading to wallboarding and furniture.

Subsequent police action may throw light on a suspect who has been seen in the vicinity. The police may then want to know:—
- (i) Can it be said *exactly* when the fire started?
- (ii) Were there any materials foreign to the premises at the seat of the fire?
- (iii) Was there any evidence of breaking and entering?
- (iv) Were the papers ignited by any traceable fire accelerant? etc., etc.

If the fire report requirements are only followed to the letter, no evidentially adequate answers will be forthcoming and, probably, the scene will not have been preserved.

As a model of perfection, therefore, it would be well if a fire investigator finds out what, if any, investigation has been done before his involvement and also what investigation is likely to follow his. He should also be aware of all other interested parties' information needs so that in his own exercise he can make notes which can be of use.

Insurance
Insurers will want to know where their liabilities lay, as, for instance, whether the terms of the policy were invalidated by any act or omission or if another party can be held responsible in damages. Most of the information required falls into the same areas that the fire service and police should be concerned with; the cause, the reasons for spread, the materials involved, etc. Because of the financial element however, there will in many cases be a need for highly quantified information, such as the quantity and value of goods.

Ways of Collecting Information
Notebooks and forms
Undoubtedly most investigation agencies use forms at some stage, generally for their more specialised requirements. There is,

though, often great difficulty in utilising the information on one authorities' form for another purpose. This underlines the greatest problem associated with forms, that of the distortion of recorded data to fit in with data storage systems. If past records of a fire are consulted one may learn only of the address, occupier, times and degree of fire brigade responses, size of fire at its maximum and cost of damage. This may be of little use if one is trying to collate information on, say, a suspected series of arsons.

Objectors to the storing and recording of more detailed information point to the fact that much so-called information on a fire is merely opinion and in the worst cases is only guesswork. It is submitted, however, that even opinion can be useful— provided it is not confused with factual evidence.

The opposite approach, done in the past by investigators is the case or scene notebook approach in which *ad hoc* information, diagrams, sketches, dirt and stains are all collected together. The result is one which may (perhaps with some difficulty) be capable of being interpreted by the investigator at a later date and has the dubious advantage of being totally unreadable by anyone else.

The problem is then to accept some degree of formalisation, in which scene performance and findings may be regulated by the necessity to fill in aspects of a form but where freedom exists to insert unplannable extra information, for example, a large 'Other Comments' box

The advantage of forms are that they can be filed and kept with other case notes. They are then subject to the efficiency of an office filing system. If they do become mislaid, however, one has not lost details of other scenes which may be the case if a general notebook is lost. Undoubtedly, the physical conditions of the average fire scene make it necessary usually to use 'notebook' notes as well. These must be transferred into more permanent records as soon as possible after the search. The legal requirements of 'contemporaneity' demand storage of those original notes. Aspects of this are discussed later in this book (Chapter 24, The Expert Witness).

Tape recorders

Hand-held cassette recorders are fairly robust and can be used in situations where writing may be difficult. Problems of intelligibility may be encountered where stray noise from equipment and wind can drown normal speech. Interviews with witnesses may fail completely because of the inhibiting effects of a recorder thrust into their faces and the fact that a slower than normal speech is usually necessary for adequate recording. Strong accents may also make recall difficult.

One must also be aware of the evidential requirements in this respect. If notes or a statement are transcribed later from a tape-recording the need for 'contemporaneity' makes it possible that the original tape recordings will be called for in evidence as these are 'original' notes. Embarrassment may ensue when all the bad language is also played back.

In complex scenes, where much information is gradually collected and much comes out of chronological order, any further information must always be added on at the end of the tape. Reviewing this for the eventual writing up of notes can be difficult as the sequential nature of the tape recording bears no relationship to the context.

Photography

The average fire scene is extraordinarily difficult to photograph effectively whether the results are for interest, training or for presentation in court. A well burnt pile of debris presents an almost monochromatic aspect which is frequently improved by the use of colour film but which also presents an almost abstract appearance on black and white. The following list of 'do's and don'ts' is not intended to be exhaustive but is the result of widespread experience.

(a) *Photographs taken while the fire is burning.* It is almost impossible to photograph a fire from within the building but external photographs can demonstrate where a fire was burning at a specific time in a large building, thus providing a record of fire development. A superb example of photographs showing fire development were those taken of the Joelma fire in São Paulo, Brazil in 1974[1].

Experimental fires have been photographed from within buildings to provide scientific record. These have, however, been taken using test rigs which can provide better facilities, such as smoke extraction and viewing ports, but they also have shown problems with smoke obscuring the areas of interest particularly in experiments involving modern plastics.

(b) *Photographs taken after the fire is out.* Most evidential material is photographed at this stage and the following suggestions are given.

(i) Do wait until the building is cool if (as is almost inevitable) flash is to be used. Steam and smoke, even in small concentrations, will show up as a dense fog and ruin the detail on the picture.

(ii) If circumstances make it necessary to take the initial photographs at night, further examination in daylight may well show details or effects not shown on the night pictures. It is as well to save time and film by postponing all except the most vital evidential photographs until daylight.

(iii) Avoid excessively contrasty film, paper or developing conditions.

(iv) Because much of the debris contains black charcoal, estimation of exposure in natural light is difficult and probably, at least one or two stops increase in exposure will be necessary over and above the meter reading.

(v) Oblique lighting will raise the contrast of char patterns if these are to be recorded.

(vi) Keep aperture stops as small as possible to increase the depths of field and definition. This will increase exposure times but if the camera is well supported, camera shake will be no problem. Wide angle/short focus lenses will mitigate some of the problems of fitting the scene into the photograph.

(vii) Colour film is useful because, contrary to popular belief, there is colour to be seen in burnt debris. Thus, details are shown better and burning patterns can be recorded more accurately. In a major case the moderate increase in cost will be justified. Colour transparencies are particularly useful. A complete 35 mm cassette can be used and the results used in debriefing sessions.

(viii) If a detail is to be photographed then this must be shown (on a separate photograph) in its context at the scene. A close-up of burnt items or debris is meaningless unless its position in the scene can be shown on a more general view *taken from the same angle*. At the same time a scale must be included on both pictures. This ensures that the object can be correctly located on the photograph (a surprisingly difficult thing to do, as a general rule).

(ix) Many photographs are taken by a professional photographer who has no knowledge of the significance of damage patterns or where the seat of fire may be. At some stage of the investigation the photographic record should be superintended by an experienced investigator. Better still, the investigator should be an experienced photographer. With cameras available which automatically focus and compute the exposure the techniques of taking adequate photographs have become easier.

(x) Stages of excavation should be covered. There is little to be gained by photographing the top of a pile of debris followed by a close-up of some evidential material.

(xi) Any significant object which is photographed should be shown *in situ* or on the ground.

(xii) An accurate record of exactly what each photograph comprises should be made. After several years, which may elapse before a civil action is heard, it might be impossible to remember, and a featureless expanse of burnt debris needs accurate labelling. Arrows on a plan showing the positions and directions of the camera are very valuable.

Video-tape recordings

This technique, as an extension of ordinary, still, photographic records, possibly has more uses in the recording of experimental work than in scene photography. Many workers are however finding it to be of great value in being able to 'pan' over scenes and to 'zoom' in onto items of specific interest. Used in this way it can provide a continuous visual commentary of the fire scene. It is most important to choose a video system which is compatible with those used by other workers in the field.

It has not yet been used much as submitted evidence in court but will, of course, be subject to the legal restrictions that are attached to ordinary photographs. These include the inadmissability of any extraneous material such as views of the investigator. Likewise, a descriptive or persuasive commentary would probably be disallowed.

The great disadvantage of hand held video-tape recording is that definition is by no means as good as with photographic film (either still or movie photography). Thus fine detail may not be accurately recorded. On some systems single frame operation is possible. It is doubtful though whether video should be considered as a replacement for still photography at the current state of the art.

Plans and drawings

As a discipline for the investigator, the analytical observation of an item, which is necessary when a sketch of it is being made, is invaluable. Details which may well have been missed by a superficial look — and superficial looks are very frequent in uncomfortable or ill-lit surroundings — can spring into full significance during sketching and labelling. Artistic talents need not be stretched, particularly if the scene or object is to be photographed; what is needed is the analysis of damage (for example, the patterns of burning, and, possibly any of the original conditions which can be deduced or inferred).

When an entire room or building is involved, some sort of plan drawing is generally necessary. Accurately drawn plans can be an extremely effective and convenient means of recording much of the available fire scene information. Plans can convey information which could not be expressed in many pages of writing, and have the further advantage that the information recorded is compact and comprehensible at a glance. Not only can the information relating to the seat of the fire be recorded efficiently and briefly; but also in the drawing up of the plans, ideas and information are consolidated.

A particular example of this consolidation of information is in the location of the seat of the fire. During the preliminary examination at a fire scene it may appear impossible to locate the seat of the fire to any accurate degree. However, when the direction of spread indications are recorded objectively on an accurately drawn plan, the facts may fit together and clearly indicate the seat of the fire. On the occasions when they do not, the plan illustrates the confusion and complexity of the particular scene. In such cases, provided it has been drawn accurately, it does at least prevent the investigator from deluding himself that he has established the exact location of the seat of the fire.

In order that all of the salient facts may be portrayed on one plan, it is necessary that symbols for all relevant phenomena and items should be adopted. It is clearly a matter of individual preference which symbols should be used, but it is convenient to adopt standard symbols where possible. Unfortunately the special circumstances of a fire scene require much information to be recorded for which there have been no published standard symbols. In a normal plan of an undamaged building merely the location and general type of a door would be portrayed. In a fire investigation plan, it is also desirable to show whether the door was open at the time of the fire, and, if so, at what angle.

Fire investigation plans are also required to record such information as the location of furniture, positions of holes in the floor and ceiling, areas of deep charring, directional indications, excavation layer structures, the positions and integrity of windows, sources of samples and the positions from which photographs were taken. It is difficult to record all of this information clearly on one sheet of paper and methods of overcoming this problem will be discussed later.

Materials
The simplest approach is to use plain paper clipped to a board. All details can be recorded on a preliminary rough diagram and these details are then transferred to the final plan shortly afterwards.

Since most corners of buildings and rooms are right angles, graph paper is superior to plain paper having the additional advantage that the plan can be drawn to scale immediately.

Another type of pre-printed paper which can be of use at fire scenes is 'isometric' paper. This material is similar in appearance to graph paper, except that it is pre-printed with a system of equilateral triangles instead of squares. It can be used for the production of isometric drawings of, for example, the floor and two walls of a room. (Fig. 6.1) Isometric drawings can be used to illustrate the interrelationship between damage to the floor and walls of a room. This information cannot be recorded on a normal plan, and may not be clearly visible in a single photograph.

The problem of drawing plans in wet conditions may be overcome by the use of one of the proprietary plastic paper substitutes. These materials, which look like a rather glossy paper, are waterproof but will accept pencil, ball-point ink, and the ink from certain felt-tip pens.

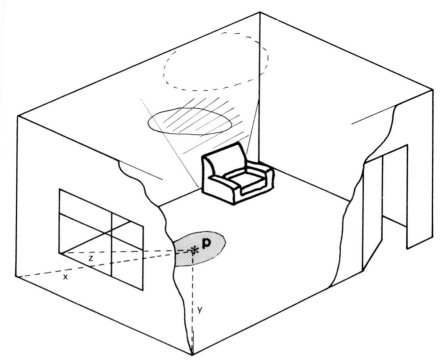

Figure 6.1.   Isometric Projection of a Fire Scene.

Methods

The most common method of fire scene plan drawing involves a preliminary rough plan drawn at the scene. The rough plan incorporates sufficient measurements and other information so that a final plan can be drawn under more suitable conditions. In the production of the final plan all available information, such as notes and photographs, should be taken into consideration.

Although there are considerable difficulties in drawing an accurate scale plan under the dirty conditions of a fire scene, especially when working on a clipboard, there are advantages in producing a scale plane at this stage. Any ambiguities in measurements show up immediately at a time when the measurements can be checked. In addition, the plan is available for its role in the objective assessment of fire seat location, at the time when this information is particularly valuable.

A detailed large scale plan of the region including the fire seat is essential, but it is not always necessary to draw a plan of the whole building. In cases where a complete plan is required, the general whole building plan may normally be drawn to a smaller scale.

Preparation of a rough plan

Mention has already been made of the use of graph paper for plan drawing. An alternative to graph paper is the use of a clipboard marked out with a conspicuous square pattern visible through a single sheet of paper. These preparations pre-suppose that the corners of the room or building in question are right angles and it is necessary to check that this is the case by visual inspection.

Fairly accurate measurements can be made using a steel or fabric measuring tape, but due to the unevenness of the floor surface and the dirtiness of the situation, many workers prefer to measure room dimensions by pacing. In most cases measurements made in this way are sufficiently accurate for investigation purposes. Typical door widths of about 0.75 metre (2' 4"), sizes of armchairs (1 m × 1 m or 3' × 3'), settees (1 m × 2 m or 3' × 6' 6") and so on may be used in the plan if the items at the scene appear to be of normal size. However, measurements are desirable if the items present are of an uncommon nature.

The exact location of an object of significance can be defined by making measurements from it to three datum points (Fig. 6.2).

As the measurements are being made, the outline of the room under consideration can be drawn on to the paper. Free-hand rough sketches are regarded as acceptable by many workers, but there are advantages in drawing the 'rough' sketch fairly accurately, using a ruler.

Recording fixed points

The positions of doors and windows together with pillars and other fixed points should be recorded at this stage. It is unsafe to assume that support pillars will be equally spaced throughout the building and it may be necessary to measure the position of each pillar if a precisely accurate plan is required.

The positions of holes or severe charring to the floor should be recorded as accurately as possible and their position in relation to the fixed objects in the room should be established.

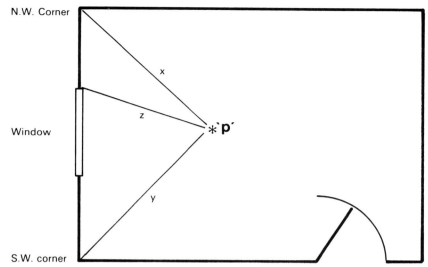

N.W. Corner

Window

S.W. corner

Figure 6.2. Locating a point from fixed reference positions. Point 'P' can be established by distances 'x' and 'y' alone but can be better determined by the inclusion of distance 'z'

Recording the positions of moveable objects

During fire-fighting, and the subsequent clearing up or 'turning-over' operations, many of the moveable objects in the room may have been displaced. The final positions of items after fire-fighting may not be of any real importance. The two positions which are of significance are that of the item when it was left by the last legitimate visitor prior to the fire, and where it was during the fire. The position prior to the fire can only be established by the interrogation of witnesses. The location of items during the fire can be established by excavation.

At this stage in the investigation it is the positions of large or important items such as articles of furniture or bodies which should be recorded. When the larger items have been located on the plan, the relative positions of smaller items can then be established in relation to them.

It may be necessary for two plans to be drawn, showing the arrangement of items prior to, and during the fire. Items are sometimes displaced by the arsonist to such an extent that all of the furniture may be in a pile in the centre of the room.

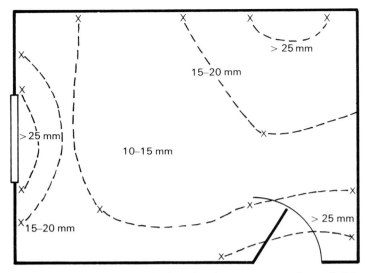

Figure 6.3. '*Contours' joining equal char depth. In practice few reliable char depth points will be available. All measurements must be taken at the same level*

Bodies found at fire scenes obviously should also be photographed. However, the exact posture of a blackened half-buried body may not be clearly apparent on a photograph and for this reason the body should be recorded on the plan in the manner illustrating its posture and the orientation of the limbs.

Recording fire seat location information
In some cases, particularly when there is difficulty in locating the seat of the fire, it can be helpful to plot fire seat location information on the plan. Contours joining regions of equal char depth can be drawn. This method has the disadvantages that it considers only wooden objects, and that differential charring on opposite sides of an item cannot be taken into account. Many workers do not regard this method as being particularly valuable. (see Chapter 7, Locating Seats of Fire).

A simpler and more effective approach is that of drawing arrows; either in the direction of spread of fire[2] or towards the apparent seat of the fire, as is the practice in most British Forensic Science Laboratories.

Information Gathering

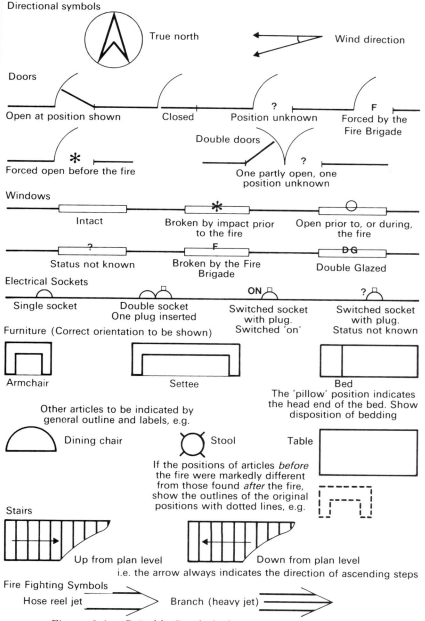

Figure 6.4. Suitable Symbols for Fire Scene Recording.

When there is a possibility that the wind could have influenced the spread of the fire, its direction must be indicated on the plan. It is also useful to indicate which direction is north. It is then possible to refer to particular parts of the room unambiguously by their compass direction.

When sufficient seat location information is available, the fire seat limitation boundary should be drawn on the plan. This boundary is defined as, 'the shortest line bounding the entire area which cannot be excluded as a seat of the fire'. This is, of course, the area defined in the term 'Radius of Error' (q.v.). The size of the area indicates the investigator's uncertainty with regard to the exact location of the seat of the fire, and frequently bears a relationship to the rate of build-up of the fire; the larger the area, the faster the rate of build-up.

Main plan
The information recorded in the rough plan should be transferred to the main plan as soon as possible but the rough plan should be retained with the investigation notes because of their 'original note' status in law.

The main plan can conveniently be drawn on graph paper, and a suitable scale such as 1 : 50 or 1 : 100 should be chosen. The drawing of the main plan would be carried out in approximately the same sequence as the rough plan, but the inevitable errors and alterations involved in the initial drawing of the rough plan can be corrected immediately.

Symbols
The symbols in Figure 6.4, with some variations, are used by some British forensic scientists.

Witnesses
These can be divided into lay and experienced witnesses (for example, the general public, and trained observers, such as police or fire officers) and considering the importance placed upon a witness' statement in a court of law, it is surprising how often the lay witness is asked to tell of his observations by someone who knows nothing of the technicalities of the subject in question. Thus, there abound statements containing misleading phrases such as 'it exploded into flames' or 'the room was completely gutted'.

Such limitations on the use of witness' statements are discussed in Chapter 7, (Locating Seats of Fire).

There is a subtle distinction between getting the best out of a witness and leading him, and any investigator who is technically knowlegable about the conditions of the fire scene and who is involved in gathering information from a witness must be aware of the distinction.

Where any investigation is concerned, the effective interviewing of a witness is the result of training and experience and is outside the scope of this book. The fire service instructions regarding statements and interviews generally emphasise the necessity of an informal, non-aggresive approach, noting such things as getting the witness away from the scene, calming him down, taking one's helmet off, taking to him man-to-man, etc. These injunctions may well be humane but do little to ensure the quality of the information coming from the witness. What is more important is that either the interviewer should know how fires behave or that he is in continual contact with someone who does. Consequently, the statement can be evaluated as it develops. In an investigation covering a series of fires previously accepted as accidental and later thought to be deliberate, several hundred statements were examined, many of which showed the effects of a non-critical acceptance of a description of events, some definitely showing a greater interest in the spectacle rather than the reality.

It is, then, clear that the eye-witness is an imperfect link in the evidential chain, having bias, faulty observation, flawed memory and emotions. He has, however, seen something which may well be of importance and every effort must be made to ensure that his observations go down in a permanent, accurate record.

If a person is involved in a fire, he may feel some responsibility for it, either because it is his property or because a close relative or friend has been injured or killed, and the shock may last for many days or weeks. It has been found on occasions when witnesses were reinterviewed several years after certain fires, that significant observations not mentioned at the time were now recalled. This recall has been, in many instances, shown to be genuine, being checked by alternative methods. Reasons for not giving such details at the time have been said to be that the initial interviews had been conducted too soon after the event and that the witness had been too shocked to think clearly. When it is realised that many statements were taken up to two days after the fires it is clear that much research into human reactions to traumatic events needs to be made.

Another distortion which can occur in a statement is that of selective observations, in which supression of some effects or events is made to shift blame in a witness' real or imagined responsibility for the fire. Again, this approach is used by the witness who wishes to be considered a hero.

Perhaps one further and most important consideration in witness' statements is regarding those that have *not* been taken. There is no rule which states how many people must be interviewed about a fire and it appears probable that on numerous occasions the number of statements taken are fewer than those potentially available. On at least one occasion where a review of a series of witness' statements was made, valuable corroboration was later given by people who had not been originally interviewed. As a halfway approach it would not seem unreasonable to have a list of interviewed witnesses made up, with brief notes as to whether they seem to have something worth saying before the actual collection of statements is made. This would make a full house-to-house enquiry, such as the police are capable of launching, a two-stage exercise which can be evaluated at intervals by the fire expert. He is then in a position to pin-point the witnesses who may well be able to contribute the best information.

Convenient though it might be to be able to categorise witnesses in advance, real-life situations do not allow such a neat solution to the problems of the effectiveness of their statements. For instance, the availability of the person is likely to be the most important consideration for statement taking and in any extended inquiry it would be a very wasteful use of manpower not to use the efficiency of a house-to-house cover made when most witnesses are at home and available. This, of course, means that the investigator performing his scene examination rarely has anything more than sketchy help from eye-witnesses. By the time visual impressions are being collected, the scene examination may have been finished and, although collaboration with the person in charge of the interviews can ensure that significant observations are spotted, an unexpected observation may make a review of the entire scene examination necessary.

As a result of these considerations it is suggested that the following are borne in mind concerning statements.

(i) If statements are taken early, there may be serious errors due to (a) emotional involvement or (b) overwhelming impressions which the observer cannot fully co-ordinate. Thus, if subsequent enquiry reveals discrepancies, the interviewer must re-interview and try to extract reasons for them.

(ii) If there is a reasonable delay (this cannot be quantified) there may be errors because of (a) rationalisation, (b) the 'guilt covering' possibility or (c) the hero syndrome.

(iii) it appears that in many cases, lay witnesses do retain, with remarkable clarity, a memory of events such as fire. Even after a seven year gap, witnesses in one enquiry, although dispersed, corroborated one another in details not mentioned in the original statements.

(iv) In spite of all this, people have frailities of detail. Asking an occupier after a fire the exact positions of all items in a room is usually a very frustrating experience. The investigator must use his expertise to attempt to corroborate or refute witnesses statements.

Further reading
Fire and Arson Photography. 1977. Eastman Kodak Company.
Using Photography to Preserve Evidence. Kodak Publications M2.

References
(1) Joelma Fire, Sao Paulo, Brazil. 1974. 'Fire Prevention' 104 FPA.
(2) Kennedy, J. 1977. Fire, Arson and Explosion Investigation.

Chapter 7

Locating Seats of Fire

Although in general use, the term 'seat of fire' is a rather loose one. In its more usual sense it means a point from which the fire has spread. Apparent seats of fire can be found which may not be the actual point of origin but which may just be the results of preferential burning conditions. Instances which come to mind are those of localised fire loading and areas of good ventilation, and care must be taken to differentiate between apparent seats of fire and the original seat of fire.

For evidential purposes the determination of the cause of a fire must depend upon a meticulous scene examination in which the original seat of fire is determined and subsequently excavated. Mere guesswork or intuition that the fire 'started somewhere over there', or a blind acceptance of what a witness said he saw, is not enough to support a contention on which a person's liability or culpability may depend.

Fire behaves in some generally predictable ways (described elsewhere in this book), allowing for differences in fire loading, room geometry, ventilation, time of discovery and method of extinction. Thus, signs are available which will point in general ways to show the direction from which a fire has travelled, how long it has burnt or how hot it got in certain areas. There should be no need to emphasise the point that unless physical justification can be demonstrated for locating an original seat of fire at a particular point, any subsequent claims as to the cause of the fire must be suspect. Such justification can be obtained by utilising directional damage patterns and other signs, although as it will be seen, there may be few instances where an individual sign is unequivocal enough to be used on its own. In its way, this part of the investigation parallels archeological field work (surveying, aerial photography, consulting the lie of existing buildings and records to decide on the best place to excavate).

If a fire has spread sufficiently to cause generalised burning, it may be difficult to locate the seat of fire precisely. Some measure of the investigator's accuracy is needed however, and in this chapter, and also in the following chapter on excavation, the term 'radius of error' will be used. Thus, if the investigator decides he has located a seat of fire within a radius of error of 1 m, he is *certain* that the original seat of fire lays within an area having one metre radius (i.e. within an area of 3.14 square metres). Two implications derive from this. Firstly, a quoted radius of error gives an indication of the degree of accuracy that the investigator is working to. Secondly, the effectiveness (and the labour involved) of the subsequent excavation is drastically affected by the magnitude of this radius of error.

Factors affecting accuracy
Accuracy in determining the location of a seat of fire is not something which can always be predicted. Apart from the technical competence of the investigator, accuracy is considerably influenced by the rate of development, the final size of the fire, the materials involved and the way the fire was fought.

Size of Fire
Clearly, a very small fire which has been confined to the item of origin and which has then been extinguished, presents no problems of location. At the opposite end of the scale, however, a

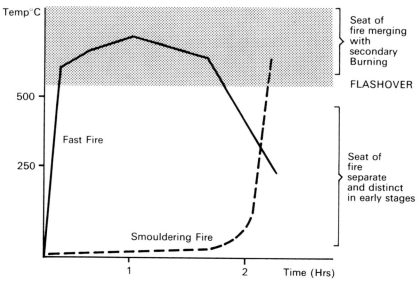

Figure 7.1. Graphical Representation of Accuracy.

fire which has involved an entire multi-storey building, which has then collapsed, makes it fairly probable that little in the way of determining the original seat of fire by a physical search can be done. The limit of accuracy may be the size of the building and could be considered to be a 'volume of error' rather than an area.

Flashover
Although only partly related to the duration of burning, the time at which flashover occurs, signals the end of the absolute separation of the burning of an object from the general secondary burning within a room. Thus, when a polyurethane upholstered piece of furniture ignites in a living room, flashover may be only minutes away (under these conditions, possibly within four or five minutes). From this point on, the original burning merges into the secondary burning to present the investigator, after the fire is out, with an evenly burnt room. Probably the major factor here in preserving any localised fire damage and, therefore, what appears to be the seat of fire is the method of fire fighting, particularly amateur fire fighting attempts.

Smouldering
Conversely, when a fire has had a smouldering origin, intense, localised destruction of items such as furniture frames, floorboards or containers will occur long before secondary fire spread takes place. Even if a delayed flashover has taken place (the ventilation induced flashover described in Chapter 19), a considerable degree of secondary burning can still fail to conceal the original smouldering seat of fire.

Fire fighting procedures
The methods used by the fire fighting team can affect accuracy to a considerable extent. The alteration of smoke travel by ventilation, the cooling effects of water and the scattering of materials when jets of water hit them are all factors which must be taken into account. In many cases, the evidence of what has been done is clear and the investigator should have little difficulty in accounting for them, as will be shown later.

The worst effects from the investigator's point of view, however, are undoubtedly 'damping down', salvage and 'turning over' procedures. These, generally, *must* be done in order to ensure a complete extinction of the fire and full protection of property, and the experienced investigator takes them into acount. Care must be taken at the fire fighting stage to see that these actions are done only where necessary and with a critical approach. Irresponsible work performed after a fire is a major reason for inaccurate results in establishing fire causes.

Salvage, as properly understood in fire brigade training, is the reduction of damage to property caused by fire and fire fighting. Such salvage (sheeting up, damming and diverting water, etc.) will greatly help the investigator, because evidence will be preserved. Indiscriminate shovelling out of the debris from a well burnt area (which, almost by definition will contain the seat of fire and all the evidential materials) must be avoided at all costs. No fire from which the debris has been thrown away can ever produce results which could compare in quality or accuracy with those of an undisturbed scene.

Directional Signposts
Some of the effects produced by a fire are truly vectors whilst some are the results of time or temperature of exposure. Particularly in the early stages of a fire, heat flow will cause assymetric effects within a building. Many of these may persist for some time into the secondary burning stage and may be available for the investigator to interpret. There are, then, numerous methods of locating a seat of fire; some will be available at every fire, some not. The following are some methods considered with their strengths and weaknesses.

Physical signs Illustrating General Locality
Low burning
This is, perhaps, one of the most basic observations. The buoyancy of flames ensures that, under normal conditions, fires will always develop upwards at a faster rate than outwards or downwards. Certainly, in a cellulosic or solid fuel fire where a 'crib' exists, this will be generally true. Smouldering fires will also frequently exhibit clear tendencies to have definite low burnt areas. These have their own specific characteristics which will be dealt with later. Modern materials have, as can be seen time and again, modified the truth of these statements. A fire burning in thermoplastic materials will cause flowing, burning droplets to cascade downwards giving charring, possibly at a lower position than the actual point of origin. If the liquid is mobile enough to

flow into the space between the joists, burning can develop attacking floorboards from below the original area. This can cause premature collapse and can simulate a below-floor or between-floor origin.

When one is attempting to characterise low burnt areas in a fire damaged building, particularly if there has been a sustained fire, much of the evidence will be hidden below debris. Careful clearance, bearing in mind the techniques described in Chapter 8, (Excavation and Sampling Techniques), will reveal those areas.

Points to consider are that floors in domestic or office premises or reception areas are generally covered with carpeting, rugs or tiles which in their own way can indicate origins and causes of fires. 'Pool' burns may be revealed (see Plate, 15A), indicative of liquid phase burning. In older commercial premises which have been modified, floors may vary in character and strength from part to part, thereby showing markedly different effects from generalised exposure to fire. Thus, weakened or split areas of floor will show an apparently greater exposure to fire in that area and simulate low points of origin. Careful excavation and comparison of the debris contents with other areas should give some indications of this possibility.

High level burning

In fires having a flaming origin where a stable thermal updraught is established, localised heating occurs, either directly over the origin, or obliquely if a venting point exists close to the origin. Established plumes of hot gases may achieve temperatures of over 750°C. Where a plaster ceiling exists, localised spalling with subsequent joist charring will rapidly develop. With a reinforced concrete ceiling, surface spalling can expose the reinforcing wires.

Factory premises with north-light roofing and/or light steel trusses will show heating effects within the roof void where unprotected steelwork can fail at a very early stage of the fire development.

High level fire spread in north-light roofs will initially follow the roof channels—any excessive spread transversely should be reflected in evidence of a wide fire area at floor level. This latter might indicate multiple seats of fire, depending on the state of flammable materials stored within the building. The early failure of rooflights, possibly remote from the original seat of fire, along the roof channels will cause localised high level damage at the

location of a seat of fire as well as showing the temperatures which may have been achieved.

The fracture of glass by thermal shock (i.e. cold to hot) requires, for window glass, a temperature differential between the hot and cold faces of about 70°C and is characterised by the random nature of the fracture pattern. This contrasts with the radial and concentric fracture patterns caused by impact, which are more completely discussed in Chapter 9. The absence of stress and 'hackle' marks on the fracture surface is a further indication of the thermal nature of this type of breakage, there being no directional component to the breaking as there is in an impact fracture. The presence of soot or pyrolysis products on one face of thermally fractured glass fragments may also give some indication of the type of origin of the fire (for example slow and smoky).

It has been commonly held that slow heating produces few cracks which, although random, roughly follow the perimeter of the pane. Certainly, in extremely slowly developing fires there is generally a very low 'density' of thermal cracks. This is probably due to a combination of low thermal stress (i.e. only marginally critical temperature gradients across the thickness of the glass) and general expansion of the glass with respect to the frame. Frequently, however, there is insufficient glass remaining in windows after any well-developed fire to observe, with any accuracy, possibly different crack patterns. Changing temperatures arising from altered ventilation states may also modify the crack pattern. There is a distinct possibility that old glass, which develops a marked brittleness with time, will develop a higher 'crack density' than new glass.

The observer must also consider the effects of double glazing or other protection such as heavy curtaining or shuttering. These will severely distort fracture patterns as a result of partial insulation of the external glass from the original fire development. With sealed double glazing units it has been known for an inner pane to show normal heat cracking while the outer pane is completely intact.

Thermal shock from hot to cold occurs when fire fighting water hits hot glass. Visual recognition of this is by the presence of 'pitting' on one surface (usually the original outer surface which may well be the opposite face to the smoke stained surface in normal conditions), (see Plate 9B). Stressing, akin to broken, toughened glass may possibly be observed.

Plate 7D. Heat distortion of a gas-filled incandescent light bulb. This occurs on the side facing the heat. Photo: B. R. G. Roberts.

The melting of glass can provide some directional information as well as suggesting maximum achieved temperatures. Electric lamp bulbs can, provided that they survive the fire fighting, indicate the hotter side and thus the direction of heat flow (see Plate 7D). Bulbs for domestic illumination are generally gas filled. Softening of the glass envelope is accompanied by an internal pressure increase and this results in the bulb bulging outwards at the softest point. Conversely, small valves, fluorescent tubes and neon indicator lamps have an internal vacuum and will collapse on the hotter, soft side. These observations must, as always, be used with caution as suspended lamps can swivel in a fire. Fixed installations, as for example wall or table lights, may be capable of giving more meaningful results.

The general softening or actual melting of glass will give an estimate of the temperature of the fire. On its own such an observation may be meaningless as to the location of the seat, but considering that flame temperatures are well above the softening point of normal window glass, localised damage may indicate locations of interest. The changes in glass with temperature are discussed in Chapter 9 and Appendix A.

Melting and distortion of metals
Sub-dividing the metal contents of buildings into structural and furnishing, temperature ranges can be deduced by the appearances of metal objects after a fire. It is of great importance to remember that in many cases these are merely temperature effects or, possibly, a combination of temperature and loading effects. Consequently, while they may well indicate the hotter parts of a fire they do not necessarily show that the fire started there. They are useful, however, in the formulation of the initial working hypothesis as to possible locations of the seats of fire.

(a) *Structural Steel Work*. Rolled steel joists, metal roof trusses, etc., particularly in modern buildings, are usually designed to cope with static loads (building mass) plus stress loads (environmentally produced) plus occupational loads, to give a safety margin of perhaps about one and a half times the total expected load. Any significant diminution of structural strength can produce rapid localised failure. Structural steel loses about 50% of its tensile strength at about 510°C and 66% of its strength at about 590°C. Fortunately for the fire investigator the progression of circumstances frequently works in his favour, in

Plate 7E. An unusual example of metal distortion. The radiator has expanded at its hotter end, indicating the direction of the major burning. Photo by Courtesy of West Yorkshire Metropolitan Police.

that, for instance, early roof venting will concentrate hotter pre-mixed flames around steel trusses. This can cause plastic deformation, visible even if the remainder of the roof eventually fails. Thus, while a completely stripped roof may show generalised sagging the originally exposed area may well show severe distortion.

Obviously, such observations can be meaningless unless the overall building construction is taken into account. Fire protection of columns and joists, specifically designed to confer substantial resistance to sagging and collapse during a fire, can cause totally misleading effects. Because distortion and collapse may well be resultant upon loading as well as strength, the presence or absence of heavy goods (e.g. cotton bales, which can absorb very large masses of fire-fighting water) must be noted. Abnormally long joist or roof spans, possibly as a result of building modifications, will have enhanced collapse characteristics.

The expansion of joists, recognised by operational fire fighters as a potential hazard in building stability in a fire, can be utilised to locate 'hot spots'. Tell-tale wall cracks, with subsequent recession of the butt ends of joists in their sockets after the final cooling down, may well show a localised hot area to have existed. As an example of this, a steel joist ten metres long and heated to 500°C will expand by about seven centimetres, assuming the coefficient of thermal expansion of steel to be an average of 14×10^{-6} metres per deg.°C.

(b) *Metal Contents.* Fitments within rooms, such as metal cabinets, shelving (particularly metal framed racking), door furniture, etc., can aid the location of hot areas and heat flow quite well. As an example of this, metal racking with its low thermal capacity will rapidly reach its 'fail' point when it is in the path of a thermal flow. Because this, similarly to smoke flow, is subject to gross changes during a fire when venting occurs, thermal signposts can exist to show whether a high level heat flow existed in an area as a result of a relatively remote fire, or whether lower distortion is present as a result of a low, nearby, seat of fire (see Plates 7E, 7F).

Plate 7F.   Progressive sagging of the hat pegs effectively demonstrates the location of the seat of fire in the centre foreground. Photo: G. Devonport.

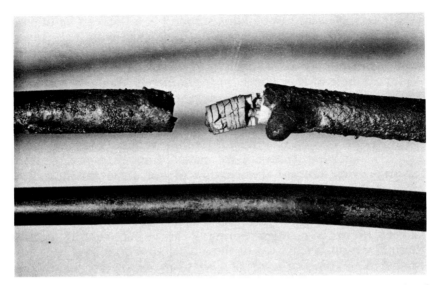

Plate 7G. The upper M.I.C.C. cable has violently arced as a result of penetration by a nail. That this is greater damage than could have been caused by ordinary exposure to a fire, can be seen by the companion cable. This latter is merely oxidised on its surface. Photo: R. A. Cooke.

Beyond the heat induced fail point of metals, melting and possibly other changes exist. These can aid the investigator in his estimation of relative temperatures within a room.

A table of melting points of metals and alloys can be found in Appendix A.

Judicious use of melting points and other factors will provide valuable pointers to areas of interest to the investigator. An example of this was found in one fire where severe melting to the copper jacket of mineral insulated copper clad cable (M.I.C.C.) in an otherwise apparently normal fire indicated localised arcing. Further enquiries revealed that immediately above this damaged cable, where a school stage had been, scenery for a school play had been nailed down a short time earlier. Because of poor earth resistance values to the circuit, a high resistance short circuit had been set up causing intense localised heating which did not, however, pass enough current to cause fuse failure. This was immediately apparent as the general temperature of the fire had never exceeded the melting point of copper, whereas the temperature of a continually arcing circuit can cause precisely this damage. (see Plate 7G).

(c) *Crystal Structure Analysis*. Some metals, notably copper, produce, under prolonged heating, internal crystal growth[3] which leads to the condition known as 'work hardening'. Attempts have been made in the past to utilise this fact by methods such as X-ray diffraction, (see also Chapter 18). Many problems surround the interpretation of such data. Work hardening is both time and temperature dependent, and fire brigade water can quench hot copper with deleterious effects. Doubtless, a marked crystal growth in one of several closely situated circuits may indicate excessive local heating, which may indicate the status of that circuit. Experiments have indicated that above external exposure temperatures of about 500°C—to be expected in a burning room — there are sufficient external heating effects to mask any internal crystalline growth.

Melting and Degradation of Plastics
The increasing use of plastics in buildings and their contents, provides the investigator with further aids; these being of more significance at the lower end of the temperature ranges which may be expected in a fire. Again, such lower temperatures can probably be used to reinforce observations of earlier heat and smoke flow, prior to full ventilation of room fires. Directional effects on plastic fitments may be quite pronounced in the earlier stages of a fire, and can provide valuable information, not only of the direction from which the fire started but of the relative intensity of the heat source.

It is probable that within the temperature range to be found in any hot gas stream coming from a fire, numerous plastics will degrade regardless of their composition. Spontaneous surface ignition due to enhanced surface temperatures may be a possible result of such exposure, but the reduction in the oxygen content in the gas stream from a fire can occasionally inhibit this.

It is impossible to cover completely the full range of commercial plastics and their fillers. The table in Appendix A gives some of the more usually encountered.

Thermosetting resins such as phenol formaldehyde or melamine formaldehyde, generally filled with inorganic materials such as calcium carbonate, titanium dioxide etc., produce rigid mouldings which are frequently found as electrical appliance bodies. These

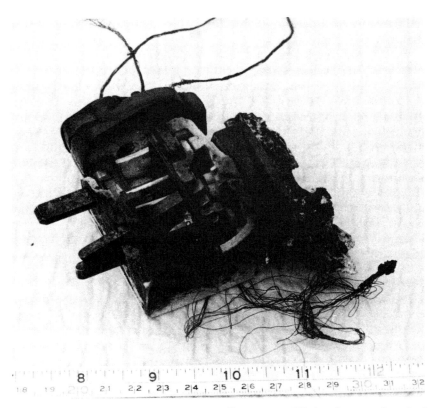

Plate 7H. Directional charring effects on filled plastic electrical components. The plugs and adaptor had not been plugged into a wall socket and had been laying on the floor when fire reached them. Charring decreasing from the outside inwards can be seen. Photo: M. J. Cooke.

do not melt, but they do char and may successfully demonstrate differences in heating from one part to another to indicate the hotter side (see Plate 7H).

A commonly encountered example of the melting and degradation of plastics which can indicate the direction from which heat has come is the well known 'sleeve' effect on wiring insulation and the related 'cindering' effect.

The sleeve effect is symptomatic of a hot wire (due to a persistent overload) charring and expanding the adjacent insulation to produce a clear sleeve around the wire. This is quite different to the effect of external heating which melts and chars the insulation onto the wire.

The cinder effect is due to the fact that as the plastic (either insulation or carcassing) heats, melts and chars, bubbles, larger on the hotter side, 'fix' in the char mass. These can be seen in cross-section using a modest magnification (frequently a hand lens is sufficient). The main problem with both of these effects is that under many fire situations, cause and effect is hard to distinguish by these methods alone. Heat will be transmitted along a conductor from a fire and simulate 'sleeving' at the extremities of the damage.

Burning Effects of Timber

(a) *Char Depth Measurement.* The measurement of char depth in burnt timber at a fire scene has frequently been the main basis for deciding the location of the seat of fire. While it is true to say that, in general, the depth and type of char can provide valuable information, its exclusive and automatic use can be extremely misleading.

Arising from the uncritical belief that within a fire environment, wood burns at a constant rate *no matter what its position is or what the localised fire loading is,* many investigators have developed 'techniques' which not only claim to locate the seat, but claim also to indicate precisely the length of time the fire has been burning. The basis for this belief has been the observation that the *mean* rate of char depth development in a standard test furnace is approximately 0.6 mm per minute (about 1/40″ per minute). Apart from the inherent error of measuring charcoal depth rather than the quantity of timber remaining (because the charcoal layer has shrunk when compared with the original wood), problems arise when this is translated into a back measurement from a 'real' as opposed to a standard test fire.

A comparison of the British Standard Specification 476 Test Furnace time/temperature curve, with those which can be achieved in real fires will immediately indicate the difficulties in translating test results in this way. Other national standards throughout the world give test fires of similar growth rate.

Charcoal is formed at surface temperatures above about 275°C[4][5] and its rate of production is very dependent on the radiation flux received by the wood surface. There are indications

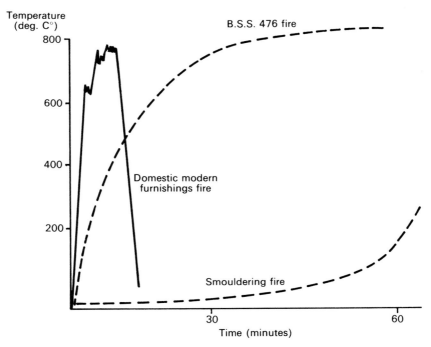

Figure 7.2. Comparison of time/temperature curves for different fires.

that the initial rate is of the same order as the quoted B.S.S. 476 value at very low compartment temperatures[6].

The indicated temperatures in Figure 7.3 assume perfect (black body) radiation (q.v.) and are, for any given radiation values, consequently somewhat lower than in actual fires. This is because radiation is absorbed by smoke and flames, and because burning objects have emissivities lower than unity.

Additionally, as the depth of char increases so the *rate* at which it develops decreases—assuming, of course, that no surface spalling, which would constantly expose fresh surfaces, occurs[7]. In Figure 7.4 at the lower temperature, the rate of char production is high. At higher temperatures this is slowed down by the insulation of the char surface.

It can be seen that on average in the standard test furnace the rate of char production *should* be roughly linear. Therefore, only if the rate of temperature increase in a room can be said to follow

94

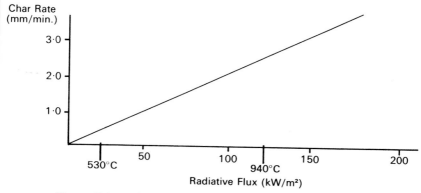

Figure 7.3. Change in char rate with varying heat flux.

standard test furnace characteristics, or possibly, if room temperatures can be assessed, can rates of char production be used as a time base for fire examinations. A fire loading of about 25–30 kg/m² (wooden cribs) may produce a fire of roughly B.S.S. 476 characteristics.

(b) *Char Patterns.* As wood chars and releases moisture and pyrolysis products, it shrinks, and the charcoal, so formed, cracks

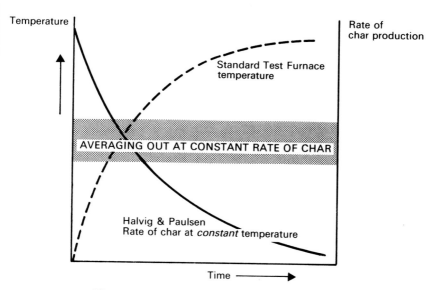

Figure 7.4. Change in char rate with time.

95

on the surface. The characteristic appearance of char pattern (the so-called 'alligatoring' or 'crocodiling' effects) has been interpreted by many investigators as diagnostic of the rate of fire development.

Reliance has been placed on such observations and claims have been made to distinguish fast fires where accelerants have been used, from non-accelerated fires by the char appearance.

To place much reliance on the appearance of char patterns is obviously dangerous. Fire development varies as ventilation and fuel availabilities vary, and frequently one may see differing char patterns at opposite ends of the same piece of wood. Char patterns are also species dependent[8]. Experiments, using different species of hardwoods under constant temperature conditions, have shown very wide variations in the charring patterns.

What does seem to be of limited use is that, in considering the

Plate 7I. The wider spaced cracks in timber char which may be caused by long exposure to a hot but smouldering fire. These can persist well into the free burning stage but interpretations of such patterns must be made with caution and must be formed with other confirmatory evidence. Photo: M. J. Cooke.

extremes of fire development and the fact that most structural timbers are softwoods, a very slow, sustained development can produce widely spaced, deep cracks running transversely to the grain (see Plate 7I). Conversely, very fast development can produce closer spaced cracking (see Plate 7J). Much surface spalling may result from rapid burning whereas the char developed in slow fires frequently shows the carbonised original surface. Confirmation of such char patterns where fast fire development occurs can be seen in the characteristic appearance of beams and rafters in roof spaces when fire has vented and exposed the wood to high temperature, well ventilated flame. It would, of course, be expected that in any fire where good ventilation existed at window or door openings, areas of relatively rapid burning will have existed according to the known relationships (see Chapter 1, Effects of Structures and Contents). Therefore, it will only be natural to see areas of apparently more rapid and, therefore, apparently more intense burning in these regions.

Further caution to be exercised in the interpretation of timber

Plate 7J.   This charcoal surface pattern is the result of exposure to rapid, free flaming combustion with a high radiative flux. Other timbers in similar fire conditions may show decidedly different appearances, depending on the species. It is dangerous to rely solely on surface characteristics when trying to determine the rate of fire development. Photo: M. J. Cooke.

char is that many timber surfaces could have had modifying properties, (paints, fire-resistant finishes, etc.), and that laminates (e.g. melamine faced blockboards, etc.) do not necessarily follow the 'rules' for solid wood.

The Arrow Theory
The knowledge that char depth bears a relationship to the total quantity of radiated heat absorbed by a combustible surface, has given rise to a technique of fire seat location called the 'arrow theory'[9]. In its simplest form the proposition is that a surface charred by radiant heat from an object does in a manner which produces, in cross-section, a deeper char, closest to the burning object. Thus, an ill-defined three dimensional 'arrow', will point away from the heat source. On a plan, a pointer in the opposite direction can be indicated. If this can be repeated for many objects an accurate 'fix' for the original seat of fire can be made.

Objections to this approach are (i) that the described manner of charring is more typical of that produced by a point source of heat, something that never occurs in a real, developed fire and (ii) much depends on accurate reconstruction. The latter, of course, is an essential part of any fire investigation but it is inherently safer to use techniques less reliant on this, if at all possible.

Instrumental Aids
Various instruments are now available which can detect hydrocarbons in low concentrations, and several authorities, frequently in the U.S.A., have advocated their use at scenes of suspicious fires. At the current 'state of the art' there are two basic approaches, either to use a hydrocarbon detector or to use a portable gas chromatograph.

(a) *Hydrocarbon Detectors.* These are capable of detecting hydrocarbons down to concentrations of parts per million in the atmosphere, and can be used as a sweep over an area to register the location of unburnt fuel concentrations. The necessary requirements for a successful instrument are that it is capable of sensitive and specific hydrocarbon detection, and that it does not suffer from false positive responses as a result of traces of pyrolysis products in the debris. One possible solution to their response to pyrolysates is to fit a 'scrubber' before the detector[10]. This consists of a solution of an oxidising agent (acidified potassium dichromate solution appears to be the most suitable) through which the vapours to be detected must pass. Roadside alcohol breath test tubes, such as the 'Alcolyser' have been satisfactorily used. Pyrolysis products, frequently being polar materials, can often be totally eliminated leaving only the less reactive hydrocarbons to pass through to the detector.

With such detectors the debris generally must be turned over before full response is possible, which counters any logical excavation of the scene. If very heavy quantities of hydrocarbons exist they can invariably be smelled. A hydrocarbon detector may, under these conditions, mark out trails or multiple concentrations and be of some use. Extreme caution must be exercised in their use by roadsides, near vehicles and if fuel supplies have been locally damaged.

(b) *Portable Gas Chromatographs.* These instruments analyse the vapours and so give specific results. For their general construction and method of use see Appendix C1. They are, however, currently cumbersome, difficult to stabilise and require debris sampling which would better serve proper laboratory analysis.

(c) *Ultra-Violet Light.* Suggestions have been made that the residues of petroleum products will fluoresce under suitable ultra-violet light. Polynuclear aromatic hydrocarbons (found in petroleum residues) do fluoresce and there are analytical procedures in petroleum and oils analysis[11] which utilise this effect. At the scene, however, the conditions are generally unsuitable for any critical approach even when using narrow band U.V. emitters. The quenching effect on fluorescence by free carbon will seriously affect any results, and many other materials (paint, plaster, plastics, and paper) fluoresce sufficiently to make most scenes unreadable. It follows also that such examinations must be made in the dark. This can be both impracticable and dangerous.

A further objection to reliance on the above instrumental methods is their pre-requirement for a fire accelerant to have been used. Negative results are therefore meaningless and positive results must be validated by all the other physical approaches, a competent excavation and subsequent laboratory analysis.

Indirect methods of locating the seat
The methods proposed in this subsection are, for the most part, the utilisation of the overall information which any competent

99

investigator should possess. Some of this will have been found before the physical examination starts; some will emerge as the investigation proceeds.

Witnesses Observations
These may be available to the investigator in some form before he starts the physical examination of the scene and it is arguable whether the scene should be examined in the light of what the witness(es) have said or *vice versa.*

Psychologically, witnesses frequently find the recollection of accurate details of the fire disturbing and difficult particularly if they have a direct involvement or interest in the matter, whether real or imaginary. Over-reaction to sights and sounds which they have probably never experienced before can give rise to exaggerated accounts of the size of flames, of rooms 'exploding' etc. There is, unfortunately, little guidance possible in how to approach witnesses, how much to believe or whether or not to 'push' him further in the hope of extracting better information. The basic rules to observe are;

(i) Never to accept in entirety what he says — there may be things added (real in the imagination) and there will invariably be important things left out. The 'witness' may well have started the fire; this must never be forgotten.
(ii) Never lead your witness — therefore, ask questions which require a descriptive answer.

Other than the obviously subjective nature of most witnesses observations are the facts that their view of the fire is untutored and frequently made from some distance away. Too much should not be read into their words, particularly when descriptive passages are involved.

Professional witnesses, such as fire officers or policemen who attend the early stages of fire fighting will, of course, fall into a special class. Their presence at the scene should ensure a more analytical view of the conditions, at least for fire fighting or rescue tactics. It goes without saying that such officers must always be invited to give their observations to the investigator.

Reversal of Fire Fighting
The way in which a fire was fought can influence the appearance of the scene and due note of the methods used must be made.

Under some circumstances the use of hoses could actually drive fire ahead of them into previously unburnt areas — possibilities such as this should be considered.

The investigator should take steps to find out what equipment was used, for example, whether fine sprays or jets were deployed. Thus, the degree of scatter of the debris, the spalling of heated surfaces, the breakage of windows, etc., should be noted and appreciated.

It is highly important to find out how and when the appliances were deployed. An example of this could be found where an apparent seat of fire was due to the area having been by-passed by fire fighting and allowed to burn later and thus longer than its surroundings. Visually, there may be little to distinguish this from an original seat of fire until the method of fire fighting is examined.

Points of Entry and Exit

When a building has been burgled and deliberately set on fire it is rare (but not impossible) for the intruder to trap himself by the fire or fires so that under certain circumstances, predictions as to the possible locations of the seats of fire and their order of ignition can be made. More references to this can be found in Chapter 15, (Arson). At this stage, we can consider that, if entry has been gained by a window, it is relatively rare for a person starting fires inside a building to get out by the same way, particularly if the access was difficult. Exits by doors could be a much more likely way, and the consequent available routes between entry and exit may well hold the original seats of fire.

Positions of Bodies

In fatal fires, bodies will frequently be found in positions which indicate that they have tried to escape by moving away from heat and smoke. It is a well known feature of statutory Means of Escape planning that people are very reluctant to move into smoke. Their positions may well indicate the direction from which smoke was coming. In a single room there is a tendency for people to face away from excessive heat or flames before they fall and so it is possible to reconstruct (particularly with the reinforcing information of carbon monoxide and smoke inhalation or inhaled heat or flame) the type of fire the deceased was confronted with.

One cautionary aspect must be considered. When many people

are presented with an overwhelming experience of heat and smoke, and particularly if they are incapacitated by carbon-monoxide poisoning or alcohol, they will not react logically. People have got lost in their own familiar rooms and have presented investigators with puzzling features of body location, (see Chapter 10, Fires Involving Fatalities).

Knowledge of Materials Present
In the testing of hypotheses of possible fire seat location one must have knowledge of the fire behaviour of the materials present. At the beginning of this chapter it was pointed out how the accuracy of results depended on the rates of fire propagation, and is thus largely dependent upon the contents. So it is then, that this knowledge can help to confirm suspicions of the direction from which fire spread, as well as to help us to determine whether the seat of fire we have found is the real, original seat of fire or an apparent seat as described below.

Apparent seats of fire
Because of the uneven way in which most fires burn, there may well be more than one area of burning in a building which appears to be a seat of fire. As one of the criteria for determining arson is more than one independent and contemporaneous seat of fire, it is very important that those elements can be proved. Again, if several apparent seats are evident it is important that their causes are recognised and the true seat of fire is properly investigated.

Apparent seats of fire are merely the results of 'spottiness' in fire development and are produced by the very factors which cause fires to spread. It is convenient then to group them under the following headings:—

Convection
As fire spread is partly convected, it follows that shafts, ducts and stairwells will all contribute to the so-called 'chimney' effects which will lift hot gases to high parts of buildings, and raise combustible surfaces to their ignition point. Under some circumstances, secondary fires may start rapidly after the initial outbreak. Any area which contains high-level stacked goods or fixtures, such as plastic light fittings or polyester roof lights may well reach their spontaneous ignition temperatures in the first few

minutes of a rapidly developing fire. Flame development increases rapidly across ceilings as the buoyant gas layer fans out; values of seven-fold over the earlier vertical development have been quoted[12]. It follows that fires from this effect can be caused by burning materials dropping down to floor level well ahead of the low-level, lateral fire spread.

Conduction
Items of high thermal conductivity, such as steel joists, metal panels or air-conditioning trunking, are able to pass heat across otherwise highly fire resistant barriers. As temperatures higher than 250°C are critical for the ignition of cellulosic materials, it follows that a dangerously high temperature can be achieved by a joist or pipe passing from a fire environment (see Plate 7K).

Radiation
Any radiation which produces heat fluxes of about 28 kW per square metre or more can cause rapid spontaneous ignition of

Plate 7K. *This metal duct passed sufficient heat through a fire resistant floor to ignite cartons placed against it.*

cellulosic materials. Values above this have been measured from flames and it has been shown that heat induced flashover, in general, is largely the result of radiation from ceiling-borne flames radiating down onto receptive surfaces. Thus, sufficient radiation may well exist across gaps to ignite remote materials, to give the appearance of a totally separate fire. Law[13] has demonstrated that this can occur from building to building via the radiation from window openings from a fully developed fire in a compartment.

Ventilation
As has been seen in Chapter 1, the rate of fire development varies as to the degree of ventilation. Relatively intensely burnt areas can be found near windows, doors and ducts. In order to check whether these are valid seats of fire or not, a comparison of each ventilated area must be made as well as establishing the direction of wind. In this way, a seat of fire found near a window could be isolated as a suspicious area.

High Fire Loading
Such areas may well have burnt persistently during fire fighting or may have ignited particularly easily. It is important to check on what materials were in that position and what form they were in. Not only the calorific value of materials, but the rate at which they burn, must be known.

Rapid Surface Spread of Flame
Bridging materials can link fire areas before general fire spread due to flashover takes over. In this way, the arsonist utilises 'trailers' between several seats of fire.

In a domestic environment polystyrene veneer sheet or tiles may be surface coated with paint or paper. This combination can cause a very rapid linear fire spread which could link pieces of furniture, or cause numerous dropping fires. If fire drops onto susceptible articles this can give the appearance of multiple original seats of fire.

Areas of Reduced Fire Resistance
Modifications to walls, floors and ceilings can cause markedly different localised burning patterns to develop. Such modifications could be caused by open hatchways in otherwise imperforate

walls, or by substituting modern plastics materials for, or possibly to complement, existing, more substantial features. Modern 'antique' pub decor now often consists of light wooden hollow beams and/or rigid, polyurethane foam moulded beams and wall panels, which possess virtually no resistance to fire.

Reduced fire resistance may also be caused by environmental factors, such as dry-rot, the dessication of wood by hot pipes, etc., thus giving rise to possible confusion of fires developing under floors.

Burning of Gases, Vapours and Liquids
In the normal progression of burning, ignitable vapours are given off from pyrolysing solids or liquefying materials. These may flow for considerable distances if they are not ignited on the spot, as may happen, for instance, in ventilation restricted zones.

A more frequently encountered situation is where a gas pipe fails during a fire and produces its own locally intense burning within the overall burning.

Aerosol cans, if involved, almost certainly will travel extensively across a burning room while ejecting burning propellant. A butane propelled aerosol hairspray container can produce a fireball of about two metres diameter and a butane lighter refill has been known to travel about twenty metres from its ignition point.

Secondary Electrical Effects
These are possible in situations where fault currents cause localised high resistance heating (See Chapter 18, Electricity). Effects of this nature may be found below floorboards or behind skirtings and may be the reason for a fire being labelled as an electrical fire when the observed feature is only secondary.

Fire Fighting Procedures
During fire fighting, as has been indicated earlier, objects may be displaced by jets and the fire front may be driven forward. An examination of fire fighting methods can indicate these possibilities which otherwise can produce intractable problems of interpretation.

One of the major problems, however, in eliminating an apparent seat of fire is that, if the area has been allowed to burn persistently after the remainder has been extinguished, then that area can show low level burning almost indistinguishable from an original seat of fire. Therefore, areas of low fire fighting priority and possible 'bulls-eyes' (unextinguished pockets of smouldering) must be identified.

These areas may possess some distinguishing features, such as excessive warmth while surrounding debris is cold, evidence of dry ash present in otherwise wet debris or even that it is still smouldering. Frequently, the materials present (e.g. fibrous natural materials) can indicate the likelihood of these possibilities.

One extremely confusing feature which may present itself to the investigator is that of fire damage from a previous fire. This may be documented, particularly if the earlier fire had occurred only a short time before. Longstanding fire damage where floorboards or joists may have been burned several years before and the damage repaired, covered over and forgotten, may give a misleading appearance to the scene. Under favourable circumstances there should be evidence of ageing, for example, dust, cobwebs and other obvious signs. Where copious quantities of water have been used in fighting the later fire this evidence could be washed away leaving the investigator with uncharacteristic burn patterns. It is important, then, that the fullest possible history of the building is obtained if any suspicion of previous fires exists.

Computer Modelling
As many of the factors influencing fire growth are now understood, it is possible to build up a predictive model of a fire in a compartment. Computer programmes have been devised to do this[14][15][16].

The fire investigator may be in a position where, having hypothesized how and where a fire started and how it then developed, he needs to be able to check his beliefs. Alternatively, he may need to see whether or not the results he has observed could also have been the results of a different cause.

A computer program for model fire growth can be used for hypothesis testing provided that accurate measurements of compartment geometry, ventilation, fire load characteristics etc., have been made. This approach has the advantage of objectivity but is currently limited in its application because it is often uncertain as to how and when some of the influencing parameters became important (e.g. the time when windows failed or whether doors were open).

There is little doubt, however, that as techniques become

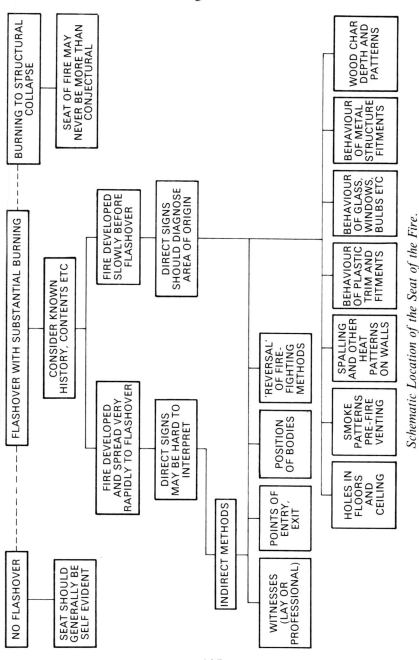

Schematic Location of the Seat of the Fire.

The following text appears within the flowchart:

- BURNING TO STRUCTURAL COLLAPSE
- SEAT OF FIRE MAY NEVER BE MORE THAN CONJECTURAL
- FLASHOVER WITH SUBSTANTIAL BURNING
- CONSIDER KNOWN HISTORY, CONTENTS ETC
- FIRE DEVELOPED SLOWLY BEFORE FLASHOVER
- DIRECT SIGNS SHOULD DIAGNOSE AREA OF ORIGIN
- FIRE DEVELOPED AND SPREAD VERY RAPIDLY TO FLASHOVER
- DIRECT SIGNS MAY BE HARD TO INTERPRET
- NO FLASHOVER
- SEAT SHOULD GENERALLY BE SELF EVIDENT
- INDIRECT METHODS
- WITNESSES (LAY OR PROFESSIONAL)
- POINTS OF ENTRY, EXIT
- POSITION OF BODIES
- 'REVERSAL' OF FIRE-FIGHTING METHODS
- HOLES IN FLOORS AND CEILING
- SMOKE PATTERNS PRE-FIRE VENTING
- SPALLING AND OTHER HEAT PATTERNS ON WALLS
- BEHAVIOUR OF PLASTIC TRIM AND FITMENTS
- BEHAVIOUR OF GLASS, WINDOWS, BULBS ETC
- BEHAVIOUR OF METAL STRUCTURE FITMENTS
- WOOD CHAR DEPTH AND PATTERNS

refined, more uses will be made of this technique, particularly in litigation where counter-accusations may need to be resolved.

References
(1) H. P. Morgan and N. P. Savage. 1980. Study of a Large Fire at St. Johns Centre. 1977.
(2) P. L. Kirk. 1969. Fire Investigation. p. 73 John Wiley & Sons.
(3) D. W. Levinson. 1977. Fire Technology (13) 211.
(4) G. S. Hall, R. G. Saunders, R. T. Allcorn, P. E. Jackman, M. W. Hickey and R. Fitt. 1972. Fire Performance of Timber. Timber Research and Development Association.
(5) G. S. Hall, *et al.* Fire Performance of Timber (Ibid).
(6) E. G. Butcher. 1976. Fire Surveyor *5* (6) 29–33 (and references therein).
(7) S. Hadvig and O. R. Paulsen. 1976. Journal of Fire and Flammability *1* (1) 57–66.
(8) G. S. Hall. 1983. Fire Resistance of Timber Elements. Timber Review TRADA.
(9) J. Kennedy. 1977. Fire, Arson and Explosion Investigation. Chicago Invest. Inst.
(10) J. Twibell, personal communication.
(11) J. B. F. Lloyd. 1971. Journal of the Forensic Science Society. Vol. 11. Nos. 2, 3.
(12) S. A. Ames, personal communication.
(13) M. Law. 1968. Radiation from Fires in a Compartment. F. R. Technical Paper. No. 20. H.M.S.O.
(14) G. Cox and S. Kumar. 1983. Computer Modelling of Fire. IP 2/83. Building Research Establishment.
(15) R. D. Peacock and J. N. Breese. Computer Fire Modelling for the Prediction of Flashover. 1982 U.S. National Bureau of Standards.
(16) H. E. Mitler and H. W. Emmons. Documentation for CFC V, The Fifth Harvard Computer Fire Code. U.S. Department of Commerce. National Bureau of Standards.

Chapter 8

Excavation and Sampling Techniques

Fire investigation is in many respects analogous to archaeology. The location of seats of fire corresponds to the initial field work carried out by archaeologists, and in both disciplines an excavation stage is normally necessary[1].

Early archaeologists dug energetically for museum specimens, tending to discard anything which was imperfect or which they found uninteresting. The first archaeologist to show a scientific approach was Lt. Gen. Pitt-Rivers, who realised that the relative positions of the artifacts which he recovered, could give information about the sequence of events and the relative ages of the recovered items. Pitt-Rivers recorded meticulously the positions of man-made articles and even items of no apparent significance. From his detailed notes and plans, subsequent archaeologists are able to test theories put forward long after his death.

Pitt-Rivers had realised two things; first that the strata laid down during the different ages, formed a sequential time record which could be used to compare the ages of buried items, and secondly, that once a site was excavated, all of this information was lost for ever, unless careful records had been kept.

Debris which falls to floor level during the progress of a fire, forms layers which correspond to different stages of the fire.

The time scale of a building fire is measured in minutes or hours rather than centuries or millennia and as a result, the fire investigator cannot expect to find the neat characteristic strata sometimes present in archaeological excavations. Large items such as partially burned joists, pipes and conduits may be buried amidst fine debris containing wood ash, charcoal, plaster, paper, fabric, glass and many other materials.

However, significant information may be acquired from investigation of the diffuse stratification commonly encountered at fire scenes and from consideration of the positions of items recovered from the debris. Exactly as in archaeology, a great deal of evidence can be lost if the debris is disturbed either during fire-

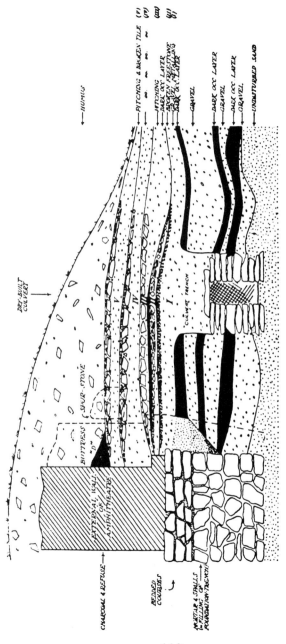

Figure 8.1. The results of an archaeological excavation showing stratification in the vicinity of an external wall of a Roman amphitheatre at Caerleon Gwent.

fighting procedures, or during an inexpert and half-hearted investigation of fire cause.

The need for excavation

Fires tend to burn upwards and debris falls downwards, with the result that the seat of the fire is likely to be buried beneath debris formed during the development of the fire. If the cause of the fire is to be established, it will often be necessary for the investigator to dig through the debris to the seat. However, there can be many possible reasons for excavation and the main objectives should be decided at the beginning of the investigation.

Excavation may be required for one or more of the following reasons:—

(1) To locate the seat or seats of the fire.

(2) To confirm the location of the seat or seats.

(3) To reconstruct pre-fire room geometry.

(4) To study events which occurred prior to the fire.

(5) To seek items said to have been in the vicinity prior to the fire.

(6) To seek incendiary devices or any accidental sources of ignition.

(7) To seek evidence of the use of liquid or other fire accelerants.

(8) To study times and temperatures.

Location of seats of fire

When it has proved impossible to locate the seat of a fire by orthodox methods, location by means of excavation is sometimes used as a last resort measure. This decision will be made in the full knowledge that some evidence may be lost with the disturbance of the debris.

Normally a regular pattern of small test holes is dug in order that the floor or skirting board may be examined. The exact positions of the test holes will be to some extent, dictated by the positions of large items such as burnt joists, distributed around the floor area. The more systematic the pattern of test holes, the more objective the assessment and comparison of floor charring can be.

In addition to the regular pattern of exploratory holes, a narrow strip excavated around the base of the wall exposing the

111

Plate 8A.   Melted lead. Lead which melted at roof level, fell on to a low shelf and solidified in the form of stalactites. The solidification of the lead (melting point 327°C) demonstrated that the shelf had been below this relatively low temperature at the time. Photograph: B. R. G. Roberts.

skirting board (if present) may give useful information regarding the variations in low level fire intensity.

Items recovered during the excavation may also indicate the position of the seat of fire. The fused lead (Plate 8a) had been found on the edge of a low level shelf at the supposed seat of a large fire. The lead had partially solidified on the shelf and had formed stalactites hanging from the edge. It was evident that the lead had originated from lead roof flashings, and clearly the temperature at roof level had been above the melting point of lead. At the position where the lead had been found, the temperature had been below its melting point. Since lead melts at the relatively low temperature of 327°C, it is clear that this point could not have been the seat of the fire. Subsequent examination, confirmed by excavation, revealed that the seat of the fire had been about 20 metres from this point.

The propane cylinder (Plate 8b) was found in the debris at ground level after a particularly destructive fire which had consumed all of the wooden floors of the building. The cylinder had been left upright by workmen on the first floor, and one theory was that the fire had been caused by a blowtorch associated with this cylinder.

If this had been the case, the fire must have started on the first floor and the cylinder would have been more or less equally heat damaged all over, except for the base on which it had been standing. When it was recovered from the debris at ground floor level, the only undamaged region of paintwork on the cylinder was that part which had been buried in the debris. The damage is consistent with the cylinder having suffered no heat damage until the floor burnt away from below. The cylinder fell into an inferno at ground level and lay partly buried at an angle in the debris.

Reconstruction of room geometry

It is not uncommon to find that furniture in a burnt room has been rearranged or removed during fire fighting operations. For a satisfactory reconstruction of events during and prior to the fire, it is necessary to establish the exact positions of all articles of furniture at the time of the fire. The legs of tables and chairs, and the undersurfaces of bookcases and doors, tend to shield the floor or floor covering in all but the very fiercest of fires. Careful excavation, using an instrument such as a small pointing trowel, can reveal these shielded areas, and the positions of most items at

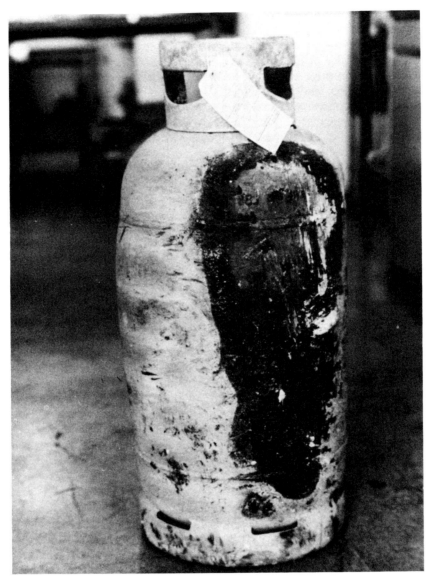

Plate 8B.   The heat pattern on this propane cylinder indicates that it had been lying on its side whilst exposed to the heat of the fire. The left hand side of the cylinder is distorted and heat damaged, the right hand side shows an area of protected paintwork. Photograph B. R. G. Roberts.

the time of the fire can normally be established. Surprisingly perhaps, the position of articles of furniture may even be established when the furniture itself has been almost completely burnt away.

Study of pre-fire events

It can sometimes be shown that the articles of furniture had not been in their accustomed positions at the time of the fire, and that some had been lying on their sides. Findings of this nature may indicate that there had been a struggle prior to the fire or that an intruder had carried out a search of the premises. The presence of buckets, saucepans or other vessels which could have contained water, near to the seat of fire, may indicate that an attempt had been made to fight the fire during the early stages. A protected area of floor covering beneath the vessel would indicate that it had been present throughout the hottest part of the fire. If all legitimate visitors to the building deny having fought the fire, it is possible that an intruder started the fire and then, surprised by its severity, tried to put it out. Displaced fire extinguishers may tell the same story.

Fires are frequently started in an attempt to conceal the evidence of another crime such as fraud, theft or murder. Arson to conceal fraud is most frequently committed by the owner, or an employee of the company whose premises have caught fire. Such fires may occur before a stock-taking or audit, and it is not unknown for accounts books or other documents to be involved at or near the seat of the fire. However, books and uncrumpled wads of paper do not necessarily burn well. A rectangle of protected carpet may provide evidence that an account book had been lying on the floor throughout the fire and the pages of the book, although charred and wet, may still be readable. Paper deliberately crumpled in order to start a fire burns more completely than a pile of flat sheets of paper, but even this may be recognisable and partially legible.

When arson is committed to conceal burglary, items may be missing or displaced. Doors, windows and drawers may show evidence of having been open or damaged prior to the fire. Details of the examination to establish whether doors and windows have been open or closed are covered more fully in Chapter 9, 'Deductive Evidence at Fire Scenes'.

When it is necessary to establish whether any articles have been stolen from the fire-damaged building it is very useful if a person familiar with the fire-damaged area can be available. The person should ideally have worked or lived in the area in question and should be able to list the items which had been present.

There are dangers in using a 'native guide' in this way. It is probable that the witness may feel that he himself is under suspicion of having started the fire by some careless act, or even deliberately. It is therefore very common for the witness to bias his account, in order that he will seem to have behaved perfectly properly. He will have unplugged all electrical appliances, and he will most certainly not have smoked. Statements of witnesses should therefore be confirmed independently where possible.

There is also a definite possibility that the witness had himself started the fire, and it is clearly advisable that he does not learn anything of the opinions of the investigators during the excavation process. For this reason some investigators prefer to keep the witness away from the excavation site, and to send items to him for identification. This indirect approach has the serious disadvantage that the witness cannot comment upon the exact location of items as they are excavated.

Recognition of items recovered from the debris
Many items commonly present in buildings, can assume a totally different appearance after being involved in a fire. They may have melted, cracked or become distorted. The surface coating of paint may have become charred or oxidised, and the article may be coated in soot. In addition, the organic portions may have melted or burnt away. It is however, important for the remains of items recovered from the debris to be recognised during the excavation process.

Identification is necessary in order to confirm or refute the statements of witnesses, to establish whether any items have been removed prior to the fire and to account for any item which is apparently extraneous. It is also essential that the typical remains of incendiary devices should be recognised.

Radius of Error
Whilst useful information can be obtained by excavation in many different parts of the fire scene, it is evident that most information regarding the actual cause of fire, will be gained by excavation at the fire seat. Here a difficulty arises. Although it may be possible

to locate the fire seat with considerable accuracy at some scenes, at many, the seat could be anywhere within a large area. It should however be possible for the investigator to draw a circle on a plan of the fire scene, and be satisfied that the fire started within that circle. The most probable seat of fire would normally be at the centre of the circle, and the size of the circle would reflect his uncertainty with regard to the exact location of the fire seat. To be certain of excavating the true seat of fire, the investigator must excavate the whole area within his circle.

Radius of error (metres)	Area to be excavated (square metres)
1	3
2	12
3	28
4	50
5	78
6	113
7	153
8	201
9	254
10	314

As the investigator's uncertainty increases, so the radius of the circle (radius of error) increases, and the area to be excavated increases immensely. It follows that the excavation at a fire with a radius of error of 10 metres, is very much less likely to be successful in establishing the cause of the fire, than one in which the radius of error is only about 1 metre. Much time and effort should therefore be devoted to locating the seat of fire as exactly as possible.

In most fires, the boundary line around the area including the seat of fire, will not form a perfect circle. Because of the geometry of articles of furniture, and the natural boundary effect of walls in the vicinity, the shape may be an oval, a semi-circle or an amoeboid shape for which no geometrical term exists. No matter what the shape, it is still of value to make an approximate estimate of the radius of error, since this can be taken into account when attempting to estimate the rate of fire build-up.

Approach to the Excavation of the Fire Seat
(1) Check that the area to be excavated is safe to work in. The

Plate 8C.   Excavation at a large fire scene. Debris from the supposed seat of fire was removed with pointing trowels and sieved twice. The survey poles mark identifiable positions at the support posts of storage racks. Photograph R. H. Ide.

118

seat of the fire is likely to be one of the most dangerous parts of the building. It is common for the floor to be weakened and for the roof to be damaged above the fire seat. It may be necessary to make the area safe by carefully dislodging loose roofing tiles, or deliberately breaking precariously cracked windows or sky-lights. At some fire scenes it may be necessary to abandon the excavation altogether.

(2) Decide upon the radius of error. All of the floor area within this radius will need to be excavated.

(3) Where practicable, plan, record and photograph the scene in general, particularly the region of the seat of the fire.

(4) Clear an adjacent area to accommodate items recovered during the excavation. This stage, though desirable, may not be practicable at many fire scenes. It should not be undertaken if there is a possibility that evidence may be destroyed. It is however, important that all materials and items recovered during the excavation proper should be retained.

Alternatives to clearing another area of floor, include placing debris recovered from the fire seat on surfaces such as plastic sheets, or doors removed from other parts of the building.

(5) Enlist the aid of a person familiar with the building and its contents.

(6) Excavate carefully through the strata, identifying each item as it is recovered from the debris if possible.

The relative positions of recovered items can be of great significance, but rearrangement of debris frequently occurs during fire fighting. Undisturbed debris can be recognised from indications such as the presence of large undamaged pieces of charred paper, protected areas on two adjacent items corresponding with each other, stratification effects, the absence of unburnt material on top of the debris and the close proximity to one another of all of the fragments which had originated from one item.

It is desirable to identify as many items and materials excavated from the fire seat area as possible. This is necessary so that everything which should have been in the area can be accounted for, and extraneous items can be recognised.

As the burnt objects are recovered, they should be temporarily stored in a safe place such as a particular region of the cleared adjacent area or on a flat surface. If stored in this way, the items are safe from loss or damage until a decision has been reached whether they are of significance to the enquiry. Items immediately recognised as being of significance should be packaged, labelled and taken into the possession of (normally) one individual, preferably a scene of crime officer. Where there is a danger of significant contamination, samples should be taken into the possession of the minimum number of individuals consistent with sample integrity.

Extraneous items and materials
In the investigation of arson, the extraneous items likely to be encountered during excavation are containers, incendiary devices, matches and 'trailers'.

Incendiary devices normally consist of some form of delayed action mechanism together with a means of ignition. The two criteria can be simply combined in the case of a fuse, which also has the advantage to the arsonist that it is destroyed during its operation. Commonplace objects such as cigarettes, lengths of string and candles have been used as fuses, but many have been unsuccessful because the flammable materials at the end of the fuse have failed to ignite. For this reason, arsonists frequently set several devices throughout the building, and a search of the unburnt rooms may reveal devices which had failed to operate.

Smouldering fuses can cause characteristic charring patterns to floorboards or whatever materials they have been in contact with.

The other type of incendiary device which may provide physical evidence at the fire seat, is the combined timer and electrical igniter. Timing devices may consist of clocks or watches (often modified by the removal of a hand) with wires attached. Other items as dissimilar as clothes pegs and integrated circuits can be used as timers.

Electrical ignition is normally effected by means of a battery and some form of heating element. Components such as these, will survive most fires and will remain in close association with one another provided that the debris has not been disturbed.

Cans or bottles which had contained liquid fire accelerants, may be found at or near the seat of the fire. Most common amongst these are five litre and one gallon rectangular oil cans. When recovered from the debris of a reasonably destructive fire, cans of this type may have lost their handles and necks as a result of the melting of the soldered joints. A search should be made for the neck of the can, in order to establish whether the cap had been in

120

position. It is often possible for a laboratory examination to establish the nature of the original markings on the can, even when the paint appears to have been completely burnt off.

Cans believed to be extraneous to the scene should be sealed, kept upright and handled as little as possible. It is also desirable that the outside of the can should be allowed to dry, otherwise it will rust and conceal identification evidence.

Bottles recovered during excavation are generally in an extremely fragile state because of the fine cooling cracks in the glass. Bottles which have been used as petrol bombs may be recognised by the presence of the remains of a fabric wick in the neck, and sometimes by characteristic soot deposition on the glass. When it is suspected that a petrol bomb has been thrown into a building, evidence that a window has been broken prior to the fire should be sought. Unsooted glass may be found at the lowest debris level, directly under the window in question. The window itself may show evidence of having been broken from outside, and a plume of relatively intense smoke staining may be present on the outside of the wall above the window.

Milk bottles are the type of bottle most commonly used as petrol bombs in the UK, having the advantages that they are free, difficult to trace and wide-necked for easy insertion of the wick.

Bottles brought to the scene full of accelerant are most commonly screw capped. When the arsonist has finished pouring or sprinkling accelerant on the floor he often throws the cap and the bottle down separately, although arsonists with tidy minds have been known to screw the cap back on to the empty bottle. Heat damaged bottle fragments seldom retain traces of fire accelerant but some bottle caps incorporate sealing disks which retain detectable quantities of fire accelerant for some time. It is often worthwhile to package extraneous bottle caps for laboratory analysis.

Fire Accelerants

Liquid fire accelerants used in the UK include petrol, white spirit, paraffin and diesel fuel. The presence of any of these agents at the seat of the fire may be recognised by smell or by characteristic char damage.

'*Crocodiling*'. Some workers believe that the burning of fire accelerants in the proximity of woodwork, produces characteristic small charcoal cubes, which differ from the normal larger cubes of charcoal on wood surfaces. Various experiments carried out at British Forensic Science laboratories and at the Fire Services College have failed to confirm this theory, and it must be viewed with deep suspicion.

Liquid burns. The burning of liquid fire accelerants poured on to a floor may produce a characteristic hard edged burn mark. Such marks have been observed on wood, carpet, upholstery fabrics and even on non-porous painted surfaces.

The hard edge of the burn mark approximates to the edge of the liquid spillage pool, and may spread along floorboard cracks. Under floorboards there may be evidence that accelerant has passed through cracks and knot holes in the wood, and there may be evidence of some burning beneath the boards. Prolonged burning in a region where fire accelerants have been used, may result in a hole in the floor, but the existence of a hole is by no means conclusive evidence of their use. Hard-edged burn marks do not demonstrate conclusively that a liquid fire accelerant had been used. Falling burning material, particularly blazing drops of melted or decomposed plastic, produce marks which may be difficult or impossible to distinguish from those made by a liquid fire accelerant. The burning of certain types of carpet can also mimic this effect.

Hydrocarbon fire accelerants have the property that they are driven away from the source of heat by a surface tension effect. As a result, after the fire has been extinguished, most of the unburnt accelerant will have been driven to the sides of the burnt area and into small gaps and crevices. It can sometimes be smelt when floor level debris, such as partially burnt carpet, is lifted during the excavation. Samples for laboratory analysis should therefore be taken from the edges of suspected liquid burning damage. Samples of partially burnt carpet or other floor covering may yield a positive analysis result for fire accelerants, even if it was not possible to smell the accelerants at the scene. Samples of skirting board, partially burnt floorboard and soil from beneath the floor may also be significant.

Samples for hydrocarbon analysis should be sealed into a container which is impervious to hydrocarbons, such as a nylon bag, glass jar or metal can. The samples should be labelled immediately with details of the location from which they were taken.

It is often desirable for one or more control samples to be

taken. These must contain the same types of material as the questioned (fire seat) sample, but should be from a source where it is believed that accelerant had not been present.

Control samples are particularly important when unfamiliar accelerants are suspected. The accelerant might be a petroleum mixture which could have been used as a solvent. The question then arises, was the solvent added as a fire accelerant, or had it been present in, for example, a floor covering adhesive? If no similar mixture is detected in the control sample, then the accelerant was limited to the region of the fire seat and did not originate from a widely used legitimate source. It is important that control samples should be packaged and stored in exactly the same manner as the questioned sample.

Sampling for liquid fire accelerants should be accompanied by a rigorous check into possible innocent explanations for the presence of any accelerant which may subsequently be detected. Had any flammable liquids been stored near to, or above the supposed seat of fire? Had there been a paraffin heater in the vicinity? Had there been any spillage of fuel elsewhere? The possibility of contamination should always be borne in mind and it is important to avoid the use of, for example, a petrol driven generator in the same room as the fire seat. When it is necessary to examine items such as containers of fuel at the scene, it is preferable that only one investigator should do this. It is desirable that he should then take no further part in the excavation except perhaps to make notes.

Solid fire accelerants

Crumpled paper is frequently used as a fire accelerant. Most commonly the paper has originated from the damaged building, but sometimes it is brought to the scene by the arsonist, in which case useful evidence of identification may be obtained from it.

Charred crumpled paper has a characteristic appearance, and certain types of paper, particularly the type used in glossy magazines, produce charred residues which can survive and remain legible after quite extensive fires. Samples of charred paper for laboratory examination should be lifted carefully with a flat trowel and placed in a shallow cardboard box.

It is sometimes suspected that the fire has been started by the use of a solid incendiary mixture. Most of these mixtures consist of an oxidising agent mixed with a reducing agent, and all tend to leave solid residues. Analysis of residues of this type may indicate which materials had been involved, but it is particularly important that several control samples should be taken from the region around the suspected area.

General Excavation
Whilst excavation at the seat of the fire may indicate the cause, a great deal of information relating to seat location and mode of fire spread can be obtained by excavation in other parts of the building. For example, consider the living room (Fig. 8.2). The furnishings include a matching armchair and settee, a television set and a metal waste-paper bin. Windows at both ends of the room are hung with flammable curtains and the pictures are suspended by flammable cords. On the floor is a fitted carpet with a foam rubber underlay.

Consider what would happen if the armchair was ignited either accidentally or deliberately, and went into flames (Fig. 8.3). The flames would steadily increase in height and would soon ignite the nearby curtain at a fairly low level, and so at an early stage in the fire, partially burnt curtains would fall blazing to the floor. The window may break due to thermal cracking at this stage. Meanwhile the flames from the chair will increase in height until

Figure 8.2. The undamaged living room (see text). Figure D. S. Loxley.

124

Figure 8.3. Development of a fire after ignition of the armchair (see text). Figure D. S. Loxley.

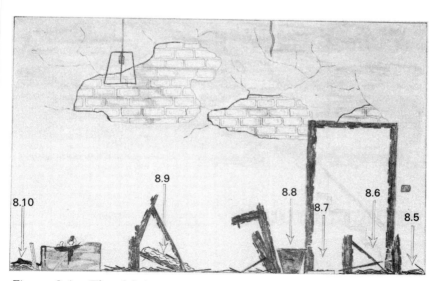

Figure 8.4. The debris remaining in the living room after a fairly destructive fire (see text). Figure D. S. Loxley.

125

they reach the ceiling, where they will spread horizontally causing heat damage at a high level. As a result, the light fittings and pictures may fall, and the curtains at the left-hand end of the room may burn through at a high level and fall to the floor. The left window is likely to break at this stage and the temperature in the room may be close to the softening temperature of glass. The settee is likely to ignite at about this stage of the fire and the thermoplastic parts of the TV set will melt. Finally all unprotected portions of the carpet will ignite, melt or char depending upon the materials involved. (Fig. 8.4).

There may possibly be some evidence that the fire had started at the right-hand side of the room but not necessarily so. In a rapidly developing fire of this type, the damage tends to be fairly uniform, and if the carpet had been made of a flammable material, a uniform low-level char may be anticipated.

Let us consider what we might expect to find if we were to excavate in various different regions of the room.

If the fire was discovered and extinguished shortly after the flashover it may be found that part of the carpet had been protected by the fall of the partially burnt curtain. On top of the curtain would be fragments of glass which had broken in the

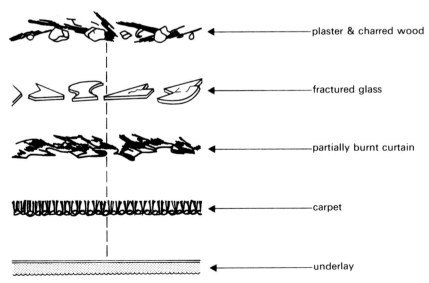

plaster & charred wood

fractured glass

partially burnt curtain

carpet

underlay

Figure 8.5. Behind the armchair. Figure D. S. Loxley.

126

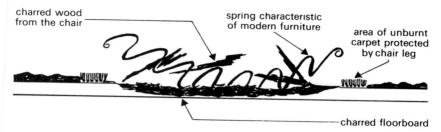

Figure 8.6. Underneath the armchair. Figure D. S. Loxley.

manner characteristic of a sudden rise in temperature. (See Deductive Evidence at Fire Scenes, Chapter 9). On top of the glass may be charred wood and spalled plaster (Fig. 8.5). The light switch, which may be recovered from the wall or floor in this general area, may still show evidence whether it had been on or off at the time of the fire.

Polyurethane foam, the most commonly used upholstery padding material in the UK normally decomposes when heated, forming flammable liquids. The flammable decomposition products burn in the manner of liquid fire accelerants producing typical liquid burns and sometimes holes in the floor. In the regions beneath the armchair and the settee there will, therefore, be

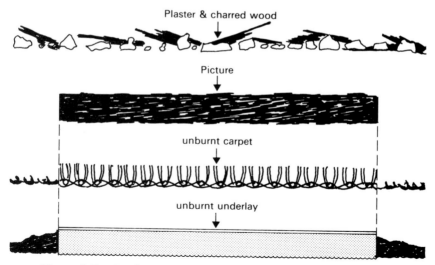

Figure 8.7.   Under the right-hand picture. Figure D. S. Loxley.

burning to the floor. However, it is still normal for there to be small unburnt pieces of carpet which had been protected by the undersurfaces of the legs of the furniture. These pieces of carpet are unlikely to have moved, even during quite disruptive fire-fighting procedures and can therefore be used to establish the exact positions of the chair and the settee at the time of the fire.

There may be a rectangle of uncharred carpet protected by the picture which fell during the early stages of the fire (Fig. 8.7). The picture is likely to be charred on its upper surface and will have been buried by falls of plaster and charred wood. (Fig. 8.7).

It may be found that the bottom papers and rubbish in the waste paper bin had not burnt, although the top papers will be

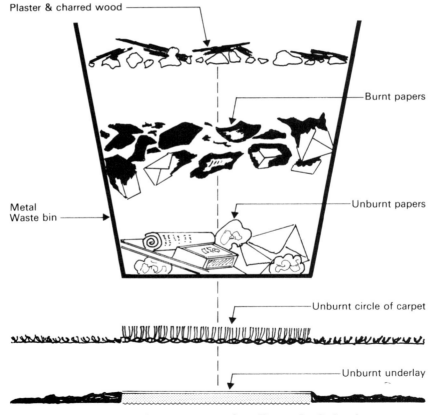

Plaster & charred wood

Burnt papers

Metal
Waste bin

Unburnt papers

Unburnt circle of carpet

Unburnt underlay

Figure 8.8. The waste paper bin. Figure D. S. Loxley.

charred. On top of the papers there would normally be plaster and charred wood. Underneath the bin there is likely to be a protected circle of carpet (Fig 8.8).

If the fire had been started by a lighted match discarded amongst papers in the bin, all of the papers would have burned and some scorching of the carpet under the bin would have occurred.

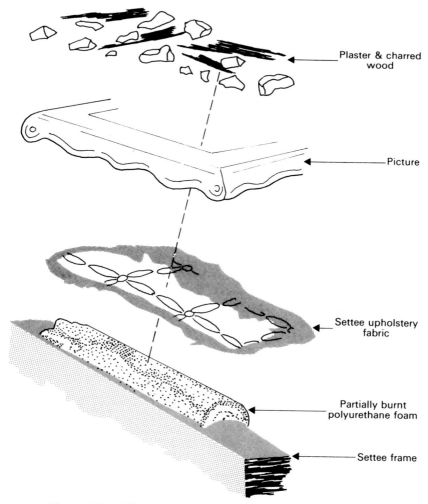

Plaster & charred wood

Picture

Settee upholstery fabric

Partially burnt polyurethane foam

Settee frame

Figure 8.9.   The picture on the settee. Figure D. S. Loxley.

The picture (Fig 8.9) fell at an early stage, before the settee caught fire. It is possible for an object such as this picture to prevent part of the settee from burning for a long period of time. A portion of settee protected in this way provides evidence that the picture fell before the settee was fully alight. Another useful result is that there is now available a sample of the upholstery foam and the fabric for subsequent laboratory examination.

The first items on the left hand side of the room to be ignited were the curtains, which burnt through at the top and fell to the floor (Fig 8.10). Broken glass, possibly distorted by the heat, and plaster followed, and eventually the TV set became heated by the fire. If the back of the set had been thermoplastic this could have melted and formed a layer on top of the other materials. This would provide conclusive evidence that the TV set had not caused the fire. If the fire had started in the set, the thermoplastic would have been the first material to land on the floor. During the excavation of this area the socket, plug and flex should be traced.

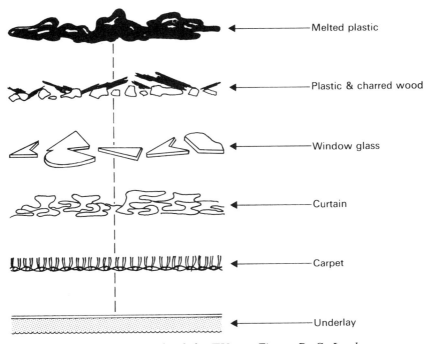

Figure 8.10. Behind the TV set. Figure D. S. Loxley.

Many supposed electrical causes of fires have subsequently been disproved because the suspected appliance had not even been plugged in.

Although layers of debris have been represented for simplicity as uniform unmixed strata, each clearly distinguishable from the one above and the one below, all those who have investigated fires know that in practice it is far more complicated than this. Much mixing of debris occurs both when it is falling during the fire and, regrettably, during clearing up operations. However, the layer of debris immediately above floor or carpet level suffers less from mixing problems than debris at higher levels, and fortunately this is the layer which normally includes the evidence which relates to the important first stages of the fire. Careful excavation of the bottom inch or two of fire debris can provide much evidence which would otherwise be lost.

Reference

(1) P. Barker. Techniques of Archaeological Excavation.

Chapter 9

Deductive Evidence at Fire Scenes

Useful evidence can be obtained by making examinations of items and materials at the fire scene. Brief examinations under fire scene conditions may suggest fruitful lines of investigation and may also prevent protracted and unnecessary enquiries. It is important however, that any examination of an item at the fire scene should be substantiated by a subsequent detailed laboratory examination if the findings are likely to be significant in a court of law.

Evidence from Glass
Glass can provide much evidence to assist in the reconstruction of the events prior to and during the fire. The breaking of a sheet of glass is a favoured method of effecting illicit entry into a building. Unfortunately firemen also effect entry in this way and they may in addition break windows to ventilate a smoke-logged building. One method of distinguishing between the two is to compare the smoke staining on the glass which has fallen from the window with that which remains in the frame. Glass which fell from the window before the fire will be free from smoke. Glass which fell from the window after the fire had started is likely to be smoke stained on one or both surfaces. The possibility that smoke stains have been washed from the glass during fire fighting must be borne in mind.

If a window was broken prior to the fire, the glass remaining in the frame may be smoke stained on both surfaces and on the broken edges. Windows which were broken or open prior to or during the very early stages of a fire, may also give rise to an abnormally intense plume of smoke-staining on the wall above.

The properties of glass
Glass is a rigid, inorganic, non-crystalline material which can for practical purposes be regarded as a solid. Unlike crystalline solids, it does not have a sharp melting point but becomes increasingly soft with rising temperature. Because of its non-crystalline state, its manner of breaking can provide significant information regarding the forces which acted upon it[1].

Figure 9.1.   A pane of glass broken by point impact at the centre. The radial and concentric cracks produce a characteristic 'cobweb' pattern.

Impact direction

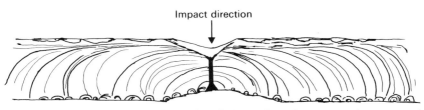

Figure 9.2.   The broken edges of radial cracks adjacent to the point of impact show rib marks which can indicate the side from which the glass was broken. The sheet of glass must be reassembled and examined under laboratory conditions. Figure D. S. Loxley.

Modes of fracture

(a) *Impact.* Sheets of glass broken by impact, crack in the typical 'cobweb' pattern, having radial and concentric cracks. Figure 9.1.

If the broken edge of a primary radial crack is examined, rib marks will be seen which can indicate which side of the window suffered the impact. Figure 9.2.

In the case of concentric cracks the rib marks are in the opposite direction to those on the radial cracks and tend to be less conspicuous.

Secondary radial cracks, or cracks distant from the point of impact can exhibit ambiguous rib marks due to a quaking effect in the sheet of glass. All direction of impact interpretations should therefore, be based upon rib marks on radial cracks immediately adjacent to the point of impact. It will be necessary to jig-saw fit the fragments of glass together in the laboratory in order to carry out this study. It must be remembered that fragments of glass falling from a window are likely to suffer further breakage when they hit the ground; these latter broken edges will show rib marks which are inconsistent with the rib marks on the other cracks.

(b) *High velocity impact.* The effect of a high velocity projectile may be to knock a cone of glass out of the window. In the case of bullet, the diameter of the hole on the impact side may approximate to that of the bullet, but the diameter of the hole on the exit side of the glass will be very much greater.

(c) *Thermal fracture.* When the temperature of a sheet of glass is raised quickly, unequal expansion causes stresses to develop in the sheet, which may then crack. Thermal cracks can be distinguished from impact cracks by their lack of rib marks. The smooth mirror appearance of the fracture surfaces is characteristic of low velocity crack propagation. The cracks are gently curved in appearance. (Plate 9A).

This smooth cracking may not always show in bottles (where considerable stresses may exist). Some aspects of heat fracture in bottles may simulate impact cracking. Generally, if enough of the bottle is recovered, the overall appearance can be of value in determining the type of fracture.

The other type of thermal cracking is caused by the sudden cooling of a hot sheet of glass. Commonly observed at fire scenes,

Plate 9A. *This soot stained window glass has been subjected to a sudden rise in temperature, and has cracked in the characteristic cold to hot manner. The wavy, smooth edged cracks are unlikely to be confused with impact damage. Photograph Mrs M. A. Taylor.*

hot to cold cracking has the appearance of many small conchoidal fractures on one surface of the glass. This damaged surface is the one which suffered the sudden cooling effect of water applied during fire fighting. It is possible therefore, to establish the direction from which the first jets of water were applied to this part of the fire.

(d) *Toughened glass.* The glass used for the side windows of most cars and the windscreens of some cars in the UK is heat-treated or toughened. In this treatment, the pre-formed window is heated to a temperature of about 650°C and is then suddenly cooled. The glass at the surface cools and hardens first, and the subsequent cooling of the glass in the midst of the thickness of the

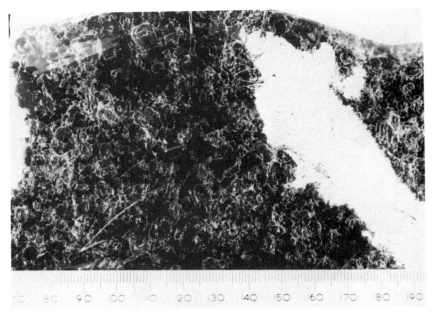

Plate 9B. This soot stained window glass has cracked as a result of sudden cooling by fire fighting water sprays. Examination of the glass will normally reveal from which side the water was sprayed. Photograph Mrs M. A. Taylor.

sheet, causes the surface glass to be put under compression and the central glass under tension.

When toughened glass breaks, it shatters into small "dice" over the whole area of the sheet, as the stress in the glass is released. It can however, withstand considerable thermal shock, possibly as much as 300°C temperature change.

The broken edges of fragments of toughened glass may show hackle lines and a central mist zone, both of which are characteristic of high velocity crack propagation. (Fig. 9.3).

(e) *Explosion damage.* Glass in the vicinity of an explosion may break in a manner superficially similar in appearance to broken toughened glass. Toughened glass is rarely fitted in buildings except in certain cases where its particular properties are required. Explosion damaged glass may be distinguished from toughened

136

Original surface   Hackle lines   Mist zone

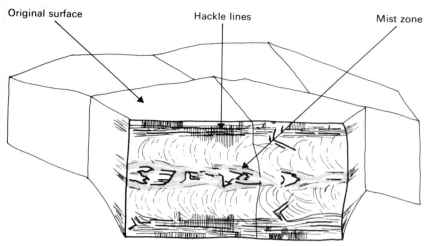

Figure 9.3. Dice of toughened glass show characteristic fracture patterns on their broken edges. The 'mist' zone is normally at or near the middle of the fracture surface. Short parallel hackle lines are also normally present. Figure D. S. Loxley.

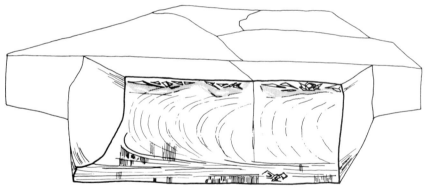

Figure 9.4. Window glass fractured by violent explosions can show a superficial resemblance to broken toughened glass. The two types of fracture can be distinguished by microscopical examination of the broken edges. Explosion fractured glass normally forms longer, larger fragments than broken toughened glass. Figure D. S. Loxley.

glass by examination of the broken surfaces under a microscope. The mist zone is displaced from the middle of the broken edge towards one of the surfaces. (Fig. 9.4).

Evidence from Smoke Records

Considerable quantities of smoke are produced in most fires. This is especially the case during the oxygen-deficient stage, when the fire has become fairly large but few windows or doors have failed. Heavy deposits of soot form on surfaces throughout the area accessible to the smoke. If internal doors have been left open or have burnt through, hot smoke spreads throughout the building at a high level, blackening the upper parts of rooms remote from the fire.

This deposition of soot provides a useful time marker, recording the positions of items throughout the building at a time when the fire had developed to a serious extent. Most of the items whose positions are of significance to a fire investigation are located in the lower parts of rooms, but fortunately there is normally sufficient turbulence and mixing for there to be some soot deposition even at quite low levels.

Evidence of security

The position and state of security of external doors may often be established by the examination of smoke records on hinges, door jambs, edges of doors, bolts and locks. Caution is necessary since smoke can penetrate extremely narrow gaps, and unless there is a draught excluder, smoke deposits may be found on the edges of closed doors; except in the few positions where there had been surface to surface contact. Smoke deposits on the external wall above a door may indicate that it had been open during the early stages of a fire, but an absence of smoke staining in this position does not necessarily indicate that the door had been closed. Smoke deposits on the hinges of a relatively unburnt door can give clear and convincing evidence of the position of the door at the time that the smoke was deposited. When the door has burnt away, the smoke deposits may be more ambiguous since there is likely to be some hinge movement during the collapse of the door, and the final smoke deposits may not necessarily indicate the original position.

The classical example of smoke deposits providing evidence of security is in the case of bolts. The securing loops of the bolt assembly can protect parts of the bolt from sooting and therefore indicate its exact position at the time that the soot was deposited. The same principle can be applied to windows and window catches.

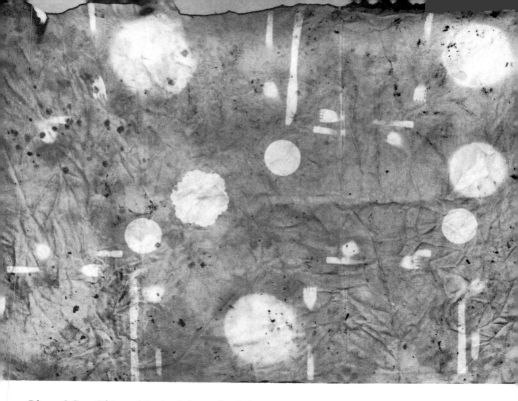

Plate 9C. This table had been laid for a meal prior to the fire. The positions of cutlery and tablewear have been recorded by the smoke staining.

The exact positions of items of vital evidential significance are frequently recorded in the same way. Photograph B. R. G. Roberts.

Positions of items during the fire

The original positions of papers, books, pens, boxes of matches and all other small items on table tops and other surfaces are clearly evident in heavily sooted rooms. This can be of particular importance in deliberately ignited fires when items have been disarranged during a burglary or in the construction of a "crib". It may be claimed by the defendant during his trial that the disarrangement occurred during fire fighting activities. The presence of protected unsmoked areas beneath the disarranged articles would refute this argument.

A fireman in breathing apparatus finding a body in a smoke filled room would be expected to carry the victim out into the fresh air in the hope that resuscitation techniques might be

Plate 9D.   Smoke record. A protected area on a two way plug adapter
which demonstrates conclusively that a plug had been in this position.
Photograph: B. R. G. Roberts.

successful. If the victim subsequently dies, a full investigation into the circumstances of the death will be required.

It is often possible to deduce the precise position of the body and the exact arrangement of the bed clothes or other articles in the vicinity, from the smoke records on the body and in the area where it had been lying.

Electrical apparatus
It can be established from heat and smoke records on plug sockets, whether there had been a plug inserted at the time of the fire, an observation of importance if the fire has been attributed to a particular electrical appliance. Electrical switches, which are frequently constructed of white thermosetting plastic in the UK, show smoke records clearly and it is often possible to establish whether they had been in the "on" or the "off" position.

Unprotected soot deposition
Soot is not deposited uniformly, even when it comes into contact with flat unprotected surfaces. The extent of deposition appears to depend upon the orientation of the surface, its temperature and the rate of movement of the smoke. Turbulent air streams resulting in whorls of smoke deposit may provide evidence of an explosion.

Cooling smoke, particularly from a smouldering fire, falls and deposits a tarry residue on the horizontal surfaces of nearby objects but not on vertical surfaces. This property can be used as a diagnostic feature of smouldering fires.

Soot deposits on the brickwork in situations where plaster has spalled, can indicate that the spalling occurred during the fire and not as a result of fire fighting jets.

Evidence from Instrument Marks
In cases of arson in a secured building, the criminal will have normally entered using force. Whilst entry by means of a broken window is a popular method, many criminals prefer the quieter technique of forcing doors or windows with suitable instruments. Larger instruments commonly used, include garden spades and forks borrowed for the purpose from a nearby insecure garden shed. Such items found discarded near to the point of entry, may subsequently be tested for fingerprints and fibre transfer, provided that they have not been seriously wetted during the fire fighting.

Smaller instruments normally brought to and taken from the scene by the criminal include:— screwdrivers, wrecking bars, chisels and knife blades. The instrument is levered sideways to widen the gap between the door and frame and eventually disengage the lock or catch. It is normally necessary to insert the instrument several times in different places before the securing system eventually fails. During this process, characteristic marks are left on the door or window edge and on the frame.

Another common method of forcing entry into buildings, is by drilling holes through window frames or doors with an auger bit. The drillings from the hole may exhibit circumferential striation marks, which correspond with imperfections in the drill. Care should therefore be taken to preserve any drillings found for a subsequent police investigation.

Criminals who intend to break into a specific building may come equipped with tools suitable for the particular target. Padlocks are often cut with bolt-croppers, and the cut surfaces of the lock shackles may reveal the type of bolt-croppers used. Wire fences and electrical wires may be cut with pliers or shears, and again the cut ends may be characteristic of the type of instrument.

Subsequent microscopical comparison of the striation marks on the cut surfaces with test marks, may provide conclusive evidence linking the particular instrument involved, with the damaged item.

Security bars may be cut with a hacksaw, and information regarding the spacing of the teeth on the sawblade and its colour, may be obtained by examination of the cut surfaces. More robust items are cut with abrasive disk power tools, oxyacetylene equipment, or very occasionally, with a thermic lance.

Criminal activities with all of these types of equipment leave valuable traces at the scene of the crime, and any evidence of their use prior to the fire should be carefully preserved.

Evidence from Footwear Impressions
Although the offender is likely to have left footwear impressions at the scene of almost every arson, these are seldom found subsequently because they are normally destroyed by fire, water or the feet of fire fighters.

Footwear impressions out of doors at night under the wet conditions of a fire ground are extremely likely to be obliterated. Footwear impressions inside the building near to the point of

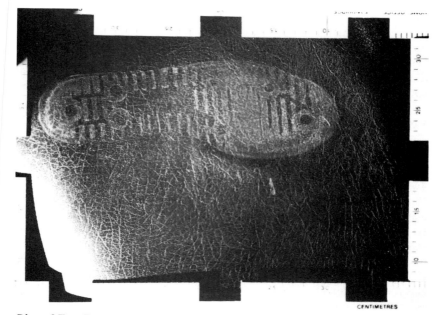

CENTIMETRES

Plate 9E. Footwear impressions should be photographed against one or more scales. It is important that the optic axis of the camera should be normal to the plane of the impression. This footwear impression had been left on the seat of a chair but was almost invisible except when viewed using oblique lighting. Photograph Mrs M. A. Taylor.

criminal entry may survive, particularly if the point of entry is recognised as such at an early stage.

Criminals entering buildings through windows, normally step on to the windowsill and then perhaps on to a table, desk or chair seat. Extremely detailed partial or entire footwear impressions may be found on the surface involved, or on sheets of paper which had been legitimately present.

It is normal for the criminal to start the fire in some area remote from his point of entry, and as a result, his footwear impressions may well survive the fire.

Footwear impressions of probable criminal origin should be preserved, for example by covering them with a clearly labelled box, because they may provide evidence of the size and type of shoe involved and subsequently, may provide conclusive evidence linking the criminal with the scene. Significant footwear impressions should be photographed against a scale ruler by a police scene of crime photographer, or recovered by one of the many other techniques now available[2]-[5]. (Plate 9E).

If the impression is on a portable item such as a sheet of paper, a chair or a desk, the whole item should be preserved as an exhibit for subsequent investigation.

Vehicle Evidence
Tyre marks
In rural areas, the offender may travel to the scene by car and park in a secluded spot, off the road near to the target building. Tyre marks may well be left in the soft ground at this point. When the arsonist has left the scene and the fire has been discovered, fire appliances, police cars or the cars of sight-seers, may subsequently be parked on the spot used by the arsonist, which was after all chosen for its convenient access to the building. During the investigation after the fire it may be very difficult to decide which, if any, of the tyre prints are of significance. In ideal cases it is possible to identify the size and type of each tyre, and to make a list of possible vehicles from the tyre width, track width and possibly from the minimum turning circle.

If a particular vehicle is suspected, its tyres can be compared with the impressions. Conclusive linking evidence can sometimes be found if sufficient accidental damage marks in the tread correspond with features in the impression.

It is not unknown for the cars of criminals to be involved in minor impacts with gate posts, walls or items of street furniture immediately before or after the crime. Flakes of vehicle paint, fragments of headlamp glass, pieces of trim or fragments of perspex may be found at the scene. These materials can be used to identify the type of vehicle involved and also to link the criminal's vehicle with the scene of the crime.

Trace Evidence at Fire Scenes
Fingerprints are the most well known example of evidence linking the criminal with the scene of crime. In the case of a successful arson, the few fingerprints not actually consumed by the fire will be difficult to develop in the damp situation, particularly with dusting agents such as the popular aluminium powder. However, small particle reagent (SPR), can be successful in damp environments. The most profitable hunting grounds for finger-

144

prints are the points of entry and exit. These areas may not be directly involved in the fire, and if they are protected from fire fighting measures, fingerprint evidence may remain after the fire has been extinguished. Good fingerprints are most likely to be found on smooth flat surfaces such as glossy painted areas and fragments of glass. A determined effort should be made to avoid touching such surfaces and if it is necessary to pick up glass fragments to examine or preserve them, they should be handled by their edges.

In cases when the offender has entered the building by means of a broken window, it is not uncommon for him to cut himself, leaving blood stains on the glass and paint work. Blood stains from scenes of crime can be grouped, provided that they have not been heated too much, and that they are reasonably fresh. In offences directed purely against property, the most likely place to find significant blood stains is at, or near the point of entry. In the case of murder or a wounding in which a fire is later started, it is probable that the blood stains will be at, or near, the seat of the fire. Blood which has been heated, darkens and can be difficult to recognise. Specific identification tests and blood grouping techniques are also likely to be impaired under these circumstances.

Directional Evidence

It is often necessary to establish the direction of travel of splashes of liquid such as blood, paint and fire accelerants. If the splashes

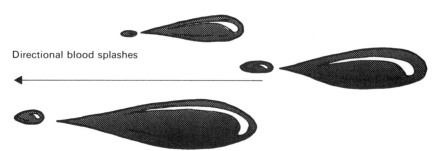

Directional blood splashes

Figure 9.5. Splashes of blood and other liquids often assume an exclamation mark shape which can indicate the direction of travel of the liquid. Evidence of this type should be carefully preserved. Figure D. S. Loxley.

have not been smeared and are still clearly visible, the direction of travel of the droplets can be determined.

The characteristic exclamation mark shaped patterns indicate the direction of travel of individual drops hitting a surface obliquely. Such factors as the possible subsequent movement of the splashed item, the effect of gravity and the possibility that the splashes originated from more than one position, must be taken into account when interpreting this evidence.

Any evidence of this type found at the scene of a suspected murder or assault should be examined by an experienced forensic biologist, who may be able to provide a detailed interpretation. From examination of blood splashes the biologist may be able to give an opinion on the number and violence of the blows, the probable respective positions of the people involved and the blood groups of the people from whom the blood came.

It is important, therefore, that any splashes of what appears to be blood, should not be touched but should be protected and brought to the attention of the senior police investigating officer immediately.

References

(1) S. P. McJunkins and J. I. Thorton. Glass fracture analysis, a review. Forensic Science 1973 ppl-27.
(2) J. S. Brennan. Dental stones for casting depressed shoemarks and tyremarks. MPFSL Report No. 24.
(3) J. S. Brennan. The visualisation of shoemarks using the electrostatic detection apparatus. MPFSL Report No. 10.
(4) K. G. Barnett and B. R. G. Roberts. The use of the Electrostatic Document Analyser for the detection of latent footwear impressions. HOCRE Tech Note 88 1978.
(5) M. J. Cassidy. Footwear Identification RCMP Ottawa, Ontario.

Chapter 10

Fires Involving Fatalities

When a person dies as a result of a fire, the investigation of the incident has two fundamental features. Firstly, as with any fire or explosion investigation, the cause must be determined. Secondly, the reasons for and the manner of the victim's involvement need to be deduced.

Because the building structure and contents, so far as the fire is concerned, are essentially static features, any reconstruction of the fire origin and spread can follow the technical outlines indicated elsewhere in this book. People, however, are mobile; in a fire the victims may become extremely mobile for short periods. They may have been instrumental in starting the fire, or they may have become unwittingly involved at any stage of the fire development. In studies of fatal fires, therefore, the investigator should be in a position to provide as much information as possible of the circumstances surrounding the victim's death. Apart from the emotive aspects of human life-loss, the strict requirements of the Coroner's investigation and the associated police enquiry makes a total scenario of events desirable.

In the United Kingdom, Her Majesty's Coroner has the duty to enquire into the causes of sudden deaths. In other countries, his counterpart may be a Medical Examiner or, possibly, an Examining Magistrate. All require answers to the following questions:—

    i. Who was the deceased?
    ii. Where did he die?
    iii. When and how did he die?

The Coroner also has a subsidiary function to make public recommendations should any avoidable hazard be discovered. These are made with a view to preventing further incidents, or to bring pressure to bear on, for example, manufacturers of faulty goods. A Coroner's Court is not there to apportion blame or to usurp the function of a Civil Court. This restriction is not so marked in other legal systems.

In certain cases, for instance, in deaths in the United Kingdom

147

at a place of work (designated under the Health and Safety at Work Legislation), assistance may be given by a member of H.M. Factories Inspectorate who may ask questions in association with the Coroner during the inquest.

It can be seen that in order to provide the information which is needed for the inquest, or, for that matter, any future enquiry, the fire investigator, must possess the knowledge, not only of how fires start and how they develop, but also of the effects fires can have in various stages of development on people as well as property. He must be aware of the evidence which can provide answers to the identification of the deceased and the cause of his death.

It must not be forgotten that fire is also used on occasions to conceal a crime and a fire fatality may in fact be a murder victim. As a criminal trial demands a strict burden of proof on the prosecution, the evidence produced in any investigation into a fire fatality must be at least up to these standards.

Identification of the deceased
In those instances where burn damage to the body is slight, formal visual identification may possibly be made by relatives or close associates of the deceased. However, in order to relieve unnecessary distress to these people, where severe fire damage or injury has occurred, identification can be more humanely achieved by the recognition of personal possessions. This may also be necessary in multiple fatalities, where several people of similar physique and age may have died, and must be done in parallel with the pathologist's post-mortem examination. As a first requirement, the fire investigator should if possible, be able to see the body *in situ*, so that those evidential materials which are essential for identity can be retrieved and seen in their proper context. Even after severe burning much of value will remain (see Plate 10A).

Frequently, movement of the body during recovery of the corpse can cause detachment of such materials. For instance, parts of the clothing of the deceased will generally be preserved under the body if it is lying on a hard floor, or in the armpits or the groin region if the arms and legs have been pressed against the body (see Plate 10B). Personal jewellery, such as finger or earrings will frequently survive the fire in recognisable form, although the fingers or ears may well have distintegrated. Watches likewise may

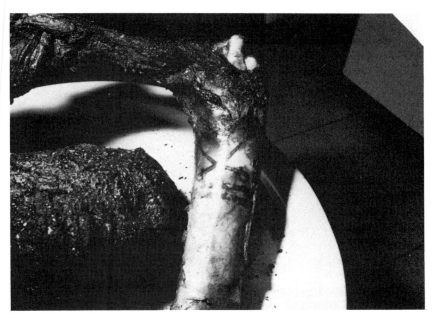

Plate 10A. Identification of the deceased. Tattoos may be preserved on unburnt skin. Here, this skin was the only unburnt part of the body. Photograph by Courtesy of Tyne & Wear Fire Brigade.

be lying associated with, but detached from, the body. Wallets, credit cards and other personal documents can be found in pockets or even detached from burnt clothing. It is obvious then that if a body is moved from its original position the recovery of these items, when there may be much generalised fire debris about, can pose problems. Careful and accurate marking of the position of the body must be made if such removal is necessary. The use of a salvage sheet to cover the original position can both preserve evidence below, and mark the location.

It goes without saying that in addition to possible identification, recovery of such items can also provide valuable evidence as to the activity of the deceased prior to or during the fire. For example, the manner of dress may show whether or not the deceased had gone to bed.

Close co-operation with the pathologist and any specialists (such as odontologists, or radiographers) is necessary, for it may well be that the combination of their findings and the

Plate 10B. Identification of the deceased by personal possessions. Here, a coat label has been perfectly preserved beneath a very badly burnt body. Photograph R. A. Cooke.

identification of personal items recovered near the body at the scene, will provide the necessary evidence of identification. Such procedures have been necessary to identify the deceased persons in several recent cases of multiple fire deaths.

Location of Death

This is not so much a problem for the fire investigator because certification of death by a doctor is the overriding factor. A point to note, however, is that since delayed fatalities may occur in a specialist hospital burns unit well away from the scene of the accident, the Coroner may not be familiar with the locale. Full information is obviously necessary to aid him.

If a victim died before the fire, it is conceivable that the place where he died was not the same place as the fire scene. Concealment of the cause of death (or of the location) has been attempted by people trying to conceal crimes, and evidence of such behaviour should signal a possible murder and an almost definitely deliberate fire.

150

When and How the Deceased Died

So that these questions can be answered, the fire investigator needs to work closely with the pathologist. But in addition to the pathologist's medical expertise, logical results can best be achieved if the fire examiner possesses some knowledge of the behaviour of people in fires and the effects of fires on people.

Deaths caused from primary ignition of clothing with no fire spread
In many cases of fire fatalities, relatively slight damage to the body is involved and the larger proportion of deaths (said to be approximately 80% in the period 1965–74)[1, 2] are attributed to the direct ignition of clothing. It is clear that 'simple' cases like these rest mainly on background knowledge of the deceased's infirmity or disability (either from extreme youth, extreme age or alcohol, drugs, etc.)[3] coupled with knowledge of the ignition hazards of fabrics etc., when considered with heat sources.

Statistics show these factors quite clearly, fatalities having peak values in the infant age groups, 0–9 years and the old-age groups of above 60 years. The advent of mandatory standards in children's nightdresses[4] in the United Kingdom and the wider requirements of flame-proofing of clothing to be found in the U.S.A. have caused deaths resulting from the ignition of clothing to drop in the last few years. Nevertheless the fire investigator must only be guided by statistics and must prove the proposition of accidental clothing ignition. Murder involving fire, or suicide by self-immolation are by no means unknown.

In a straightforward accidental death resulting from the ignition of clothing while the victim was alive, the pathologist will normally find evidence of vital reaction of pre-death skin burns. This includes the blistering and reddening of surface skin and under layers respectively. It may not be particularly clear at post-mortem examination whether or not the victim has inhaled smoke or flame, and blood samples may not show any significant carbon monoxide levels, particularly if the victim was a heavy smoker. However, the pathological signs of death by shock and burns are usually clear.

One peculiar development which may occur from a fire of this type is that of the progressive and total combustion of the body. If the victim is lying on a bed or in a chair the reasons for this are usually clear, because the mass of smouldering upholstery can obviously support the general combustion of the body. Sometimes

Plate 10C.   Total, self-sustaining combustion of a human body. The initial heat has been provided by the open fire and the body has gradually rendered down and burnt.

the body burns without the apparent aid of any external fuel. In the past this has been believed by some to be a 'spontaneous combustion', when the corpse almost completely burns away leaving just the extremities, causing little or no fire spread beyond it (see Plate 10C).

152

The requirements for this to happen should be that (a) the victim has some degree of body fat (an almost inevitable condition), (b) he or she has been fairly well clothed and (c) an ignition source exists which is capable of a sustained heat output for some time. The body then 'renders down' with the fat burning slowly, probably using the clothing as the wick[5]. Investigation of these effects has shown that usually the radiative heat output is remarkably low and that the burning probably takes place over a considerable period of time. Speculative stories of people suddenly and dramatically bursting into flame and burning to ashes at extremely high temperatures have been a source of wonder in the popular press from time to time. These stories lack adequate research. Bodies which have burnt to the condition described, obviously present enormous difficulties for the pathologist as little tissue remains. Providing the explanation of the cause of death may then rest largely on the investigator.

In all deaths in which clothing is suspected of being the prime ignition source, the characteristics of that clothing must be

RELATIVE IGNITION HAZARDS OF FABRICS

Fabric type	Examples of trade names	Susceptibility to ignition		Melting point (min.) °C	Remarks
		Flame	Smouldering		
Wool	—	Low	Low	Chars	Forms intumescent layer
Cotton	—	High	High	Chars	Rapid spread of flame
Rayon (Acetate)	Tricel	High	High	290–300°	Burns rapidly
Nylon 6	Enkalon	Low	Low	210–216°	Melts into skin
PVC/ Polyvinylidine Chloride	Saran	Low	Low	160° Chars	May not burn
Polyester	Crimplene -Terylene Dacron	High	Low	250–260°	Melts and spreads flaming droplets
Acrylics	Acrilan Courtelle Orlon	High	Low	Decomposes/ chars	High surface spread of flame
Modacrylic	Dynel	Low	Low	190°	Used to modify acrylic fibres
Polyolefin	Courlene	High	Low	108–113°	Spreads burning droplets
Polypropylene	Meraklon	High	Low	165–175°	Spreads burning droplets

understood. The relative susceptibility of fabrics to ignition sources is shown in the table above.

Made-up fabrics can be mixtures of fibres which will modify their ignition characteristics, and furthermore, surface modification (e.g. fluffy pile fabrics) can increase the surface spread of flame quite dramatically. Interlinings, such as can be found in padded or quilted garments, may present a special burn hazard to the victim, particularly when they consist of polyurethane foams or polyester fibre.

Work clothing may well become impregnated with flammable solvents, and in domestic accidents petrol, lighter fuel, paraffin, methylated spirits or other flammable solvents could be involved. Thus, in all cases of suspected primary ignition of clothing, when by its nature the clothing does not appear to be especially flammable, a check for the presence of solvents both at the scene and on any remaining garments should be made. Reference to the analytical methods and flash points in other parts of this book should be made.

Deaths occurring as a result of general fire spread
Notwithstanding the fact that most fire casualties occur as a result of the primary ignition of clothing, many fatalities remain which occur in fires which have spread some distance from their points of origin. Some of these fires may well have originally been intimately associated with the victim (e.g. a person falling asleep in an armchair which smoulders, and later freely burns as a result of a dropped cigarette end). But an increasing proportion involve people originally remote from the fire who are overcome by smoke and combustion products. The preponderance of plastics in modern furnishings appears to be the cause of this, with the current trend showing no significant decrease in fatalities in domestic dwellings[6] in spite of improved medical and resuscitation facilities.

As indicated in Chapter 1, modern polyurethane upholstered furniture can cause flashover conditions within perhaps, four minutes from ignition with the production of extremely large volumes of heat and smoke. The configuration of the average house seems to be peculiarly well adapted for the rapid propagation of these products, and numerous instances exist of families having been trapped and overcome by smoke in the upstairs rooms within one or two minutes of the discovery of fire.

154

Nor are these fires confined to homes. Furniture storage, manufacturing and retail sales premises have provided some notable multiple fatalities, as for example the Woolworths (Manchester) fire in 1979 in which ten people died, or the Stardust Disco fire in Dublin in 1980.

It follows then that a toxicological and pathological examination of the deceased needs to be made in order to provide the essential details of the cause of death.

Carbon monoxide

By far and away the most important combustion product where fire fatalities are concerned is carbon monoxide. It is present in all combustion processes apart from stoichiometric combustion (which rarely takes place in burning buildings). Thus, in any ventilation controlled fire, that is a fire which has significantly spread from its item of origin, or in any smouldering fire, the production of carbon monoxide becomes a serious hazard to any unprotected person exposed to smoke. At low levels of concentration the victim may survive for some time (minutes to hours) while at high levels, survival may become critical within seconds. The age and robustness of the victims also determines their survival chances, ignoring any additional factors which may be present, such as intermediate combustion products, for example, cyanides etc., (discussed below). Polyurethane foam upholstered furniture is capable of producing lethally high concentrations of carbon monoxide within one or two minutes of ignition.

The mechanism of carbon monoxide poisoning is partly the substitution of oxygen in the oxyhaemoglobin component of blood by the carbon monoxide molecule, thus forming carboxyhaemoglobin. This is a relatively stable molecule which prevents the oxygen transfer necessary for life. The result for the victim is that, say, a 50% saturation of carboxyhaemoglobin is equivalent to losing half of his blood oxygen. As haemoglobin has a several hundred times greater affinity for carbon monoxide than for oxygen, it follows that even low concentrations provide risk if there is sustained exposure. An example of this can be seen in the fact that a heavy smoker can achieve peak values of about 10% carboxyhaemoglobin in his blood. There is reason to suspect that further, more complex effects are involved. These could include the blocking of oxygen transfer within nerves and tissues because of carbon monoxide combination with cytochrome[7].

Carboxyhaemoglobin levels of about 50% saturation or higher are usually accepted as being fatal.
Some typical effects of carbon monoxide can be seen in the table below.

EFFECTS OF CARBON MONOXIDE

Concentration in air (ppm)	Symptoms
50	Threshold limiting value and maximum allowable concentration in work places
100	No poisoning symptoms for several hours
200	Headache after 2–3 hours, collapse after 4–5 hours
400	Headache and nausea after 1–2 hours, collapse after 2 hours. Death after 3–4 hours
800	Collapse after 1 hour. Death after 2 hours
1500	Death after 1 hour
3000	Death after 30 minutes
12500	Unconsciousness after 2 or 3 breaths. Death in 1–3 minutes.

Source: National Materials Advisory Board 1978 National Association of Sciences.

As to the concentrations of carbon monoxide which may be expected in a fire, work performed at the Fire Research Station, Borehamwood[8] indicates that values of 0·2%–3·3% (2,000 ppm–33,000 ppm) in air can be achieved in test fires of simulated living rooms. These are well into the lethal range of concentrations shown above. The higher range of values is found in fires containing polyurethane upholstered furnishings.

While not strictly speaking fire fatalities, deaths from carbon monoxide poisoning occur when exhaust gases from gas appliances or oil heaters, or car exhausts are allowed to accumulate in occupied areas.

An analysis of his blood will indicate that the victim has been exposed to a lethal concentration but will not, of course, necessarily indicate the source of the carbon monoxide. Testing, *in situ*, of the suspect appliance is therefore necessary. It is of paramount importance that any such tests are carried out recreating as closely as possible the known conditions at the time of the fatality. This can be difficult; frequently the conditions have been changed prior to the investigator's arrival at the scene. For instance, during a cold winter a fatality of this nature had occurred during an outside temperature of about −10°C, the suspect appliance being a gas-fired central heating boiler with a flue extending through a cavity wall. Before investigation could take place, not only had the boiler been serviced, but a thaw had set in. Although a crack was found in the flue which could have leaked sufficient carbon monoxide via the cavity wall to the deceased's room, complete reconstruction was impossible, as a hypothesised ice blockage in the flue had melted, the burners had been readjusted, and the boiler was by then working more or less correctly.

In other cases mobile heaters in rooms may have produced carbon monoxide because of doors and windows having been sealed. Rescue of the body and the subsequent ventilation of the room by the rescuers will doubtlessly disturb this.

Tests on heaters, etc., in rooms must obviously be performed with an absence of risk for the investigator, so readings should preferably be made by remote measuring apparatus. Suitable devices, such as the Draeger colorimetric adsorption tubes, or specific gas detectors connected via a sampling tube leading from the room can be used.

Further intermediate combustion products
As has been indicated previously, numerous other intermediate products of combustion are produced in any fire because of the imperfect ventilation of flames. Of major importance to the investigator of fatal fires, are those produced by burning plastics.

In spite of public alarm at the physiological effects of these, little is actually known about either their contribution to deaths in fires, or the concentrations in smoke which can be achieved in actual fire conditions.

(a) Cyanides have probably been investigated more closely than any other intermediate product and blood cyanide levels have been estimated from time to time in deaths from fires involving polyurethane foams, nylon or natural protein fibres, such as wool. Fatal levels have been recorded of 1·0–15·0 mgm/litre of cyanide (CN) in blood resulting from inhalation of pure HCN gas[9]. Occasionally values approaching these have been noted in fire victims. Accurate analysis of the blood of fire victims has its problems however, because spontaneous generation of cyanide can occur if the blood is sampled after a delay (fire damaged bodies are usually in a poor condition for preservation)[10]. Furthermore, inhaled or ingested cyanide levels have been found to fluctuate with time, this possibly being due to the cyanide becoming protein bound[11], and are probably inaccurate. In routine tests it has usually been found that sufficient carbon monoxide is present to account for the victim's death.

(b) Hydrogen chloride, produced by burning PVC, has the effect of making even a light smoke intolerable and probably induces violent coughing leading to hyperventilation. Such an effect would accelerate carbon monoxide absorption. It is generally understood that 100 ppm (0.01%) of HCl in air is impossible to breathe. No reliable method exists to test a victim's blood for HCl absorption due to the natural chloride content of body fluids.

(c) Anoxia (lack of oxygen) is frequently overlooked as a contributory cause of deaths in fires and, until routine oxyhaemoglobin measurement was possible (as with the CO-oximeter described in Chapter 23), was rarely tested for. The human body reacts to a depletion of its oxygen supply as shown below.

RESPONSE OF HUMANS TO CHANGES IN OXYGEN CONCENTRATION

Concentration of O_2 per cent	Response
21	Normal concentration in air
15	Rapid fatigue, loss of co-ordination
10	Faulty judgement
6	Collapse
5	Death in 4–5 minutes

Rapidly developing fires can strip the oxygen from the air extremely quickly before failure of the windows allows a freer ventilation. Simultaneous measurements of the carboxyhaemoglobin and oxyhaemoglobin of the blood of victims of large, rapidly developing fires has shown that oxyhaemoglobin levels can be severely depressed. This will obviously enhance the effects of other more actively toxic agents such as carbon monoxide. Test fires[8] have shown that with modern furniture the minimum oxygen content in a room fire may be of the order of 1% to 12.6% in the emitted smoke. These are admittedly somewhat different conditions than for a house fire in which the victims may be away from the room which is actually on fire. However, oxygen depletion of this order may help to explain the occasional carboxyhaemoglobin saturation figures in the lower lethal range (i.e. 50%–60%) in modern furnishing fires.

(d) Alcohol is not considered here as an intermediate combustion product. As an intermediary in reducing reactions, inducing carelessness and lowering the threshold of survival capability, alcohol is frequently associated with fire fatalities. Harland and Woolley[3] have, in an intensive study of the toxicology of fire fatalities in Glasgow, shown that in the majority of cases, alcohol was present in considerable quantities in fire victims. There was little evidence to show that the presence of alcohol clinically modifies the effects of carbon monoxide. This is now open to question[12]. Alcohol may actually increase the victim's tolerance to a small extent. Some caution must be exercised when the blood of a fire victim is analysed for alcohol. Bacteria can, under some circumstances, generate alcohol in blood if no preservative is present in the blood sample. This was found to have occurred in the Moorgate Train Disaster (1975) when bodies had been in elevated temperatures for over two days before recovery. Fire victim's bodies are not, generally speaking, in a good condition after burning and, unless a blood sample is taken shortly after death, may contain alcohol generated within the body.

The Behaviour of People in Fires

A study of the reactions of people finding themselves involved with fires has recently been published by Canter[13]. This work also explores the psychology of a wide range of subjects including fire setters.

In any attempt to reconstruct the movements of a fire victim, or to investigate the reasons why a person died, the psychological effects of heat and smoke must be recognised. Indeed the basis of the UK Means of Escape Legislation and similar codes in other countries is the recognition that normal rational behaviour is frequently lost when a person is faced by a fire. People generally will not willingly go into smoke (particularly hot smoke) and will frequently run with the smoke travel, even although certain circumstances, such as building geometry, mean that by so doing they are putting themselves into further danger.

Victims suddenly faced with overwhelming circumstances when totally unprepared, cannot be expected to behave in the manner of, say, a trained fireman and if in addition they are faced with this emergency in the dark, awakened from sleep or have the additional burden of children or dependents in separate rooms, their movements can seem to defy reason in the cold light of an investigation. As has previously been mentioned, many fire victims may be under the influence of alcohol or may be in the primary stages of carbon monoxide poisoning. These factors again may be responsible for apparently irrational or irresponsible behaviour. It is imperative then that the investigator does not fall into the error of assuming irresponsibility or culpability for one person's survival in the face of other deaths.

The Recognition of Murder
A case could be made that every fire in which a body is found should be investigated as a possible murder. Fire is such a good destroyer of evidence that numerous cases of arson associated with murder have probably been missed. In some circumstances the murderer clearly attempts to destroy the body completely even at the risk of a comparatively rapid discovery of the crime, because of the discovery of the fire. In any event, the reasoning appears to be that the elimination of such clues as fingerprints and blood stains may so sufficiently disturb the evidential links, that connection with the murderer becomes difficult if not impossible (Plates 10D, 10E).

The investigator must also bear in mind the fact that arson which causes death may also result in a murder charge. This would put the burden of proof on the investigators to demonstrate arson *and* that the victim died as a result of the fire. It must not be forgotten that there have been many instances in which the victim was killed directly by fire which was used as the 'weapon'. The main subject of this section is however, the investigation of a pre-fire murder with subsequent fire development.

It follows that in such a circumstance the fire itself will have been deliberately started (ignoring the occasional freak condition in which a purely accidental fire follows a homicide). The investigator will be faced with the following problems:

(a) Can the victim be identified?
(b) Was the victim dead when the fire started?
(c) Is there evidence to show that the fire was deliberately started?

(d) If so, was it started with the intention of destroying evidence, either of the body or connected with the body?

(e) Is there any physical evidence remaining which can indicate how the victim died?

(f) Is there any evidence at the scene which can indicate who committed the offence?

It can be seen that these are not all novel questions to the arson investigator. It is the emotive nature of a murder enquiry which places such special emphasis on the answers. Cross examination of the expert witness generally reaches its peak of intensity in a murder trial, so that more perhaps, than in any other type of incident is perfection in proof required.

Where the detection of a deliberate fire is concerned, the normal procedures and reasonings of an arson investigation will be applied. Indeed, it may be somewhat simpler where a body has obviously been involved and has obviously criminal injuries; the *indication* of arson is immediately apparent. The *proof* may be more difficult to find and the investigator should never merely assume arson, even when external circumstances seem to be obvious. Elegant fire raising methods involving timing devices or trailers will probably be absent, as the murderer will in most cases, resort to more obvious methods to try to give a fast destructive burn. Petrol or other fire accelerants feature frequently in this type of case.

Fires started with the intention of destroying the body

These pose special problems both for the investigator as well as the murderer. On the one hand the seat of fire will usually be centred about the body thus destroying or modifying evidence quite severely. For instance, if the fire has burnt for a long time estimates of the time of death in which the pathologist depends on body temperature measurements, will be invalidated. On the other hand it is generally difficult to destroy a body completely by fire, and much evidence of value can remain.

Some research has been carried out on how a body burns by observing the rate and mode of destruction in crematoria[14]. It is of interest to note that crematoria operate at about 680°C to 850°C, which is the temperature range frequently encountered in flashover conditions. The burning conditions are however, rather different to those in a building, in that crematoria design incorporates adequate all-round ventilation of the burning corpse (to avoid smoke), a situation which rarely obtains in real fires. Consequently, a body raised off the floor on a 'hearth' burns faster than one directly on the floor. Thus, as could be expected, data from cremation observations is likely to err on the rapid side. There are some cases where the fire conditions do tend to parallel a cremator. These can frequently be found in car fires where the body is suspended on a metal seat frame. Nevertheless, the data has some relevance since the murderer may have attempted to destroy the body and the evidence with it, it can be seen that progressive burning is from the limbs inwards and shows some definite patterns. The observation of abnormal burning patterns to a body when compared with its surroundings may help the investigator in solving the method of ignition.

RATE OF BURNING OF CORPSE IN CREMATORIA (680°–850°C)

Time (min)	Observations
5–10	Limbs burning on surface
10–15	Limb bones exposed. Ribs exposed
15–20	Skull exposed. Exposed limb bones splitting
35	All flesh burnt away from limbs. Torso remaining. Skull splitting
90 (approx.)	Corpse reduced to calcined bone

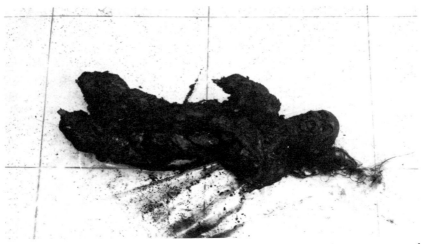

Plate 10D. The normal, severe burning to a body exposed to a protracted fire. Photograph by Courtesy of Durham Constabulary.

162

Plate 10E. The reverse side of the body in Plate 10D, showing the evidential materials which can be protected (hair, ligature, marks of brassiere). Photograph by Courtesy of Durham Constabulary.

As these are the results of a limited number of tests it is clearly unsafe to treat them with any great degree of accuracy, particularly in room fires where no artificial ventilation to aid combustion exists, but they do show the durability of the human torso in fires. Sufficient torso will often still remain to note smoke inhalation into lungs, evidence of strangling or asphyxiation by pathological changes or evidence of recent sexual intercourse. In spite of considerable burning to the arms and upper body, cord used for strangulation can be preserved in skin or tissue folds or on the protected under-side of the body. This demonstrates yet again, the need for a careful examination around the corpse *before* it is removed. Blood carboxyhaemoglobin levels, blood grouping and toxicological analyses can also be carried out after apparent severe burning of this nature, so on no account should the investigator discount the possibilities of obtaining substantial evidence from a badly burnt body.

Obviously, the discovery of wounds or trauma to the body must raise the possibility of murder, but it must not be forgotten that a person collapsing, perhaps in a smoke filled room, may suffer injuries. Falling glass from say, light fittings later involved in fire, can cause severe lacerations so that all injuries observed must be considered in their scene context.

Recognition of Suicide
Self-immolation (the burning of oneself) has, at times, been noted as an ultimate political or religious protest (as in the case of the Bhuddist monks in Vietnam) but is far from unknown in the Western world as a form of suicide. Frequently the would-be suicide wishes to let the public know what he or she is doing and witnesses to the act are frequently available. The most usual manner in which this type of death occurs is by the person pouring petrol or some similar fuel over himself and then igniting his clothing. As these acts are often done in public, from the investigator's point of view, only the checking of the means of ignition and the fuel used is necessary. This will be done bearing in mind the results of any toxicological analysis to check for alcohol, drugs, etc., which may help to explain the person's state of mind.

It has been known for people to be murdered in this way—the main difference from suicide being essentially that murder would most probably take place without witnesses. Suspected self-immolation in private then should be double-checked to eliminate any possible crime. In the drug trafficking world, punishment for a bad 'dealer' or a person not paying for his supplies has been said to take this form.

Suicides lacking other means to kill themselves have been known to seal themselves in a room which they have then set on fire. If the sealing is effective the victim dies from carbon monoxide poisoning and the fire may go out or at least go into a smouldering phase.

A person who has set fire to himself will very frequently show characteristic burn patterns. These result from the fact that initially he is either standing or sitting upright and ignites himself from the front. Rising flames then cause preferential burning around the hands and upper chest and more noticeably, under the chin, nose and cheeks. As it is very difficult to inhale when surrounded by flame pathological signs will frequently be deficient in the characteristics of flame and smoke inhalation although there may be burning in the mouth and throat. Carbon monoxide levels in the blood will often be very low; however, analysis of the lungs may well show the presence of the inhaled fuel from *before* the fire.

The recognition of more orthodox suicides where an accidental fire follows may pose serious problems for the investigator. Obviously, toxicological analysis of body fluids or any remaining organs will be used to assess drug overdoses. Mechanical methods of suicide, such as hanging, shooting, self-inflicted stabbing or cutting may well be partly masked by a subsequent fire. For example, a person having hanged himself may in a subsequent fire appear to have been garrotted, the suspending cord having been burnt away. There are few recorded cases available, and the coincidence of a fire subsequent upon a suicide appears to be of low probability. The investigator must not, however, fail to consider the possibility in any attempted reconstruction of a fire fatality.

References

(1) N. Bailey, Life Risk Study. 1979 Home Office SAB Publication.
(2) G. Charlton. 1979 Personal Communication.
(3) W. A. Harland, W. D. Woolley. Fire Fatality Study—University of Glasgow IP 18/79. 1979 Building Research Establishment.
(4) Nightdresses Safety Regulations 1967.
(5) D. J. Gee. 1965 Medicine, Science and the Law. Vol. V. pp. 37–38.
(6) P. C. Bowes. Casualties Attributed to Toxic Gas and Smoke at fires. 1975 Fire Research Note 1025.
(7) L. R. Goldbaum, T. Orellano and E. Dergal. 1977 Aviation, Space & Environmental Medicine. 969–970.
(8) K. N. Palmer, W. Taylor and K. T. Paul. Fire Hazards of Plastics in Furniture and Furnishings—Fires in Furnished Rooms. CP 21/76. 1976 Building Research Establishment.
(9) R. C. Baselt. Disposition of Toxic Drugs and Chemicals in Man. Volume 2. 1978 Biomedical Publications.
(10) M. Ansell and F. A. S. Lewis. 1970 Journal of Forensic Medicine 17, (4) pp. 148–155.
(11) A. S. Curry. Poison Detection in Human Organs, 2nd Edition. 1969 Charles C. Thomas.
(12) L. A. King. 1983 Human Toxicology 2 155–157.

(13) D. Canter (Ed). Fires and Human Behaviour. 1981 J. Wiley & Sons.

(14) N. F. Richards. How Did It Start? 1980 I.F.E.

Chapter 11

Explosives and Explosions

Techniques of fire and explosion investigation are analogous, and just as explosions may occur as a result of fires, fires can be caused by explosions. Although the detailed investigation of an explosion is a task for a specialist, every fire investigator should be familiar with the basic principles of explosives and explosions. More detailed information on the subject can be found in several excellent specialised books and papers[1]-[9].

Types of Explosion

An explosion is a physical or chemical change resulting in the sudden, violent release of energy. Heat, light, gaseous products and shock waves, or combinations of these are normally produced.
Chemical explosives may either deflagrate or detonate.

Deflagrating explosives

Deflagration is a form of rapid burning, which normally occurs only as a result of the ignition of mixtures of flammable materials with oxidising agents. For example, a pile of gunpowder (a mixture of charcoal and sulphur with potassium nitrate), deflagrates when ignited. The ignition of a mixture of a flammable gas in air would also normally result in a deflagration.

In a deflagration the reaction spreads through the mixture as a result of thermal conduction and radiation, the normal mechanisms of fire spread. Deflagrations normally propagate very much more rapidly than typical fire spread, because of the greater reactivity of the constituents of the mixture.

Although deflagrations occur most commonly in mixtures of fuels with oxygen-rich compounds, other mixtures such as zinc dust and sulphur, and even single compounds such as ammonium dichromate can deflagrate.

Detonating explosives

High explosives, such as gelignite and TNT are designed to detonate in use. Detonation is a very much more rapid process than deflagration and involves velocities above about 1500 m/s (metres per second). It is evident that the detonation of a 4 oz stick of gelignite takes only microseconds from start to finish.

In detonation, the reaction progresses as a result of a shockwave. The shockwave is normally initiated by the operation of a detonator inserted into the explosive mixture. The shock wave momentarily subjects the explosive to a pressure of many thousand bars, compressing the explosive in the region through which it is passing to a high density. Reaction then occurs and the explosive decomposes forming gaseous products at a high temperature. The energy is released extremely rapidly, building up and accelerating the shockwave which passes on to reach and detonate the next region of unreacted explosive.

It is possible to detonate high explosives such as gelignite by burning; the flame front accelerating through the very reactive material can eventually produce a shockwave which causes the remainder of the explosive to detonate.

Clearly if the piece of explosive is too small for the flame front to reach the critical velocity, no detonation will occur and the explosive merely deflagrates. Burning can therefore be a safe but disquieting method of destroying small quantities of high explosive. It is not recommended that anyone but an explosives expert should destroy high explosives in this manner.

Condensed phase and dispersed explosions

Irrespective of whether an explosive detonates or deflagrates, its initial state affects the form of the final damage. The reactive material prior to the explosion may be in the form of a compact mass of solid or liquid (condensed phase) or distributed through a relatively large volume (dispersed).

Clearly gas and dust explosions fall into this second category, and they almost always deflagrate rather than detonate.

Container explosions

Many explosions occur as a result of the mechanical failure of containers subjected to internal pressure. The pressure inside the container is often due to compressed gas or gas mixtures. However, liquids stored at temperatures above their boiling points in pressurised vessels also cause many explosions, the so-called BLEVES (boiling liquid expanding vapour explosions).

Containers can also explode as a result of a reaction enhancement effect such as when a deflagrating explosive is ignited in a sealed tube. This mechanism is commonly employed in pyrotechnic manufacture.

The collapse of a building following the ignition of a gas mixture could be regarded as a special case of container burst.

High Explosives

Materials formulated for use as high explosives are normally solid (condensed phase) and are capable of detonation.

The military uses of conventional high explosives such as TNT (trinitrotoluene) and RDX (cyclonite) are well known.

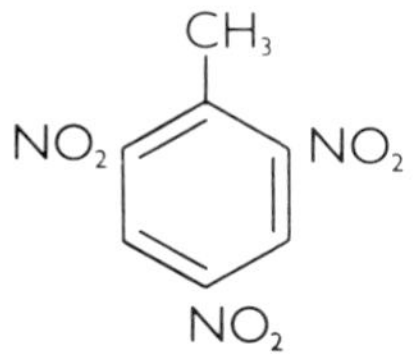

Trinitrotoluene 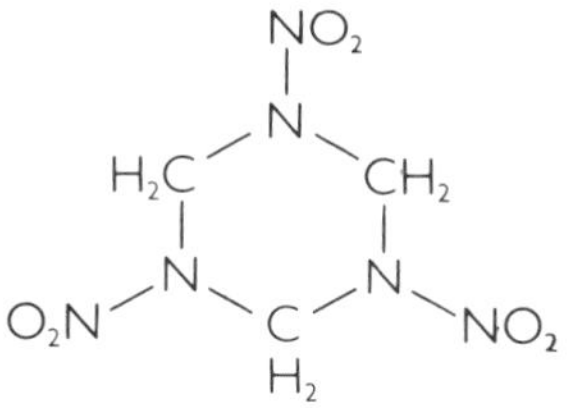   RDX

Commercial uses of high explosive include quarrying, mining together with demolition, and millions of tons of explosive are used each year. Methods of security are improving and it is becoming increasingly difficult for criminals to steal high explosive from legitimate users.

Many commercial explosives include nitroglycerine as a constituent.

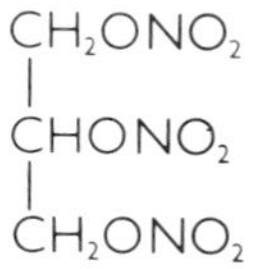

$$CH_2ONO_2$$
$$|$$
$$CHONO_2$$
$$|$$
$$CH_2ONO_2$$

Nitroglycerine

Nitroglycerine is a violently explosive, unstable, oily liquid which for reasons of safety and ease of handling is normally absorbed in a solid mixture, forming a dynamite or gelignite explosive. If they have been stored under the correct conditions, high explosives are stable and safe to handle. Most high explosives can be safely dropped, cut or even burnt in small quantities. Improperly stored nitroglycerine-based explosives may 'sweat' and exude liquid nitroglycerine, making them unstable and liable to explode when mishandled.

High explosive mixtures other than the conventional

commercial and military types may be encountered. Terrorist organisations use mixtures which are of varying sensitivities but which can normally be made to detonate under suitable conditions. Home-made mixtures do not normally react to completion, and as a result, considerable residues may remain for analysis after the explosion.

Accidental detonations can occur in chemicals legitimately stored in warehouses or in chemical works. Any situation in which for example, liquid oxygen comes into contact with organic material (particularly grease) may result in a detonation.

Other materials capable of detonation include nitrocellulose, organic peroxides, acetylene, ethylene oxide and many azides. Large quantities of ammonium nitrate or sodium chlorate can detonate in fires, although the presence of organic materials such as wood or paper may be necessary for the detonation to take place[10].

Brisance
The term 'brisance' refers to the shattering power of an explosive. High explosives are in general, brisant, but the degree of brisance may be varied according to the application. For example, a desirable property of a quarrying explosive might be that it should lift large fragments of rock without shattering them, whilst a military high explosive may be required to cause as much fragmentation and damage as possible. Military high explosives are therefore designed to be more brisant than most commercial explosives.

Recognition of condensed phase detonations
The detonation of a quantity of high explosive would normally be expected to cause a crater in the ground unless it occurred at a high level. Even in this case however, there may be evidence of shattering of brickwork or other structural material in the immediate vicinity of the explosion. It is possible to form an approximate estimate of the size of the charge involved, from the size of the crater, but this is dependent upon the medium, the type of explosive and the height of the explosion above the ground. There can therefore, be considerable problems in attempting to estimate the weight of explosive involved.

Detonations may produce shattering damage to walls, characterised by a network of cracks induced by tension in the material. Sometimes, especially in the case of concrete walls, the

170

shock wave passing through the wall may cause a layer of the concrete to spall from the wall on the side opposite from the explosion.

Another characteristic of a detonation, is the rapid fall-off of degree of damage with increasing distance from the centre of the explosion. Dispersed deflagrations in buildings may cause more widespread damage than condensed phase detonations, but the damage at the centre of the explosion is likely to be very much less extreme.

Location of the seat of the explosion

Because detonations show a characteristic rapid fall-off in damage intensity, it is likely to be easier to locate the seat of this type of explosion than that of a dispersed explosion.

The position of the crater or any other region of shattering of building material, is a good indication of the position of the explosive material. The direction of displacement of items can also be used, but the possibility that items may have been moved during the fire-fighting or rescue operations must be borne in mind. The movement of a heavy item is likely to provide a more reliable indication than that of a light item, whose motion may have been influenced by the wind.

Distortion and bending of metal objects can give an indication of the direction of the blast. Items which incorporate flat metal panels in their construction may show 'dishing' effects; long metal objects such as pipes, railings and lamp standards may bend away from the blast.

Fragments from the exploding item may embed themselves in wood or plastic in the vicinity, giving further information to locate the seat of the explosion. Care must be taken to distinguish fragments which had formed part of the item which exploded, from secondary fragments projected by the blast.

It is important that all directional indications should be recorded on a plan of the area drawn to scale. The indications can then be seen in perspective and considered in association. It is also important that the scene should be photographed from various angles before too much disturbance takes place.

Condensed Phase Deflagrations

Materials such as gunpowder, cordite and match-head composition normally deflagrate when ignited. This means that unless they are confined, moderate quantities of these materials

171

produce very much less blast than detonating explosives. For this reason unconfined deflagrating explosives tend to have an incendiary rather than a shattering effect.

Gunpowder, is one of the most commonly used of the deflagrating explosives. Its burning behaviour is very much influenced by its physical state and the manner of its packing.

Correctly packed for the purpose in a narrow tube, gunpowder can form a delay fuse which burns slowly and steadily before reaching the main charge. If for some reason the gunpowder becomes loosely packed, then the flame can flash down the tube giving a very much reduced delay period. If gunpowder is ignited whilst confined in a container, a reaction enhancement effect can occur. The reaction rate accelerates rapidly as the pressure inside the container increases and, as a result, the container explodes violently. Many of the sound-producing fireworks and explosive signals depend upon this principle.

Deflagrating explosives react very much more slowly than detonating explosives, and can therefore be used as cartridge propellants. Another widespread use of deflagrating explosives is in the manufacture of pyrotechnics.

Pyrotechnics

The science of pyrotechnics, though commonly supposed to relate only to fireworks, includes a wide range of military and commercial applications, and a pyrotechnic device may be defined as follows:—

A device constructed to react exothermically, producing light, heat, sound, shockwaves and gaseous, liquid or solid products, or any combination of these.

Pyrotechnic devices can be divided into the following major categories:—

(1) *Light producers* such as fireworks, flares, signal rockets and flash charges for photographic purposes.

(2) *Heat producers* which include igniters, incendiary devices, heat-transferring trains and fuses, welding and cutting devices and food warming mixtures.

(3) *Sound producers* including whistling and exploding devices.

(4) *Smoke formers* intended for use as distress signals, for air flow testing or for fumigation purposes.

(5) *Gas producers* which can be used as a compact source of

energy to operate ejector seats, to start engines, or to generate a desired product such as oxygen or tear gas.

Pyrotechnic devices normally contain a solid mixture of reactants, one of which is a source of oxygen, and the reaction, once initiated is normally self-sustaining. It is however, perfectly possible for pyrotechnic devices to be constructed using liquids, such as petrol, single compounds such as ammonium dichromate or materials which do not contain oxygen.

Investigation

Pyrotechnic devices, whether commercially manufactured or not, are normally more likely to have incendiary effect than explosive. Commercially manufactured pyrotechnics are normally encased in strong, flame-resistant cardboard tubes and it may be possible to identify the type of device involved from the tube and from the remaining design of the outer surface.

In the case of home-made pyrotechnics, it is seldom that the maker achieves a stoichiometric mixture of ingredients, and commonly, sufficient unreacted mixture remains for chemical tests. (See Chapter 23 Laboratory Analysis).

Many home-made pyrotechnics and incendiary devices are ill conceived and owe more to optimism than to scientific knowledge. Incompletely burnt or unburnt devices can provide a great deal of evidence, including finger prints and they should not be handled before the arrival of a Scenes of Crime Officer.

Dispersed explosions

Dispersed explosions take place in diffuse media such as mixtures of air with gases, dusts or vapours. They are, almost without exception, deflagrations although detonations can occur under certain conditions. The most commonly encountered type of explosion in this category is the gas explosion.

The ignition of a serious leakage of piped or bottled gas indoors can cause almost total destruction of a building. For such an explosion to occur, the gas must be in a concentration within its explosive limits, and there must be a suitably energetic source of ignition, normally a spark or a flame. (See Chapter 18).

Methane (natural gas) is the fuel gas normally used in Britain, and this has an explosive range between 5% and 14% in air. For an explosion to occur, the gas must fall within its explosive limits in the immediate vicinity of the source of ignition. Since methane has only about half the density of air, a steady leakage of this gas

Plate 11A. Petrol bomb. An experimental throwing of a small petrol bomb. Petrol bombs have been judged by an appeal court to be subject to the provisions of the Explosive Substances Act. Photograph: R. H. Ide.

will tend to rise to the upper part of the volume available to it, and begin to fill the building from the top downwards. The eventual ignition of the methane/air mixture may have a more destructive effect in the higher part of the building or room.

Both the flammable gas butane, and petrol vapour are significantly denser than air and tend, in a draught-free environment, to fill rooms from floor level upwards. The resulting explosion on ignition may show characteristic low level damage.

Naturally, some mixing of the gas or vapour with air will occur by diffusion. In addition, in the case of gases, high velocity leakages will result in turbulence which will cause the whole available volume to be filled by a homogenous gas/air mixture.

Petrol bombs

Petrol bombs have been held by the Court of Appeal in the UK to be Explosive Substances for the purpose of the Explosive Substances Act 1883 (Regina v Bouch 1982).

A petrol bomb or Molotov cocktail is an improvised incendiary grenade, normally constructed from a glass bottle filled with a flammable liquid and normally incorporating a means of ignition, such as a wick.

The principle of the device is that when thrown against a hard surface, the bottle breaks scattering fuel in a cloud of droplets and vapour. The flame of the wick ignites the cloud causing a fire-ball which is typically about 3 metres across (although it can be substantially larger). Various additives may be incorporated with the fuel, these are normally surfactants, such as soap or detergent, although pyrophoric mixtures have been used. Particularly violent explosions have occurred when unlit petrol bombs have been thrown into an enclosed space, and the vapour has subsequently ignited.

Fuels other than petrol have been used in Molotov cocktails and, clearly, any liquid with a fire point below the ambient temperature is capable of forming a fire-ball. However, violently thrown paraffin filled devices can also form fire-balls, probably as a result of the formation of small droplets, which ignite in the same manner as a dust explosion.

Higher boiling range and relatively viscous flammable oils such as diesel fuel, do not normally form fire-balls when used in Molotov cocktails. However, the spilled oil is still likely to be ignited eventually by the flame of the wick, and the device may therefore, have a considerable incendiary effect.

Dust explosions

Dispersed explosions can also occur in dust clouds[7][11]. The conditions necessary for a dust explosion to take place are that:—

(a) the dust must be explosible.

(b) the dust suspension must be of a sufficiently high particle concentration.

(c) the dust particles must be of an appropriate size.

(d) there must be a source of ignition.

(e) oxygen or another reactive gas must be present.

Explosibility

Most materials which are flammable in bulk are likely to be explosible when dispersed as dusts. However, in addition, a number of materials not readily flammable in bulk, such as zinc or aluminium, can explode violently if ignited when finely dispersed.

Materials commonly accepted to be capable of exploding include coal, flour, starch, sugar, wood flour, sulphur and certain metals. High flash point combustible liquids can, when dispersed into fine droplets, explode in a manner analogous to a dust cloud. Liquid mists of this type can be produced by high pressure leakages or by violent events such as crashes or impacts involving the rupture of containers of flammable liquid.

Dust particle concentration

Dust explosions require a dust particle concentration above a lower limit, which varies with the material, but which is typically about 0.03 kg/m^3. Flammable dust clouds above this concentration can occur in cyclones, and in association with grinding processes. The appearance of such a dust cloud is similar to a thick fog, and it is unlikely that a person in such an atmosphere would be unaware of it, as could be the case in a vapour/air mixture. They are unlikely to be encountered in well run flour mills except in certain limited areas. However, two-event explosions can occur in which a preliminary explosion or accident, causes dust to be disturbed forming a cloud. This dust cloud then ignites causing widespread destruction.

Size of particle

Clearly, the more finely divided the substance, the greater is its surface area in proportion to its weight. Two effects result from this:—

(a) the greater the surface area, the more readily the material can burn in air, because the burning reaction takes place at the air/solid interface.

(b) the greater the surface area/weight ratio, the greater the 'wind resistance'. As a result fine particles will remain dispersed in the air for far greater periods of time than coarse particles.

Ventilation Induced Flashover

When fires burn in conditions of limited ventilation, and especially when the fire has been smouldering for a long time, flammable gaseous pyrolysis products accumulate. These products do not necessarily ignite at first, particularly if there is insufficient oxygen present. It is possible under certain circumstances, for the pyrolysis products to ignite explosively when air is allowed into the burning room or building.

Generally the pyrolysis products are diluted with non-flammable gases, such as carbon dioxide and it is also the case that they may be liable to deposit as a gummy layer on cool surfaces. For these reasons, ventilation induced flashovers do not frequently occur, even though it is normal fire brigade practice to ventilate fires (See Chapter 3, The Effects of Fire-Fighting).

Certain materials appear to be particularly prone to the production of dangerous pyrolysis products, and one such material is latex foam (Chapter 1, Structures and Contents). An explosion occurred in a store at Chatham dockyard killing two firemen. Subsequent investigation indicated that latex foam mattresses had been smouldering, producing a characteristic flammable, cold, white, smoke. Whilst firemen were searching and ventilating the building, an explosion occurred causing much of the flammable material in the vicinity to ignite. The explosion was violent enough to break some windows in the building but it did not cause any structural damage[12].

Vapour cloud explosions

It is possible for a large gas or vapour cloud, ignited in air, to produce a violent explosion even though it is not confined. A well known example of this phenomenon occurred at Flixborough in 1974, when a large cloud of cyclohexane and cyclohexanone mixture was released by the failure of a pipe linking two reactors.

The vapour cloud expanded and rose rapidly, entraining air as it did so. When it ignited, very rapid flame speeds developed (in the order of 100 metres/second). The resulting blast caused widespread damage to the chemical works and to buildings in nearby villages. (Plate 11B).

It is not fully understood how such high flame speeds could occur. One theory is that particles of dust suspended in the cloud became heated by radiation from the nearby flame front and caused gas near them to ignite prematurely causing a leap-frogging effect[13]. An alternative theory is that pipework and other obstructions on the chemical plant caused turbulence. Turbulence can cause very considerable flame acceleration in dispersed explosions.

Plate 11B. Unconfined vapour cloud explosions can cause considerable damage. The ignition of a vapour cloud at Flixborough resulted in blast effects which demolished buildings. The debris in the foreground includes the remains of three cars. Photograph R. A. Cooke.

Fires and explosions involving large quantities of material do not necessarily behave in the manner which might be predicted from the results of small scale experiments.

Dispersed detonations
It is possible in certain uncommon situations for a gas/air mixture to detonate. The mixture would normally have to be in a long duct or pipe and ignition would necessarily be in a position which would allow flame front acceleration along the duct. It would normally be necessary for the duct to be at least 60 times as long as it was wide.

Sources of ignition
Dispersed explosions of all types require a source of ignition. Electrical, mechanical and chemical sparks, flames and hot surfaces can all ignite dispersed mixtures.

In the case of a leakage of gas in a building, possible sources of ignition include pilot lights, heating appliances and electrical sparks from appliances, switches or motors. The source of

178

ignition will not necessarily be at the region of maximum damage because of the tendency of the flame front and resulting pressure wave to accelerate away from the point of ignition. It is not unknown for a householder who has ignited a leaking portable gas appliance to have been relatively uninjured while his house fell in ruins all around him.

In the case of deliberately induced explosions involving gas or petrol vapour, candles or heating appliances may be left in the building to ignite the mixture when it reaches the correct concentration. In such cases the mixture can ignite prematurely, sometimes while the arsonist is still making his preparations.

Dust explosions can occur as a result of a major fire. Part of a building may collapse resulting in the disturbance of a quantity of dust which has been deposited in some inaccessible place over a long period of time. Dust explosions can also be caused by mechanical sparks resulting from the entry of a metallic foreign body into a grinder or cyclone.

Recognition of dispersed explosions
Normal deflagrating dispersed explosions produce very much less violent pressure surges than do condensed phase detonations. However, a very small pressure rise can be sufficient to demolish walls and to raise roofs. Structural damage of this type vents the

EFFECTS OF BLAST OVER PRESSURE ON COMMON BUILDING ELEMENTS

Structural element	Failure	Approx. blast pressure acting at right angles to plane of element. (kN/m^2)
Glass windows, large and small.	Shattering usually, occasional frame failure.	3.5 to 7
Corrugated asbestos panelling.	Shattering.	7 to 14
Corrugated steel or aluminium panelling.	Connection failure followed by buckling.	7 to 14
Wood siding panels, standard house construction.	Usually failure occurs at the main connections allowing a whole panel to be blown in.	7 to 14
Concrete or cinderblock wall panels, 200 mm or 300 mm thick (not reinforced).	Shattering of the wall.	14 to 20
Brick wall panel, 200 mm or 300 mm thick (not reinforced).	Shearing and flexure failures.	48 to 55

After Glasstone (refs 17 & 18).

Plate 11C. Gas explosions in buildings can result in the collapse of complete walls. The damage is likely to be widespread and general throughout the room or rooms where the gas had been present. Photograph by Courtesy of West Yorkshire Metropolitan Police.

explosion and it is for this reason that higher pressures are not developed.

The effect of a dispersed explosion may be to push down a whole wall almost intact, although as the wall falls it tends to break up in mid-air. (Plate 11C).

Less destructive dispersed explosions may vent through the weaker parts of the structure such as the windows. These windows may show a cracking pattern characteristic of an explosion (See Chapter 9, Deductive Evidence at Fire Scenes). There may also be evidence that the roof has been lifted, although it may have fallen back into place. There will be no crater and there is unlikely to be any localised shattering of brickwork.

Container Explosions

Violent explosions can occur as the result of the bursting of boilers, water heaters, gas cylinders etc. Many such explosions occur during fires when the contents of sealed containers are heated. The bursting of a relatively small container can produce a very loud noise, and it is common for eye witnesses to report that they had heard one or more explosions during a fire.

Fire-induced container explosions
Many sealed containers are present in both domestic and industrial premises, and in most cases they are filled with a material capable of producing an internal pressure when heated. Of the commonly encountered sealed containers, cylinders of compressed gas are the most likely to produce a violent explosion in a fire. Liquefied petroleum gases (LPG), such as propane or butane, are commonly used as industrial and domestic fuels. A fire involving a cylinder or pressure vessel filled with LPG will cause the internal pressure to rise with the rising temperature. In addition to the pressure rise, the walls of the cylinder may be weakened by the heat, especially in the head space region above the liquid level.

Eventually the pressure vessel may split, allowing the liquid contents to burst out and vaporise. Ignition of the vapour is likely to take place almost immediately after the release, but cases have occurred in which the vapour has spread for some distance before igniting. When the vapour does ignite, it is likely to form a fireball of considerable size and great ferocity.

Such fireballs will vary in size, depending upon the quantity of fuel involved. A 125 gramme butane gas lighter refill container may produce a fireball of between 3 and 6 metres in diameter, while the tanker which exploded near the Spanish camp site at San Carlos de Repita, contained approximately 20 tonnes of liquefied gas (propylene) and produced a fireball about 400 metres ($\frac{1}{4}$ mile) in diameter.

The increasing use of LPG as a fuel, and its transportation in larger quantities has given rise to concern in some circles regarding the possibility of an increasing number of very serious accidents[14].

Most British propane and butane gas cylinders incorporate a pressure relief valve which is intended to prevent bursting of the cylinder under conditions when the gas pressure may rise.

If the gas pressure in the cylinder rises above a certain predetermined figure, the pressure relief valve opens venting gas.

The operation of a pressure relief valve normally prevents bursting of the cylinder, but a horizontal jet of flame about 5 metres long may result. During the investigation of fires which have involved LPG cylinders, allowances should be made for regions of severe burning caused by the operation of these valves.

LPG in motor vehicles

A growing use of LPG is as a fuel for motor vehicles. Although many conversions are carried out by reputable companies, inefficient operators have also entered the field, and some of the installations are not necessarily safe.

During the filling procedure too, short cuts can lead to danger, and it is possible, by disregarding proper filling instructions to over-fill a fuel tank. Manufacturers of the systems, instruct that there should be a specified ullage space above the liquefied gas, and a dip tube leading to a bleed valve should ensure that visible evidence is given when the tank has been filled to the maximum acceptable level.

Liquefied petroleum gases have a very high coefficient of thermal expansion and as a result, the liquid in an over-filled tank can expand under warm conditions until the tank is hydrostatically full. Any further rise in temperature causes a further expansion of the liquid, exerting an immense pressure on the tank which then bursts causing considerable damage to the vehicle even if it does not ignite.

Expansion ratio.	Propane	Butane
Liquid to vapour.	274	233
Coefficient cubical expansion per °C at 15°C.	0.0016	0.0011

The coefficients of cubical expansion of these two liquefied gases are several times that of water.

The presence of a fuel tank containing 80 litres or more of LPG in a crashed or burning car presents obvious dangers to firemen and the public[15].

Plate 11D. The remains of a tank which had contained liquefied propane. When involved in fires such tanks can explode and may fly considerable distances due to the reaction effect. Photograph Courtesy Tyne and Wear Fire Brigade.

Other container explosions

Very violent explosions can result from the bursting of boilers and other vessels when they are over-pressurised with steam or gas. Almost all large vessels designed to contain a gas or vapour under pressure have some form of safety valve or bursting disk. Any fault which results in an explosion is likely to have, as a contributory cause, some fault to, or interference with, the safety valve.

When investigating a pressure vessel explosion it is necessary to establish not only the reason why the pressure had exceeded the critical level, but also why the safety valve failed to operate. It is not unusual to find that safety valves have been tampered with, perhaps because the frequent operation of the correctly set valve has been a source of annoyance or inconvenience to nearby workers. For the same reason it is possible that bursting disks could be replaced with different and stronger materials. Another reason for an explosion may be that for an unforeseen reason the pressure in the vessel rose very much more rapidly than had been anticipated, and that loss of gas through the safety valve had not been sufficient to cope with the build-up of pressure.

Other container explosions may occur in vessels which, although not designed to withstand pressure, suddenly suffer an internal production of gas, vapour or heat.

Mode of failure of pressure vessels

When a container bursts as a result of internal pressure, it is normal for it to break up into a small number of relatively large pieces. This can be contrasted with the effects of a detonation when any metal in the immediate vicinity is likely to be shattered into small pieces. In the case of a cylindrical container of uniform strength, it is more common for it to split longitudinally than circumferentially.

In a cylindrical vessel, the pressure at which it would burst in a longitudinal direction is given by:—

$$p = \frac{d \, ft'}{r}$$

where p is the pressure
     d is the thickness of the wall
     ft' is the ultimate tensile stress of the material
     r is the radius of the cylinder

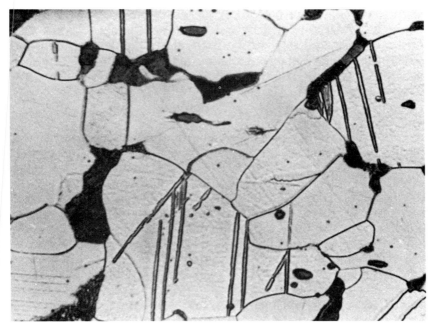

Plate 11E.   Neumann Bands. These bands are characteristic of explosive damage to ferrous metals and can be observed by microscopical examination of metallurgically prepared specimens. Photograph D. J. Hanks.

The formula is only capable of giving an approximate idea of the pressure involved, and wide variations may result if the cylinder is not uniform or the metal has been affected by heat.

The pressure required to produce a circumferential split is given by:—

$$p = \frac{2d\, ft'}{r}$$

It is evident from this that the strength of a cylindrical vessel to resist internal pressure in a circumferential direction is twice its strength in a longitudinal direction.

Pressure bursting of vessels constructed of ductile materials may be distinguished from detonation damage by the characteristics of ductile failure. There may be thinning of the metal near the edge where the failure initiated, and the split in the metal is likely to have propagated as a shear tear, which may show chevron marks indicating the direction of propagation of the split. Metal damaged by a detonation is likely to crack in a brittle manner and this will be particularly the case at the point where the cracks began. Neumann bands may also be found in metallurgically prepared specimens of detonation-damaged ferrous metals. (Plate 11E).

Implosions
An implosion is a special case of failure of a sealed container as a result of differential pressures. It is necessary for certain procedures to take place in a vacuum. The commonest everyday example of an evacuated vessel is the cathode ray tube of a television set. It is possible for cathode ray tubes to implode if subjected to force or thermal shock. However, the pressure difference involved cannot be greater than atmospheric pressure and with this relatively small pressure difference there is seldom any great damage caused by the implosion of a modern television tube, although the fragments of glass can travel many metres.

Certain items of laboratory apparatus commonly used evacuated, include Buchner flasks and desiccators. Implosions in such glassware have on rare occasions resulted in fatal injuries from flying glass.

Reaction enhancement in pressure vessels
A chemical mixture which might normally be expected only to deflagrate if unconfined, may burn more rapidly in the confined situation of a sealed container. As the pressure increases (as a result of rise in temperature and accumulation of gaseous products) so the rate of reaction can increase. Consequently, the container may burst with greater violence than might be expected simply as a result of gaseous over-pressurisation.

Investigation of Explosions
Whilst it is true that no two accidental explosions are alike, a systematic approach is still vital during the investigation.

Safety
Structural damage to buildings may pose a threat to the investigator and in the case of explosions there is no recovery of stability such as may occur in fire-damaged buildings on cooling.

In the case of terrorist attacks, there is the possibility that additional 'follow-up' devices may have been planted nearby to be detonated by timers or by remote control. For this reason explosion scenes of this type should be searched for 'booby-traps' by military or civilian personnel trained in this work and the investigation of the explosion should **not** begin until the area has been cleared.

One of the most hazardous situations the explosives investigator is likely to meet is when a device has not exploded as intended and still remains in an unstable condition. Untrained personnel should not attempt to disarm such a device, but it may be necessary for someone to look at it in order to decide whether the bomb disposal squad should be called out.

If it is not known whether the item is an explosive device, the approach will obviously depend upon the degree of suspicion felt, nobody should go near to it if there is any reasonable cause to suspect that it is explosive. As much information as possible should be obtained from people who have already been near to the item. It may also be possible to make an assessment using binoculars.

If it is felt necessary for an examination of the item to be made, only one person should enter the hazardous area. He should make his check as quickly as possible, without actually touching the item. If he observes wires or lines attached to the item, or if it is smoking, he should withdraw immediately. On no account should he use a personal radio, since this could actuate the device. For the same reason, lights or electrical apparatus in the vicinity should not be switched on or off. It is possible for explosive booby traps to be set to explode when doors are opened or items moved. The investigator should bear this, and the fact that it could be actuated by remote control, in mind when in the vicinity of the device.

If as a result of this examination, or for other reasons, it is believed that explosive may be present, the appropriate Explosive Disposal Unit should be informed and the area should be evacuated to a radius of 100 metres (200 metres if the device could be a car bomb).

All relevant witnesses, including anyone who has seen the item at close quarters, should be retained until the arrival of the disposal team. More detailed advice is available in the UK from the staff of the Joint Services Explosive Ordance Disposal Report Centres.

Other dangers may exist at the scenes of explosions in chemical works. It is possible for plant to have been weakened or distorted in the explosion, or for critical control processes to have been interrupted. Under these circumstances, it is possible for a second explosion or fire to occur as a direct result of the first. The advice of production managers, chemical engineers and others associated with the company should be sought, to establish whether there is a substantial quantity of any reactive or toxic chemical still remaining.

Type of explosion
It should be established as soon as possible whether or not there has been a significant explosion at all. It is common for witnesses to report that they had heard explosions during fires. Many items are likely to explode in a fire and, apart from cans and bottles, any hollow, sealed item can burst when heated. Cement asbestos roofs disintegrate violently and loudly when heated and the collapse of part of a structure may be interpreted as an explosion if heard but not seen.

If it is evident that an explosion has occurred, then it should be established whether a high explosive, pressure vessel or dispersed phase was involved. Diagnostic features of each type of explosion are summarised below.

Indication Characteristic	High Explosive	Pressure Vessel	Dispersed Phase
Crater.	Commonly formed if explosion near to ground.	Can occasionally be formed, particularly if vessel buried.	Highly unlikely.
Localised shattering of brickwork.	Common near to seat of explosion.	Damage more likely to be caused by impact of flying fragments.	Unlikely.
Spalling of concrete on side of wall opposite to explosion.	Fairly common.	Unlikely.	Unlikely.
Effects of explosion fall off rapidly with increasing distance.	Normal.	Possible, depends on size of vessel and its wall strength.	Not normal.
Directional indications fairly clearly defined.	Common.	Common.	Not normal at seat of explosion.

Indication Characteristic	High Explosive	Pressure Vessel	Dispersed Phase
Widespread fairly uniform damage.	Highly unlikely.	Can occur.	Normal.
Explosion lifts roof and pushes down entire walls.	Unlikely with small devices.	Possible.	Probable.
Fragments of metal produced.	Common. Fragments may be small and very distorted.	Normal. Fragments will normally be large.	Improbable.
Neumann bands found in ferrous metal.	Probable.	Unlikely.	Improbable.
Long-lived fire ball.	Improbable.	Depends on contents.	Possible.
Centre of explosion and region of most damage do not coincide.	Improbable.	Possible, depends upon movement of vessel.	Possible.

Materials Involved

High explosives

High explosive (condensed phase) incidents normally involve mixtures or compounds deliberately produced, either by commercial manufacturers or by terrorist groups.

Traces of unreacted explosive normally remain at the scene of the explosion. Material which had originally formed part of the device, or which would appear from its disrupted structure to have been near to the seat of the explosion, is likely to be of evidential significance and may bear minute traces of explosive. Relatively large quantities of explosive may be retained by plastic items which had been part of or near to the device[16].

Extremely sensitive methods of detection are available and for this reason stringent precautions must be taken to avoid the possibility of contamination. For example, in the case of an explosion caused by a terrorist device, the homes of suspects may be searched, and it may be required that the hands of the suspects should be swabbed for explosive residues. It is important that no officer who has attended the scene or handled explosives should subsequently come into contact with the suspect or his possessions.

189

In the case of accidental high explosive incidents, it is likely that the materials involved had previously been thought to be relatively safe under the prevailing conditions. A normal line of enquiry would be to establish whether any conditions had changed immediately prior to the explosion. It is also important to establish whether the official regulations and precautions quoted by the Works Manager or his equivalent were actually carried out in practice.

Dispersed explosions
The materials likely to be involved in dispersed explosions, flammable gases, vapours and dusts are by their nature, transient, and might not be thought to be likely to remain in detectable quantities after the explosion. Whilst it is by no means always possible to detect gas and vapour residues, the increased sensitivity of current techniques makes their detection a serious possibility.

In the investigation of explosions thought to have been caused by gas leaks, a 'chicken and egg' problem can arise and there may be dispute whether the gas leak caused the explosion or the explosion caused the leak.

In many cases, gas leak investigations are likely to be fairly straightforward because the leak need not necessarily be at, or near the region of severe damage, and can therefore be demonstrated to have occurred before the explosion. It should always be borne in mind, however, that other materials besides natural gas can cause dispersed explosions and the finding of a leaking gas pipe does not preclude the possibility that for example, petrol vapour or bottled gas was the actual cause.

High Explosive Device Searching Procedure
Whenever possible, attempts should be made to preserve evidence. Fragments of the significant items which had been close to the centre of the explosion will have been scattered widely. Fragments may be found in the crater (if any), embedded in woodwork, on the ground, on nearby roofs, and particularly at the bases of walls and kerbs.

Significant fragments in the gutter can easily be washed away if it rains or if hoses are in use. For this reason it may be worth while to search gutters at an early stage.

The scene should be searched systematically dividing the area

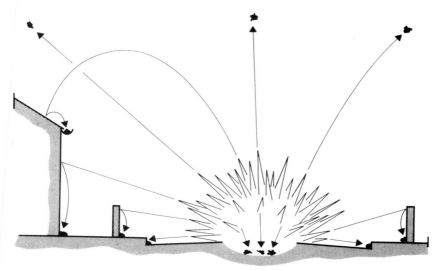

Figure 11.1. Fragments of an exploding device travel in all directions, but show a tendency to accumulate at the bottoms of vertical surfaces. The whole area must be searched, but care must be taken to preserve fragments in gutters etc in the event of rain.

Fragments may be found on the roofs of buildings especially on the downwind side of the explosion. Figure D. S. Loxley.

into sections, and subjecting each section to a fingertip search. Recovered items should be labelled according to their locations. If a significant fragment is recovered from a particular area, it is well worthwhile to search that area particularly carefully, because fragments are often found grouped together.

It is important to search rooftops and gutters because many fragments will have been projected upwards. It is possible for the trajectory of the lighter fragments to be affected by the wind and, therefore, more fragments may be found on the down-wind side of the explosion seat.

Small fragments can normally be packaged in polythene bags, but if the presence of commercial or military high explosive is suspected, nylon bags should be used.

Following the fingertip search, it may be thought necessary to sweep up the remaining debris for a subsequent laboratory search. New brooms should be used if possible, to avoid dangers of contamination from previous scenes. Most local authorities are prepared to lend the Police or Fire Brigade brooms from their stores if they can be convinced that the situation is sufficiently serious.

The sweepings should be put into large plastic bags, new dustbins or cardboard boxes for transportation to the laboratory.

References

(1) R. J. Harris. The investigation and control of gas explosions in buildings and heating plant. 1983 British Gas.
(2) S. Fordham. High explosions and propellants. 1980 Pergamon.
(3) J. Stoffel. Explosives and home-made bombs. 1972 C. C. Thomas.
(4) C. H. Johansson and P. A. Persson. Detonics of high explosives. 1970 Academic Press.
(5) R. Meyer. Explosives 1981 Verlag Chemie.
(6) H. J. Yallop. Explosion Investigation. 1980 Forensic Science Society.
(7) K. N. Palmer. Dust Explosions and fires. 1973 Chapman and Hall.
(8) S. E. Chandler. Fire incidents involving explosions in Great Britain. BRE current paper CP 55/77.
(9) W. M. Croft. Fires involving explosions, a literature review. Fire Safety Journal 1981 24 3.
(10) Sodium chlorate risks to be reconsidered. Fire Eng. Journal 1979 39 14.
(11) F. C. Lloyd. Dust explosions and powder flammability. Fire Eng. Journal 1980 40 21.
(12) W. D. Woolley and S. A. Ames. The explosion risk of stored foam rubber. BRE Current paper CP/36/75.
(13) S. R. Moor and F. J. Weinberg Nature 1982 290.
(14) Concern over LPGs piecemeal control. Fire Eng. Journal 1980 40 31.
(15) G. M. Threadgold. That crashed car may be LPG-fuelled. Fire Eng. Journal 1976 36 7.
(16) D. G. Higgs and T. S. Hayes. Post detonation traces of NG on polymeric materials, recovery and persistence. J. For. Sci. Soc. 22 p. 343.
(17) Samuel Glasstone. The effects of Nuclear weapons April 1962.
(18) D. Drysdale, N. Kemp. Concept selection: flammable atmospheres. Architects Journal 7 March 1979.

Chapter 12

Vehicle Fires

Fires in vehicles have for some time been regarded as amongst the most difficult to investigate. The particular problems presented by these fires are that they can quickly burn to completion, they may involve considerable quantities of fuel and there is normally no structural woodwork.

However, when properly investigated, vehicle fires can yield much useful information. A relatively uniform distribution of trim, window glass, upholstery material and carpet throughout most modern cars can provide valuable directional heat indications. The fact that most vehicles are mass produced, makes possible a comparison between the burnt vehicle and an unburnt model of the same type. Above all, the relatively small size of most vehicles makes it possible that every part of the debris can be examined in detail if necessary.

Despite improving safety technology, the number of car fires in the UK is increasing over 5 times as fast as the number of cars on the roads[1].

Car Fires
Moving car fires
Except in the case of road traffic accidents, it is fairly uncommon for cars to burst into flames whilst in motion. In the case of cars deliberately burnt for insurance purposes, it appears to be more common in the USA than in Britain for the owner to claim that the fire had occurred whilst the vehicle was moving[2].

Several factors act together to lessen the probability of ignition of a moving vehicle:—

(a) Any electrical fault is likely to be noticed by the driver or passengers during the smoky initiating stages.

(b) Some parts of the car are effectively air-cooled by its movement. This can sometimes prevent the surface of the heated item from reaching an appropriate ignition temperature.

(c) Accumulations of the vapour of petrol or other fuel may be swept away by the air currents before they reach a high enough concentration to ignite.

193

Immediately the driver stops the car to investigate the smell of smoke, the situation changes. The cooling effect of the air is considerably reduced and any leakage of volatile fuel is able to build up vapour into a flammable concentration. It is at this stage, shortly after stopping, that actual ignition is most likely to take place. However, if ignition does occur in the engine compartment of a moving car, the fanning effect of the slipstream can result in very rapid fire development.

Sources of ignition present in the engine compartment include electrical sparks, electrically overheated wiring and the exhaust manifold. Materials which can be ignited in the engine compartment include petrol, lubricating oil, grease and wire insulation (normally PVC on modern cars). In addition, many items in the engine compartments of modern cars are constructed of plastic, and the spare wheel may also be stored in this compartment.

Any fault leading to a fire in the engine compartment is likely to demonstrate itself to the driver in one of three ways:—

(a) The performance of the engine is likely to be adversely affected either by a deterioration in the fuel supply due to a leakage of petrol, or by inferior cylinder head ignition due to loss of electrical power.

(b) A smell characteristic of the fault may be detected. The smell caused by a petrol leak is self-evident. Alternatives could include the smell of burning PVC insulation or the burning of any other material displaced so as to come into contact with a hot region of the engine.

(c) Abnormal sounds may be heard. A loose flammable item dislodged inside the engine compartment may be heard during its displacement prior to the fire.

Flames are less likely to be observed than smoke at this stage. If they do occur, they are likely to be smoky and orange/yellow in colour. All of the materials legitimately present in the engine compartment burn in a manner characteristic of hydrocarbons.

Electrical faults are more likely to occur either during the very early life of a new car, when the electrical system has been modified, or after damage which has affected part of the wiring. It is unusual for a fault in wiring insulated with PVC, to cause a fire. Normally, electrical overheating results in damage to the insulation accompanied by dense pungent smoke.

Fires in the passenger compartments of moving cars are uncommon, but when they do occur, they are most likely to have been caused by an activity of one of the occupants. It is conceivable that misuse of smoking materials could cause a fire in a moving car but normally the fire would be discovered and existinguished before it became dangerous. For the same reason children are unlikely to cause a serious fire whilst playing with matches, being in the close vicinity of an adult whilst the car is being driven.

The experience in the USA is that some fires in which the driver claims to have been moving, were in fact deliberately ignited by him whilst the car was parked in a secluded place.

The investigation of a suspicious fire of this sort will largely follow the pattern of the investigation of stationary car fires. However, in this case any evidence that the car was not drivable, will rebut the story of the owner. Information of this nature may be forthcoming from neighbours or may be obtained by examination of the engine or of the scene. If the car could not have propelled itself to the scene of the fire, it must necessarily have been towed, pushed or carried there. Evidence of towing may be visible on the front bumper.

Accident-induced car fires

Several studies have been carried out to investigate the incidence of fires breaking out after serious road traffic accidents. In all studies it was found that a very small proportion of vehicles involved in accidents, actually caught fire. Austin and Wagner found that only 0.22% of the 12,909 accidents which they investigated had resulted in fire[3]. A similar figure of 0.29% was found by Gloyns, MacKay and Chattergee[4]. Siegal and Nahan found that fire occurred in 1.68% of accidents that they studied[5].

These figures are surprisingly low when it is considered that accidents frequently result in a spillage of petrol and damage to electrical systems.

Certain types of accident were shown to be more likely to result in fire than others. Accidents in which the vehicle rolled over, particularly those in which it came to rest inverted, were found to be more likely to cause fires than normal accidents. Clearly accidents of this type are more likely to result in a spillage of fuel than those in which the vehicle remains the correct way up.

Gloyns et al. estimated that 56% of all identified fuel leakages came from the fuel filler cap and pipe region. Vehicles with rear engines and petrol tanks in the front are thought by some to be more likely to ignite, because the fuel tank is more likely to rupture in a frontal impact. However, the surveys carried out to investigate this possibility are ambiguous, some tending to support the theory and others to refute it[6][7].

Stationary car fires

In the majority of car fires requiring investigation, the car is thought to have been stationary when it ignited. The information required for the investigation may be obtained from four sources; the owner, the Fire Brigade, the first witness and from examination of the scene.

Since it is possible that the fire had been started by the owner himself, the information obtained from him should not necessarily be regarded as accurate.

The following information will be required from the owner:—

(1) When the car had last been driven.
(2) Where it had been left.
(3) Whether it had been secure.
(4) Whether the keys or any valuables had been left inside.
(5) Whether there had been any recent faults, modifications or damage.
(6) When the car had last been seen in an undamaged state.

Information will also be required from the person who discovered the fire. e.g.:—

(1) The time and circumstances of discovery.
(2) Whether any doors had been open.
(3) Whether any windows had been broken or open.
(4) The size and position of the fire.
(5) The colour of the smoke.
(6) Whether there had been anybody else in the vicinity.

Car fires develop very quickly if there is sufficient ventilation, and for this reason the account of the first witness may seem to be at variance with that of the fire officer. The state of the car at the time of arrival of the appliance will normally be evident from the final condition after extinguishment because car fires are generally quickly extinguished. The wind strength and direction at the time of the fire should be established before any attempt is made to locate the seat of the fire.

Plate 12A.   Cars can burn rapidly provided a window is open to allow sufficient oxygen for combustion. Photograph A. J. Bolister.

Location of the seat of fire

It is possible to locate the seat of a car fire with reasonable accuracy in many cases. Most cars can be divided into three regions, the engine compartment, the passenger compartment and the boot, and it is seldom difficult to establish in which of the three compartments the fire started.

If the fire started in the passenger compartment, it is often possible to locate the seat of the fire with a precision of about one quarter of the total area with reasonable certainty, particularly if the fire was extinguished before all of the flammable contents had been burnt. The burning pattern to the paintwork on the outside of the car may give good indications of the point of ignition of the fire. However, car fires are very much affected by the wind and allowance must be made for this effect when forming an opinion.

Several stages can be recognised in the effect of heat on painted metal.

(a) At relatively low temperatures, paintwork remains undamaged although some darkening and wrinkling may take place.

Plate 12B. Burnt car evidence of insecurity. Unburnt paint at the top and rear of the window of the rear door indicate that this door had been open throughout the fire. Photograph R. H. Ide.

(b) Somewhat higher temperatures normally result in blistering or creasing of the paint film. The temperature at which this effect occurs depends upon the type, thickness and freshness of the applied paint.

(c) Charring occurs at a higher temperature and the paint becomes black and flaky.

(d) The highest temperatures result in ashing of the paint. Although the colour of the final powdery deposit depends to a large extent upon the original composition of the paint, it is in most cases a light yellow or brown at this stage.

Areas of paintwork first heated by the flames inside the car are likely to be ashed, whilst the areas which became heated at later stages in the fire may be only charred.

The distribution of charring to the paintwork is particularly useful in comparing the extent of burning on the left and right hand sides of the vehicle. However, the burning levels at the front and rear of the passenger compartment cannot be so easily compared, because there is often a higher fire loading towards the front.

Paint char patterns on car doors provide good evidence to indicate whether the door had been open or closed at the time of the fire. The effect is most clearly seen in cases when the door had been wide open, but evidence is generally present if a door had just been ajar. The exact position of the door may be established by examination of smoke records on the hinges.

The upholstery materials used in cars frequently generate enough heat in a fire to cause the roof to sag significantly. Whilst the sag may be more pronounced above the seat of the fire, this is by no means always the case and the region of maximum roof sag appears to be influenced more by the direction of the wind than by the position of the seat of the fire.

Melted glass and metal in the car may give directional indications, but caution is required. Unmelted, broken, toughened glass may have failed and fallen to the floor at an early stage in the fire. Melted glass will have remained in the window until a later stage. The presence of melted glass in a burnt car does not, despite popular belief, indicate that a flammable liquid must necessarily have been used as a fire accelerant. The burning of the upholstery material alone, is capable of melting all of the windows of the car under suitable conditions.

The effect of wind is to cause greater heating to the items and materials on the leeward (downwind) side, and it may be that windows on this side of a car may melt whilst the others do not.

The small light bulbs in a car, particularly those beneath the dashboard, can also provide fire seat location information. The bulbs, which are vacuum filled, tend to collapse on the hottest side.

Interpretation of this type of evidence may be complicated by the fact that some of the bulbs and associated wiring may have become displaced during the fire.

Melted metal in a car fire is best used comparatively. Items which have partially melted give the best locational information. Many different component manufacturers are involved in the production of one car. All of these companies may use alloys of different compositions and therefore of different melting points. For this reason it is dangerous to interpret temperatures in absolute terms unless the alloy or metal is known, or unless a laboratory test has been carried out.

Cars which catch fire in secluded rural areas may completely burn out before they are discovered. However, in most cases, the Fire Brigade arrives whilst the car is still burning and extinguish it before all of the flammable material inside has been consumed. Under these circumstances, there may be some residues of seating material or interior trim remaining. These residues, by their presence may indicate that the fire started in another totally burnt region of the car. Carpets can provide especially useful evidence of this type and it is always valuable to excavate down to this level in each quarter of the passenger compartment. The degree of burning to an area of carpet in the passenger compartment will be influenced by its proximity to the seat of fire, but the presence or absence of rubber mats must be taken into account.

The underside of the car should also be examined if this is practicable. The heat damage to the underseal may give an indication of the position of the seat of the fire. In addition this is the only method of recognising a fire set under the car. The thickness of the carpet and the number and position of any rubber mats affects the extent of the heat damage to the underseal. It should be recognised that leakage of petrol from a fire-damaged fuel line may result in a pool burn under the car.

Examination of the car

It is essential to record identification data such as the registration number, make, model and colour of the vehicle.

(a) *Burning patterns.* The damage pattern to the body of the vehicle should also be recorded. This can be by means of photography or by sketching the damage patterns onto standard outline drawings of stylised cars.

(b) *Other ignition attempts.* Although the seat of the fire may have been located, it is important to examine the other less damaged regions. It is not uncommon for an arsonist to attempt, unsuccessfully, to ignite a car at the petrol tank or in the engine compartment. On failing, he may re-ignite the car inside the passenger compartment. Despite the subsequent successful passenger compartment fire, there is still likely to be evidence of the first attempt. Matches, crumpled paper or evidence of volatile fire accelerants may be present in the engine compartment. The petrol cap may have been removed and paper inserted into the filler pipe. Petrol or other fire accelerants may have been poured over the outside of the car.

200

There may also be evidence that a bonfire has been ignited underneath the car. Any bonfire of this type is likely to have been constructed of materials taken from the vicinity and on one occasion at least, it was possible to establish a link between charred material under the car and the contents of a nearby rubbish skip.

(c) *Security*. The state of security of the car immediately prior to the fire must also be established. Experiments have shown that it is difficult for a fire to take hold inside a car if the windows and doors are all closed. After an initial period of flames, the interior of the car becomes smoke-logged and the fire will either self-extinguish, or burn slowly, sometimes for hours, until a window breaks allowing the development of a ventilated fire.

Many arsonists are aware of this problem and as a result, leave a door or window open during the fire. In the case of petrol-assisted fires, it is not uncommon for the car to be ignited by means of a blazing torch thrown through the open window.

The position of a window at the time of the fire can be established by examination of the window winding mechanism inside the door. In addition, the broken glass from a window wound down before the fire will be predominantly inside the structure of the door, whilst little of the glass from a closed window falls inside the door. It is sometimes possible to find a record in toughened glass which indicates its position in the door.

As has been previously mentioned, it is possible to establish whether a door had been open or shut at the time of the fire by examination of paint charring patterns. Examination of the door catch mechanism may reveal whether the door had been locked or unlocked.

The security of the boot lid and bonnet should also be considered, but it should be borne in mind that it is common practice for fire fighters to force these open in order to establish that all of the fire had been extinguished.

(d) *Removal of items*. Whether a car has been ignited by its owner or by another person, it is likely that the arsonist may have been tempted to take items from the vehicle. Amongst items commonly taken are:— tool kits, wheels, radios, cassette players, batteries, spot lamps and wing mirrors. If the car has been ignited by the owner, some items, particularly batteries, wheels and tyres, may have been replaced by inferior substitutes. A substituted battery may be difficult to recognise unless the arsonist has been

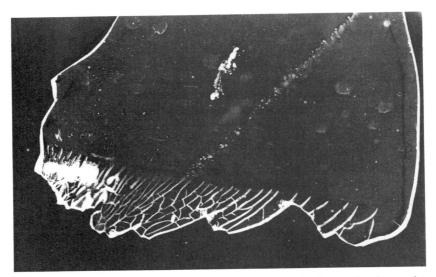

Plate 12C. Toughened glass can be annealed by the heat of a fire and it will then behave like normal glass. This car side window had been half wound down prior to the fire. The part of the window inside the door was protected from the heat and broke in the manner of toughened glass. The part of the window above the door has cracked normally. Such evidence can indicate the exact position of the window at the time of the fire. Photograph Mrs M. A. Taylor.

so careless as to fail to connect it to the leads. Even if the battery is found to be unconnected after the fire, care must be taken to establish that it had not been disconnected as part of the fire fighting procedure.

Substituted tyres are likely to be of clearly inferior quality and those portions of the tread remaining may well be bald. In addition the wheels may not match each other (even to the extent of being different sizes) and not all of the wheel nuts may be present. Cases have been reported in the USA in which tyres have been removed and the vehicle driven for some distance on wheel rims[2]. Such an occurrence would be readily recognisable by the absence of any tyre remnants (particularly the two bead wires) and by the presence of abrasion around the circumference of the wheel rims in question.

The removal of tyres from wheel rims is extremely difficult without proper equipment, and this type of evidence is unlikely to be commonly encountered.

(e) *Accident damage.* There may be evidence that the vehicle had been recently involved in an accident or had broken down. The owner may have one of two possible motives for setting fire to his vehicle after an accident, he may simply be wishing to claim the full insurance on the vehicle, or he may be attempting to destroy evidence which might link him with the accident.

In the latter case, it is unlikely that the very front part of the vehicle (the region most likely to provide useful contact evidence) will have been fire-damaged. Under these circumstances, it is not unknown for the owner to cause further damage to the front of his vehicle with a hammer or similar instrument.

(f) *The interior of the car.* Despite apparent almost complete destruction in the passenger compartment of a burnt car, it is generally still possible to identify and position most of the items which formed the original contents of the vehicle. This is particularly true of items which had been on the floor. Although incombustible items such as keys, bottles, metal cans, knives and coins might be expected to remain, it is also common for flammable items to be recognisable. Boxes of matches, newspapers, banknotes and even balls of crumpled paper have remained in an identifiable state after cars have burnt almost to completion.

On the other hand, items supported by seat springs at a high level in the fire may burn to almost complete destruction. Human bodies in this situation may continue to burn over a long period of time, heated by a small pool of fat which has been rendered from the body and which continues to burn beneath it. (See Chapter 10, Fire Fatalities).

When a badly burnt body is present in a car, it may be necessary for identification purposes to make a search for articles of personal jewellery in the ashes beneath the seat.

(g) *Examination of the engine compartment.* Attempts to ignite fires in engine compartments are less likely to succeed than those in the passenger compartments. However, accidental fires are more common in the engine compartment; these fires may be rather limited in effect and may not spread to the other parts of the car. Arson attempts in the engine compartment may be recognisable by the presence of fire accelerants, such as paper, straw, oil soaked rags or spilled flammable liquids. Matches may also be present.

Accidental fires are most likely to be caused by electrical overheating or by the ignition of a petrol spillage. It is not normal for the PVC insulation of wiring to ignite even when substantial overload currents flow. The normal effect is for the wire to become extremely hot and for the insulation to partially melt and char with the formation of pyrolysis products in the form of dense acrid smoke. The insulation may split in a spiral pattern and may shorten in regions where the wire had been curved. The net effect is that the insulation tends not to remain in contact with the heated wire. Ignition seldom occurs but when it does, it is probably due in part to the presence of oil, grease and dust on the insulation.

When evidence of severe electrical heating is found, there is always difficulty in establishing whether the heating caused the fire or was a result of damage by the fire to insulation elsewhere. If it is possible to locate the exact seat of the fire, this information can be used to determine between the two alternatives.

In the case of electrical equipment such as dynamos, ignition coils and motors, there is likely to be evidence that the item of equipment had been hotter than its surroundings if it had overheated and caused the fire.

Leakages of fuel in the engine compartment undoubtedly can cause fires but it is surprisingly unusual for leaking petrol to ignite. The operating temperature of the exhaust manifold of a car can vary between about 200°C–600°C. The normal auto-ignition temperature of petrol is quoted by many as 246°C, but there is in fact, considerable variation depending upon the exact composition of the petrol. Ignition also depends upon variables such as the nature of the surface involved, the geometry of the contact zone and the concentration of petrol vapour. Ignition of leaking petrol may be caused by electrical sparks at the commutators of motors and dynamos, or sparks originating from or associated with the ignition system. For leaking petrol to ignite, it is normally necessary that the engine of the vehicle should be running or should have stopped immediately prior to the fire.

(h) *Searching the scene in the vicinity of the car.* The authors have set fire to many cars for experimental and training purposes, and it has become clear that considerable evidence can be gathered from the scene in the vicinity of the car.

Cars incapable of self-propulsion must be towed or pushed to the chosen scene and evidence in the form of tyre marks, damage to bumpers or hand prints may be found.

If the vehicle has been left in gear, it sometimes happens that the engine may start when the fire reaches it, causing the car to move forwards or backwards a few metres. It cannot necessarily be assumed therefore, that the final position of the car after the fire was its position prior to the fire. This possibility should be taken into consideration when tyre marks and burn patterns on the ground are examined.

When arson is suspected, the area in the vicinity of the burnt car should be searched for containers, matches and anything which could have been used as a blazing torch or taper. In addition, it is possible that the arsonist has removed items of value from the car, and has hidden them in the vicinity, intending to return and recover them later.

Lorry Fires
Moving vehicle fires
Faults in moving lorries are more likely to result in fires than faults in moving cars. This effect is to some extent a result of the greater energy involved, but overheating of certain types of load can occur. In addition, a lorry driver is not so closely associated with the whole of his vehicle as is a car driver and he may not therefore, be aware that he has a problem at the rear of his vehicle. Overheating can occur in axles, in brakedrums and in tyres.

Partially deflated or heavily overloaded tyres flex more than is intended by the manufacturers. During the flexing process, frictional forces can result in considerable overheating of the tyre, particularly in the thicker shoulder region. Ignition of the tyre may not necessarily occur whilst the vehicle is actually moving, because the outside surface of the tyre is air-cooled to a certain extent. It is possible for an overheated tyre to burst into flames very shortly after the vehicle has stopped.

A similar effect has been known to occur when hot or reactive loads have been carried. Materials are sometimes loaded into lorries immediately after a production process involving elevated temperatures. Although the material might normally be expected to cool safely in small quantities, the large bulk which falls within the capacity of some lorries may suffer self-heating. A mixture of incompatible materials as a result of bad stowage, can also result in self-heating of the load.

Other fires in loads have been attributed to stowage of loads against interior lighting and to damage to electrical circuits during loading.

Accident induced fires

Diesel fuel is very much less easily ignited at normal temperatures and pressures than petrol and a pool of diesel fuel cannot normally be ignited by an electrical spark or even by a flame. Lorries can, however, burst into flames immediately after an impact and there are several mechanisms for this. Some lorries have in the engine compartment a canister containing ether pressurised with carbon dioxide or some other gas. These canisters, whose function is to assist the starting of the diesel engine, can rupture in an accident, releasing a cloud of ether droplets and vapour. Ether is one of the most easily ignited of common substances, and if there is any source of ignition in the vicinity, a fire-ball will result.

In particularly violent impacts resulting in rupture of the diesel fuel tank, it is possible for diesel to be sprayed out forming fine droplets. These droplets can be ignited in a manner analogous to a dust cloud explosion. Because of the viscosity of diesel fuel and the fact that diesel fuel tanks are normally positioned in regions not vulnerable to impact, fuel droplet ignition is an extremely unusual event.

When a lorry carrying a load of flammable liquid is involved in a crash, an ignition or explosion may occur, depending upon the properties of the liquid.

Fires in stationary lorries

Fires in stationary lorries follow a similar pattern to those in stationary cars. The main difference occurs, in the case of long distance lorries, when the driver uses the cab as a sleeping compartment. This situation gives rise to the risks associated with smoking in bed and with the use of small bottled-gas cooking appliances.

Similar logic may be used in locating the seat of a fire in a lorry, to that used in a burnt car, but the wind is likely to play an even more significant part in influencing fire spread in a lorry. Problems may arise if the load had been particularly flammable or if a glass fibre cab had been involved.

References

(1) M. Coates. Car fires, driving home the dangers. Fire Prevention 152. 13.
(2) Carter. Arson Investigation: Automobile Fires.
(3) Austin and Wagner. Proceedings of the 18th Conference of the AAAAM 1974 Toronto. pp. 89–103.
(4) P. Gloyns, G. M. MacKay and Mrs C. Chatterjee. Post-collision vehicle fires. April 1975. Accident Research Unit, Birmingham University.
(5) Siegel and Nahum. Vehicle post-crash considerations. FISITA International Safety Conference. SAE paper 700435 May.
(6) Porter. Burns in Automobile Accidents, Second J Plast Reconstr. Surge 2 104–108.
(7) Garrett and Stern. A Study of Volkswagen Accidents in the United States. 1968. Cornell Lab. Report VJ 1823–R32.

Chapter 13

Heating, Cooking and Lighting

Many accidental fires are caused by the misuse or malfunction of heating, cooking or lighting equipment. Even in normal operation, more energy is released by the use of these types of appliance than by most other domestic processes.

Open Fires

With the increasing constraints now applied to the emission of smoke from domestic premises, open fires are becoming less common. Many are still used however, and a number of accidental fires are caused by them each year.

A properly constructed fireplace and hearth is designed to prevent the possibility of flammable items such as wooden joists from being heated unduly during the use of the fire place.

The burning coal or wood fire is carried on a cast iron grate, which is openly constructed to allow ventilation from beneath and to allow ashes to drop through.

The hearth must be constructed of a fire resistant material and must extend for a distance of 0.84 m in front of the grate. Burning material rolling off the fire will land on the hearth and should self-extinguish safely. It is common practice for a hearth to be bounded by a fender, which is intended to prevent burning material from rolling beyond the edge.

The smoke from the fire escapes up the flue, providing much of the draught necessary for the proper burning of the fire. The flue is normally lined with a smooth clay or cement lining, which enhances the draught and lessens the deposition of soot.

Possible causes of ignition

A fire can occur under an improperly constructed hearth as a result of a fall of burning material through cracks or gaps.

Joists or other wooden structural members can protrude under the hearth, and can be ignited by the heat. Wooden shuttering accidentally left in position during construction can be similarly ignited.

Accidental fire spread is however, more likely to occur by ignition of materials in the room. Radiated heat or burning

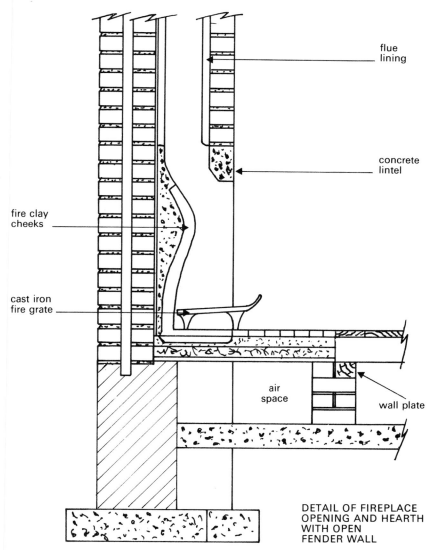

Figure 13·1. Chimney, Flue, Fireplace and Hearth construction.

material falling from the fire, can ignite nearby flammable materials, such as airing clothing or stacks or fresh fuel. It is also possible for the clothing of a person standing, sitting or lying near to the fire, to be ignited.

209

Accidental fires have also resulted from attempts to light open fires using unsuitable fuels or techniques. Petrol and paraffin have been used, and on at least one occasion, a fire resulted from the use of a butane blow torch for this purpose.

Accidental fires can occur at a higher level, and in many cases they commence as a result of ignition of soot or tarry deposits in the flue. Structural woodwork in the vicinity of the flue or chimney breast can be ignited[1], and this may smoulder for a long period before going into flames.

Faults in the brickwork or in the pointing of the flue may allow fire penetration into the roof or interfloor space. Thatched roofs present a particular problem in this situation.

Recognition of fire cause

For a house fire to have been caused by a domestic open fire, it is obvious that this must have been burning during or prior to the accidental fire. Except in cases where hot water is provided by a back boiler, it would be reasonable to expect that the weather should have been cold at the time. Accidental fires are most likely to occur if circumstances have changed, for example when a hearth fire is lit for the first time in the autumn, or if an abnormally large amount of fuel was used on a particularly cold night.

Fires due to defective hearths and those originating in or near the flue, are easily recognised from their position. Fires which result from coals rolling from the grate onto a carpet, or from the ignition of airing clothes, can be very much more difficult to recognise. However, even in these cases, it will normally be possible to locate the seat of the fire with sufficient accuracy to indicate the cause.

Fixed Gas Fires

Domestic gas fires operate using a piped supply of natural gas which passes through a venturi system at the burner, entraining air and producing pre-mixed flames. The gaseous combustion products pass into a flue and are vented to the outside of the building.

Much of the heating effect is by radiation, and since pre-mixed flames are non luminous, most gas fire designs depend upon the use of radiants. Radiants are constructed of a ceramic material, and are shaped in such a manner that parts of them quickly reach bright red heat, and consequently radiate heat horizontally into the room (see page 271).

Possible problems

Flue faults. Although a properly installed gas burner produces clean and smoke-free flames, the flue still needs to be cleaned at intervals.

An improperly maintained flue can result in a significant build-up of soot and debris, causing fumes to enter the room. Since the fumes contain significant quantities of the poisonous gas carbon monoxide, a number of fatalities have occurred as a result of this.

Ignition of material in the room

Gas fires share with most other heating appliances the possibility that material placed too close to them could ignite. They are therefore fitted with dress guards which prevent loose clothing from coming into contact with the radiants. Any normal flammable material which comes into contact with the dress guard should not be ignited by the radiated heat, even if the contact is fairly prolonged.

A tragically common cause of fatal fires, is when small children left alone in a room heated by a gas, electric or open fire, play with spills of paper, igniting them from the fire. Many modern furnishing materials can be easily ignited by burning paper, and such fires can develop rapidly, killing the occupants of the house.

It is possible for the ceramic radiants of a gas fire to crack or break. When this happens, the broken radiant is normally prevented from falling out of the fire by the dress guard, but it is possible for a piece of hot ceramic radiant to fall from a gas fire. If the fire has been installed on a non-combustible hearth, the fallen piece of radiant will not normally cause any problem. In the absence of a hearth, it might be possible for a hot fragment of ceramic radiant to ignite certain types of carpet.

Gas fires installed by amateurs to replace previous open fires, may not necessarily be fitted in accordance with the appropriate codes of practice. The original hearth opening may be covered with a sheet of hardboard, chipboard or some other combustible material. Fires have occurred in which flammable backing boards have been ignited by heat from the back of the gas fire.

211

Recognition of a room fire caused by a gas heater
For a gas heater to have caused an accidental fire, it must necessarily have been turned on. It is often possible to check whether or not the appliance had been turned on, without actually disturbing the position of the control knob. Evidence will be destroyed by the movement of controls and this should not be done unless it is essential. If it is necessary to alter any of the controls during the investigation, it is important to mark the original position of the control by scratching a line on it and on the side panel of the fire. The control should be returned exactly to its original position after the examination.

Plastic, fabric or burnt paper closely associated with or attached to the front of the gas heater, may indicate that this material had been ignited by the fire. However, it is possible for paper and other material to be thrown into the vicinity of a gas heater by the force of a fire-fighting jet.

LPG Cabinet Heaters
These heaters consist of a portable flueless radiant gas fire, connected by a length of flexible hose, to a cylinder of compressed butane.

The gas fire operates on the same principle as a normal gas fire, but because it is flueless, there is some danger that the atmosphere in a poorly ventilated room may become vitiated. Many of these heaters therefore incorporate a vitiation device, which cuts off the supply of gas to the burners if the pilot flame is not burning satisfactorily.

In conditions when the air has become vitiated, the lower oxygen concentration causes the pilot light to go out or to burn with an abnormal flame. The thermocouple hot junction of the vitiation device cools, and causes a control valve to close.

Problems
In an appliance containing many litres of liquefied butane, any form of misuse or any serious fault is likely to have dramatic consequences.

There have been many accidents in which losses of gas have occurred during the changing of a cylinder. Defective or dirty cylinder valves, or failure of the user to comply with the recommended procedure, can allow the escape of a considerable volume of gas. If there is a source of ignition nearby, a very destructive explosion is possible.

Any serious leakage of gas which occurs whilst the appliance is operating, is almost certain to be ignited by the hot radiants. Damage to or deterioration of the flexible hose can result in a gas leakage, and it is not unknown for a hose to become disconnected from the cylinder.

The presence of a cabinet heater in a burning room is also a cause for concern. There is a serious likelihood that the gas cylinder may become involved in the fire and there is a possibility of an explosion. If a pressure relief valve operates under these conditions, large volumes of butane will be released horizontally under pressure. The burning of this vented gas may give rise to misleading burning patterns.

Paraffin Heaters

Paraffin heaters used for domestic purposes are of two main types, convector and radiant. These two types depend upon totally different principles and will be dealt with separately.

Paraffin has a fire point significantly above normal ambient temperatures and, as a result, it is not possible to ignite a pool of the fuel without subjecting it to heat.

For this reason the paraffin must be either absorbed upon a porous wick, or heated to an elevated temperature in the burner[2]. A third possible method of ignition, is to introduce the paraffin into the combustion chamber in the form of an atomised spray. This last method, although a preferred technique in certain central heating boilers, is not convenient for use in small portable heaters.

Convector heaters

Convector heaters normally depend upon a tubular wick whose height is adjusted by a rack and pinion mechanism. The burner is supported on top of the fuel tank, and paraffin climbs the wick by capillary action. In most types of convector heater, the height of the wick should be adjusted so that a blue flame results when the chimney assembly is in place.

Problems

Convector heaters are generally designed to be fairly tall but slim, and they are therefore often used to heat passage ways and

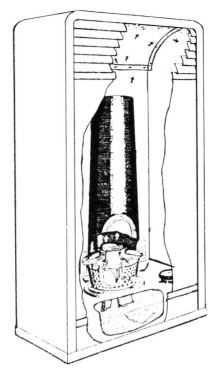

Figure 13·2   A paraffin convector heater

entrance halls of houses, since they do not obstruct appreciably the passage of the occupants of the building. In such positions not only are they more vulnerable to being knocked over, but the consequences of a fire caused in this way are likely to be more serious. The newer convector heaters incorporate devices which are intended to extinguish the flame when the heater is tilted, but many unprotected heaters are in regular use.

Fluff and dirt which have accumulated in the burner and chimney can possibly ignite. It is also possible that clothing or furniture in contact with the heater might catch fire, but normally the casing temperature of a convector heater is far too low for ignition to take place.

Radiant Heaters
Most radiant paraffin heaters operate using the drip feed

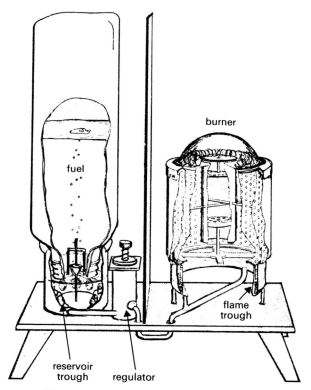

Figure 13·3   A paraffin radiant heater

principle. Fuel feeds from a removable glass or metal reservoir into a trough until it finds its own level.

The rate of flow of fuel is controlled by the feed tap. Paraffin in the burner trough is heated by an igniter wick, whose function ends when the paraffin in the trough has reached its fire point. The flammable vapours then burn on the surface of the wire gauze dome, heating the room by convection and radiation, and heating the surface of the fuel in the trough. Fuel flows from the reservoir trough at a rate controlled by the tap, and is replenished from the fuel tank on demand.

Problems
It will be evident that it is essential for the heater to be fairly level. If the burner trough is higher than the reservoir trough,

215

insufficient fuel will reach the burner and the heater will not reach the desired temperature or may be impossible to light. If the burner trough is lower than the reservoir trough, too much fuel will reach the burner and the result could be flaring, or possibly spillage of burning fuel.

Most radiant paraffin heaters are fitted with adjustable feet, intended to allow the heater to be levelled on an uneven surface. However, householders do not necessarily adjust the level of a heater every time they move it.

Apart from the problem of level, draughts can affect the older type of drip feed heater causing flaring which has resulted in many fires[3]. Radiant heaters manufactured more recently, have been made very much less susceptible to draughts. Other problems which can occur include leakages, contamination of the fuel with water, and use of an incorrect fuel such as petrol.

In addition to the fire hazard, this type of heater has been responsible for a number of deaths from carbon monoxide poisoning.

Electric Reflector Fires

The two-bar reflector electric fire is still commonly used in a form which has remained almost unchanged for many years. The two bars consisted originally of a ceramic core spirally wound with a heating element wire, each bar rated at about one kilowatt.

Normally one of the bars is controlled by a switch, but the other bar comes into operation immediately the appliance is connected to a power supply. The radiant heat is reflected in the chosen direction by a chromium plated reflector trough which in some models can swivel in a vertical plane.

The elements in operation are electrically live and at bright red heat, and it is necessary for them to be protected by a wire dress guard. Some of the modern versions of this design use heating elements which are protected by a quartz tube. This design ensures that no live wiring is readily accessible, and also decreases the probability of ignition of material coming into contact with the bar. However, some form of dress guard is normally incorporated in this type of heater too.

Problems

In common with all forms of portable heater, electric fires can be placed in close proximity to flammable items. Fires have also been

216

caused when electric trough reflector heaters have fallen, or been placed, face downwards on the floor. Fires which have started in this manner normally show characteristically severe damage to the floor boards in a very localised region.

Electric Fan Heaters

In this type of heater, loosely wound spiral elements are situated in the air flow of one or more electrically driven fans.

The elements are separately controllable to a total of two or three kilowatts. The system is protected from overheating by one or more bimetallic cut-outs situated above the heating elements.

Problems

If the air intakes or outlets are blocked, or if the fan motor fails, the element rapidly overheats causing the bimetallic cut-outs to operate.

It is possible for partial obstruction of an air intake to result in the serious overheating of part of the element, whilst the bimetallic cut-out is still effectively being cooled by a narrow air stream.

Since the operation of the fan creates a suction effect, it is possible for papers or curtain fabric to be drawn into contact with the air inlet. Overheating of the element could eventually result in the ignition of flammable materials forming part of the heater, the curtain or other obstructing material, or of certain types of carpet.

Night Storage Heaters

Night storage heaters take advantage of the fact that it is economical for electricity producers to sell electrical power at a cheaper rate during periods of low demand. Time switches set and sealed by the Electricity Board, ensure that the cheap rate electricity is only supplied to the consumer during selected low demand periods, particularly at night.

Night storage heaters consist of a large mass of bricks or other inert material, heated by interwoven electrical elements.

A thermostat offers some temperature control, and thermal cut outs and fusible links may also be present.

Problems

Despite warnings from the manufacturers, users frequently stack material on and against these heaters. If the material is a good thermal insulator, the surface temperature of the heater will rise with the decreasing heat losses to the air. Eventually thermal cut-outs will operate preventing any further electrical heating of the appliance. However, heaters of this type have a very high thermal capacity, and the temperature in the centre is very much higher than the normal surface temperature. The possibility therefore exists, that the surface temperature in the insulated region could rise to a level capable of igniting the stacked material.

Cooking Appliances

A large number of fires are caused each year by cooking appliances. Hogg[4] found that the overall fire risk from electric cookers was about three times that of gas cookers. She also reported that over 95% of fires caused by cooking appliances arose from misuse rather than malfunction.

FIRES IN ELECTRIC COOKERS

Fault	Fire Incidence
Misuse	1401
Faulty thermostat	16
Faulty switch	5
Earth fault	8
Defective insulation	6
Short circuit	2
Collapse of insulating material	2
Fault in installation	4
TOTAL	1444

Because of the absence of a visible and possibly audible flame, an electric cooker is inherently more likely to be left switched on accidentally than a gas cooker. There is a particular danger in the case of electric cookers with ceramic hobs that they could be used as an extra work surface area, and then accidentally be switched on. Manufacturers recognise this problem and take measures such as the incorporation of indicator lights and the positioning of control knobs out of the reach of children.

The commonest form of ignition by a cooking appliance, is the chip pan fire. A chip pan may be left unattended whilst the cook answers a telephone or works at another task somewhere else in the house. The temperature of the fat or oil can rise fairly quickly from normal cooking temperatures (in region of 200°C) to its spontaneous ignition temperature (310°–360°C).

Fat or oil spilled at normal cooking temperatures through a flame will not normally ignite, but spillage on to an electric heating element at dull red heat (550°C or above) will normally result in ignition.

Fires in ovens occur more frequently in those heated electrically than those heated by gas. It is possible that this effect may, in part, be due to the atmosphere in a gas oven being more inert than that in an electric oven.

Ignition of clothing

It was found that the clothing worn by the user of a cooker is more likely to be ignited by gas flames than by electric heating elements. In general it is to be expected that the clothing of the user of a cooking appliance is likely to come into only brief contact with a flame or hotplate, and in this short period of time, ignition by a flame is more possible.

Recognition of cooking appliance fires

Recognition of these fires normally presents little problem. Apart from the fact that these are generally eye-witnesses, the location of the seat of the fire in the kitchen and the time of day (normally just before a meal time) immediately indicate the type of fire. Subsequent investigation will establish the position of the cooker controls and the types of cooking vessel involved.

Lighting

Incandescent lights

The most common form of domestic lighting is the incandescent light bulb. A fine, coiled, tungsten filament is raised to white heat by an electric current.

The filament is held in the desired position by support posts which are insulated and supported by a glass base. The glass envelope of the bulb retains an inert atmosphere around the filament; usually an inert gas such as argon is used, but sometimes, particularly in the case of small bulbs, the envelope is evacuated.

The envelope temperature normally reaches between about 100°C and 300°C, but very much higher temperatures can be attained if heat losses from the envelope are lessened by insulation[5].

219

The envelope temperatures of high intensity, incandescent filament spot lights, will not necessarily be any higher than those of normal incandescent bulbs, although several shop and dance hall fires have been attributed to contact of paper decorations with spot lights. In an enquiry of this type, experimental temperature measurements should be made on similar lights, before attributing the fire to this cause.

Fires caused by incandescent bulbs
The envelope temperature of a bulb is not normally high enough to ignite cellulosic materials. Small amounts of paper or fabric in contact with bulbs can scorch but do not normally ignite. Larger quantities of paper or cloth have an insulating effect and cause the envelope temperature to rise significantly, resulting in ignition of the material.

If the bulb is broken, the filament remains glowing for a few seconds, but in the presence of air, white-hot tungsten burns, forming white or yellow deposits of tungsten oxide. It is possible for the hot filament to ignite combustible material in contact with it. This is particularly significant in road traffic accidents, when spilled petrol can be ignited by the filament of a broken bulb.

Fluorescent Lights
Fluorescent lights consist of a sealed tube filled with mercury vapour at a low pressure, and coated internally with a mixture of compounds which fluoresce in ultra-violet light.

A choke is present in the circuit to assist in the starting of the lamp and to prevent a harmful rise in voltage.

Operation
When the current is switched on, a starter circuit operates causing a voltage surge energetic enough to initiate a discharge in the mercury vapour of the fluorescent tube.

The discharge results in the emission of light, particularly in the ultra-violet region. This ultra-violet light impinges on the coating on the inside of the tube, which fluoresces, emitting visible light.

This is an extremely efficient method of producing light from electricity.

Dangers of ignition
Fluorescent lights do not produce much heat, and the envelope

temperature is unlikely to exceed 60°C, except in the region of the cathodes where the temperature may reach 80°C.

Chokes can overheat, and a number of fires have been attributed to this cause, although some difficulty is likely to be experienced in proving this conclusively from residual evidence.

Tungsten Halogen Lamps

A tungsten halogen lamp differs from a conventional gas-filled incandescent bulb in that a low partial pressure of a halogen such as iodine or bromine is present. The tungsten vapour, which would normally deposit on the glass envelope, combines with the halogen to form volatile halides and the envelope temperature is kept sufficiently high to prevent these from condensing. The halides disassociate in the vicinity of the incandescent filament and an equilibrium state is reached.

The envelopes are constructed of vitreous fused quartz or Vycor, which can withstand the high temperature necessary. The greatly reduced volume of a tungsten halogen lamp allows economic use of more expensive but more effective gases such as krypton and xenon instead of the more normal argon. In addition, the smaller size of the envelope results in improved mechanical strength, and allows higher gas filling pressures. This reduces evaporation and increases filament life.

Problems

Tungsten halogen bulbs operate with envelope temperatures which can be as high as 600°–900°C[6]. Flammable materials in contact with a quartz envelope at such temperatures are likely to ignite in a short time.

Some tungsten halogen bulbs operate at a high internal pressure and it is possible for these to explode under certain circumstances[7]. Traces of sweat left on the quartz can cause the bulb to fail, and some display lights require to be arranged to within about 5° of horizontal otherwise they may eventually shatter, as a result of differential migration of the halide. Several fires in shop windows have been attributed to this effect.

Lighting Systems Involving Naked Flames

Whilst almost all lighting commonly encountered is electrical, naked flame lights persist in certain applications. Many people store candles in case of power cuts and for lighting at dinner parties and seasonal festivities. Oil lamps and pressurised butane lamps are used by campers and by householders where there is no electricity supply.

Problems

Because they are not in frequent use, naked flame lights can cause fires by misuse. Few householders now possess candlesticks and as a result, when candles are used, they are stuck to saucers with wax or wedged into the necks of bottles. The candle may therefore be unstable and can cause a fire by falling onto or against a flammable material.

Oil and pressurised gas lamps are designed to some extent with stability in mind but if overturned they are very likely to cause fires.

Another danger can be when naked flame lights are positioned close to or underneath a flammable item such as a curtain. At Christmas, candles may be incorporated into decorative arrangements which can include crepe paper and evergreen foliage. Few people today illuminate Christmas trees with candles, but if a dry spruce tree is ignited at a low level, the rate of spread of flame is dramatically fast.

It would be possible for a kerosene lamp to be filled with an incorrect fuel such as petrol or methylated spirit, and this was the cause of many fires in the early part of this century. Now, most people are familiar with the smell and properties of the liquid fuels and such accidents are rare. It is however possible to fit the wrong type of butane gas cartridge to a pressurised gas lamp. Several manufacturers market lamps designed to accept a particular cartridge; some cartridges release gas by operation of a valve, whilst others are pierced by a protruding blade inside a gas-tight rubber seating.

Use of the wrong type of cartridge or incorrect fitting of an acceptable cartridge can allow a sudden release of butane, resulting in a fire or explosion.

References

(1) B. Beland. Fire places and chimneys as fire causes. The Fire and Arson Investigator. Vol. 33, No. 3, p. 10.
(2) J. F. Fry and R. E. Lustig. Fires associated with kerosene burning appliances in dwellings. Fire Research Tech. paper No. 4.
(3) Effect of draughts on the burning of portable oil heaters. DSIR SO 47–222.

222

(4) J. Hogg. Fires associated with electrical cooking appliances. Fire Research Tech. Paper No. 9 1963.
(5) P. A. Funnell and R. H. Ide. Unpublished work.
(6) J. R. Coatin. Lamp materials. The Metallurgist and Materials Technologist 1975, p. 510–514.
(7) M. J. Buckley. Letter. Fire Prevention 152, p. 25.

Chapter 14

Recognition of Types of Fire

In the previous chapters some specific aspects of fire damage patterns have been discussed and their relevance to the investigator has been considered. This chapter, together with the chapter on arson, is concerned with whether particular types or causes of fire can leave tell-tale signs.

Many of the ideas presented will already have been discussed in one form or another elsewhere in this book but a restatement of them in this particular context will not be out of place.

Characteristics of Fires with Different Origins

Slow fires

Fires with smouldering origins require very special conditions for their development. Suitable materials, usually finely divided cellulosic substances, can smoulder provided that a suitable sustained heat input combined with insulation is available. Typical materials capable of allowing smouldering to develop include:—

Traditional furniture (coiled springs and vegetable fibre stuffing)
Piled sawdust
Baled cotton
Latex foam
Corrugated cardboard
Baled or stacked hay
Cellulosic fabrics (cotton or rayon)

Although it is possible to induce smouldering directly in polyurethane foam (see Chapters 1 and 20) it is more frequently a smouldering cellulosic cushion or some other sustained incandescent heat source which transmits the heat to the foam.

Smouldering from a cigarette end requires a pile of materials which are not only susceptible as the above mentioned materials are but which must also be arranged so that the cigarette is buried or, at the very least, in firm contact. Cigarettes are frequently blamed as a cause of fire even when these conditions are clearly

224

not available. For example, a cigarette landing on a typical carpet would, at the most, merely produce a small burn which would not develop beyond the immediate locality of the glowing tip. Similarly, a cigarette landing on a sheet of paper would be very unlikely to produce anything more than a slight localised charring. Even in waste bins where there may be a considerable amount of torn and crumpled writing paper it is difficult to produce anything more than a minor smouldering fire which may last for only a few minutes. Absorbent tissues can, however, smoulder for a considerable time.

Smouldering may result also from spontaneous heating to ignition in haystacks, in unstable chemical mixtures or by radiation as with wood close to hot flue pipes.

Materials which would normally be expected to burn freely may, after initial flaming combustion, settle down to a smouldering mode in a vitiated atmosphere (that is, in which there is not enough oxygen to support free flaming). For instance, an average sized living room contains about enough oxygen to support the flaming combustion of only half of an average polyurethane foam upholstered armchair. If the doors and windows are shut and remain intact, fire in such furniture may die down to a quiescent phase contrary to its more recognised behaviour.

Because of the slow rate of heat transfer away from the smouldering materials the fire damage pattern is usually one of very heavy localised destruction at the site of smouldering contrasting with lesser burning effects elsewhere. For example, there may well be a hole in a floor or a piece of furniture which has been totally consumed in a room in which the remaining furniture, although surface burnt, is largely intact (see Plate 14A). The windows, although cracked, may remain in place and the wall and ceiling plaster may still adhere to their supports. Cold surfaces, such as windows, will have collected condensed pyrolysate tars. Horizontal surfaces will collect deposits of soot and tars showing a marked difference from adjacent vertical parts.

It is very difficult to assess the time that a material has been smouldering. Undisturbed furniture of both traditional and modern types could smoulder for some hours before eventually bursting into flame. The presence of draughts can accelerate this process dramatically. It has, for instance, been possible with a sustained draught of about 1 m/sec (about 2 m.p.h.) to induce free

Plate 14A. The localised destruction which can be seen after a piece of furniture has smouldered for a considerable time. Photograph by Courtesy of Cheshire Fire Brigade.

flaming in corrugated cardboard carton 'flats' in contact with a cigarette end within five minutes. Sawdust trails may smoulder at about 5–6 cm/hour in still air. Draughts of one metre per second can double this rate. Evidence exists to suggest that this increase is linear for higher draught velocities.

Rapidly developing fires
Fires which spread quickly frequently show obvious signs of extreme thermal shock in materials. These have already been discussed in Chapter 7 (Locating Seats of Fire) but, in summary, these may include effects such as surface spalling of plastered walls and ceilings and, because of the small time interval between origin and total involvement of the compartment, will exhibit very even burning and poor fire seat location characteristics (see Plate 14C).

For a fire to spread rapidly it must have had either a very high thermal output at source (as for example a boil-over from an over heated fat pan which then spreads to other kitchen equipment) or

Plate 14B.   Flattened and distorted springs can be caused by persistent smouldering inside traditional furnishings. Here, springs, left after a burnt divan bed has been removed, show such an effect. Photo: R. A. Cooke.

have spread to highly flammable materials (such as hanging fabrics or fuel soaked materials). Thus, rapidly developing fires frequently have their origins in a flame rather than a glowing or smouldering source.

Because a fire developed rapidly it does not necessarily mean that it is suspicious provided that the analysis of the incident shows that the materials which were present were normally capable of producing that type of fire growth.

On occasions the rapidly developing phase is a secondary effect produced from a sustained slow origin. Such a situation could be found in a ventilation induced flashover (q.v.).

Some examples of normally rapidly developing fires are as follows:—

(a) High energy output.
(i) Ignition of liquids above their fire points.
(ii) Bursting and ignition of aerosol containers filled with LPG propellant.

227

Plate 14C. The characteristic remains of a fire involving polyurethane upholstered furniture in a living room. Photograph by Courtesy of Cleveland Constabulary.

(iii) Spillage of large quantities of extremely hot materials (e.g. molten slag, embers, etc.).
(iv) Ignition of airborne materials (e.g. dust suspensions, vapour concentrations)
(v) Ignition of unprotected foamed plastics, such as polystyrene or polyurethane foams.
(vi) Burning fuel from fractured pipe-lines.

Such sources can produce tens or even hundreds of kilowatts of heat energy after ignition. This can raise local temperatures sufficiently to cause very rapid fire spread in what might be considered to be low risk surroundings. As an example of how much heat power can be produced by burning objects, a 150 gm newspaper, crumpled up and burnt could emit heat at a peak rate of about 80–90 kilowatts.

(b) Susceptible Conditions for Flame Spread.
(i) Continuous fuel beds of finely divided materials (e.g. shredded paper).

228

(ii) Contaminated surroundings (e.g. oil soaked floorboards).

(iii) Materials with high surface spread of flame characteristics (e.g. nitrocellulose lacquered surface coatings).

(iv) Adverse arrangement of materials (e.g. cartons or boxes stacked on top of each other).

(v) Fire spread into pre-heated surroundings (e.g. flashover effects).

(vi) Fire spread into abnormally dry areas.

(vii) Forced ventilation of burning areas (e.g. by wind).

The above list is not intended to be exhaustive but does illustrate the variety of reasons why a fire may, on occasions, spread unusually quickly. It is important to remember that in most of these circumstances a prerequisite of a rapidly spreading fire is ignition by a flame source.

Accidental fire types from different causes

Having looked at the fire characteristics in the sense of rates of development, the investigator needs to consider what possible findings may result from particular causes of fire.

The following frequently considered causes of fire have been dealt with in more specific detail in other chapters. It may be found useful to consider them in summary form.

Children with Fire. Children, particularly the very young, who experiment with fire will very frequently leave signs of small 'trial' fires, matches scattered about or other evidence of play. These may take the form of dens, and very often the fires will have been lit in 'secret' places, for example, in cupboards. Children will use ideally available tinder, such as papers, straw or other easily ignitable materials.

Cooking appliances. Normally, one would find such fires in kitchens and they would involve cookers, fat pans or fabrics in contact with them.

The fact that cooking may take place in unusual surroundings by people living rough should not be overlooked. In these cases the cooking apparatus may be substandard or unorthodox. Gas rings or camping cookers may be encountered together with bedding or other soft furniture. Such fires may develop rapidly, this resulting from flames setting fire to fabrics. There should be ample evidence of utensils at the fire seat.

Electrical appliances. The appliance must be capable of emitting sufficient heat to set fire to its surroundings.

Plate 14D. Focussed heat. A characteristic burnt scar produced by a shaving mirror focussing the sun's rays. This may happen on sunny days, even in winter. Photograph I.O.W. Fire Service.

Radiant electrical heaters (see Chapter 18) may ignite materials if they are closer than about 2–4 inches from the dress guard. Other electrical apparatus will probably need to have developed a fault to cause a fire. This, in turn, should result in evidence of arcing or fusing.

Flues. Evidence of deep charring with a very slow initial fire development channelled along the flue path should be found. This will probably be so contrasted with the burning in an open room, if fire has broken through, that there will be little problem in identifying it. Frequently, these fires develop after some change in use, such as uprating boilers or switching on again after a summer break.

Focusing of heat. In Chapter 17 (Physical Processes in Fire), mention is made of the capabilities of concentrating the suns rays by lenses, mirrors, or 'bulls-eye' windows. Other items could be involved and water carafes, curved silver trays and even glass grave ornaments have been quoted as being responsible.

Fires of this nature often start as a slow smouldering but in reasonable British sunshine a shaving mirror could ignite cotton curtains remarkably quickly. If the suspected item has been on a shelf or table, small, possibly intermittent, arc shaped burns may be found where the sun has been focussed but has not achieved sufficient heat to ignite the surface (Plate 14D).

Before this cause of fire is considered, it must be established that focussing can take place. Mere curvature of a piece of glass is not enough; it must have a converging lens or mirror effect. Moreover, if the proposed point of ignition does not coincide with the focal point of the suspected item effective concentration of heat will not occur.

Frictional heating. These fires will be limited to situations where movement of bodies exist. Many will be in workshops where moving belts can bind against the fixed parts of machinery. Binding brakes or wheels on vehicles may also be responsible.

Evidence of movement should be available. This may include 'scoring' where badly adjusted parts have rubbed against each other. The rise in temperature due to friction can be very fast but the energy expended is also often noted in loud noises or power losses before the fire is discovered. Delayed fires due to frictional heating can occur when rubbish under belt drives may have been ignited and may smoulder for some time.

Heating appliances. These have been discussed in detail in a previous chapter (Chapter 13, Heating, Cooking and Lighting). Appliances in fixed positions and correctly installed are likely to have non-combustible surroundings and effective guards to prevent most accidental ignitions. The main problem from the investigator's point of view is that many susceptible materials (cotton, for instance) burn away so completely that evidence of their presence against the heater may be hard to establish.

Mobile heaters may have been badly positioned so that upholstery or curtains can be set on fire. Fire seat location logic may well show a seat of fire concentrated around such an item. It must be remembered that, as they are likely to carry their own fuel supply, fire reaching them will probably set fire to the fuel and thus produce intense localised burning, irrespective of whether the apparatus was originally involved or not.

Hot surfaces. In many respects fires from this cause may

resemble fires from flues. The temperatures attained by the surfaces must be capable of igniting the suspected materials; this is discussed in Chapter 17 (Physical Processes in Fire).

Smoking materials. A cigarette end requires specific conditions to start a fire and in most instances the development will be slow, as indicated at the beginning of this chapter. Fires have been attributed (wrongly) to cigarettes falling onto carpets, flooring or other flat surfaces. The investigator must be able to demonstrate that sufficient finely divided or fibrous materials have been present to develop smouldering from the cigarette end (Plate 14B).

Spillages of fuels. This could be a pre-fire condition because of bad working practices and areas found to be so contaminated might lead the investigator to believe that a deliberate use has been made of a fire accelerant.

Contamination of areas by leakages during or after the fire can, of course, present toxic exposure hazards to anyone involved in a close examination of the debris. There may be very little difference in the appearance of a fuel leak occurring before the fire or caused by the fire. There will, however, generally be a considerable difference in the initial fire development.

Storage of hazardous materials. Substances which can react together may be found in close proximity when a fire hazard is unknown or ignored. Examples can be found which involve oxidising and reducing agents in contact with each other. If sufficient of these materials are present, exothermic reactions may eventually develop spontaneously into flaming combustion.

Spontaneous ignition can also be initiated by heat as, for example, when electric light bulbs become submerged in grain, carpets, paper storage, etc. Fires of this nature are frequently indicated by a slow smouldering development and the damaged remains of the bulb can generally be recovered.

The storage of waste materials has from time to time resulted in fire because of ignorance of their properties. Several incidents have been recorded of polyester resins (containing styrene monomers and organic peroxides) and yellow chromate primer paint residues (which are oxidising agents) spontaneously heating in waste bins in paint spray shops. In these cases it has generally been attempts at good housekeeping, when floor or cubicle sweepings have been dutifully put into waste bins, which have caused the fires.

Welding and cutting. There should be clear evidence of the work

:hat has been done. Heat transmission from one metal surface to another may well ignite materials which have not been seen or considered while the work was being done. In most cases the fire will be detected during work or very shortly after it, as the temperatures involved (greater than 1500°C) are clearly sufficient to ignite most combustibles very rapidly. Sparks from cutting may travel some distance and drop down through holes onto rubbish. Again, these fires should be detected fairly rapidly.

Chapter 15

Arson

Arson is recognised as a major cause of fires in most countries, and regardless of the legal system under which a nation operates, the essential ingredients for the offence are very similar. Minor variations may exist in some cases, such as whether or not the damage was actually caused by flame and not merely heat (this distinction existed in English law before current legislation).

The current Criminal Damage Act 1971 in the United Kingdom preserves the Common law offence of arson in Section 1 (iii) and defines it as the unlawful damage by fire of property belonging to another—a distinction observed in a recent case[1] when an employee, paid to set fire to his employer's own property, was held not to have committed arson because he had a reasonable belief that he had permission so to do, irrespective of the employer's motives. In this chapter, however, the term will be used to cover all cases of deliberate or reckless fire raising.

The legal proof of arson is difficult for fairly obvious reasons. Firstly, the interpretation of the evidence at a fire scene to establish a definite cause presents problems and is, in many cases, imprecise. This frequently runs contrary to the requirement that the prosecution should prove its case beyond reasonable doubt. Secondly, the penalty on conviction can be high (a maximum of life imprisonment) especially when lives have been put at risk. This, again, leads to a heavy burden of proof on the prosecution. Thirdly, the placing of a suspect at the scene and actually committing the offence, when the crime may only be discovered some time after the suspect has covered his tracks, presents obvious problems.

Thus, special emphasis must be placed on the interpretation of the results from an investigation, and the investigator must learn to recognise the signs that may lead him both to suspect and to deduce that arson has been committed. In many cases a careful study of these may also suggest the type of person who may have been responsible (see Chapter 16, Fire Setters). This can, of course, be of great help to a police investigation team in the assessment of possible suspects. Care must be taken, however, not to be too rigid in these interpretations. The investigator must obviously possess an enquiring mind and, arguably, should work from the proposition 'prove that it is *not* arson' in order to expose any weaknesses in his logic. He must also realise that in a court of law the onus is on the prosecution to prove that it *is* arson and so must develop positive proof of the offence. He must be aware of the strengths and weaknesses of his evidence and form his conclusions accordingly.

Some of the more diagnostic signs of arson are treated below in the order in which they may become apparent; at the fire itself, during the investigation or when the investigation results are compared with other evidence or witnesses stories.

Reasons for Suspecting Arson from General Circumstances
Evidence of Forced Entry
This should be noted by the first crew attending the fire. The building may be insecure, not showing definite signs of forced entry, as, for example, when a padlock has been cut from a hasp and completely removed. Broken windows should be noted for evidence of impact fracture, and doors and window frames, if open, should be noted for evidence of tool marks. If at all possible, all known or suspected points of criminal entry and exit must be preserved. There may be some occasions when a fire can be fought from an alternative point in order to preserve such evidence.

Repeated or Numerous Fires
There may have been several fires in the building before. This is not always appreciated by the first attendance if the other fires have occurred during other watch duty periods.

There may, alternatively, have been several fires locally showing a pattern of similar times, type of premises or owners. Patterns of this nature can take some time to recognise, particularly if the fires are spread across different divisions, brigades or police forces. Experimental approaches have been made to form inter-service discussion links so that patterns may be noted at an early date. This is of great importance when dealing with the repetitive arsonist who appears to move onto bigger and better fires as time goes by.

The Same Person Present at Different Fires
Many arsonists like to have a good look at their handiwork.

Often they will seek a good viewpoint and so may not always be amongst the onlookers immediately surrounding the fire scene. The opportunity for discovering an offender who repeatedly starts fires usually lies in the hands of the police patrols who should, during crowd control duties, keep a sharp look-out for familiar faces who have no connection with the property. At a major incident a senior fire officer, who is more likely to have covered fires in an area over several different watches, may well recognise a regular on-looker.

Fire Fighting Difficulties

Items may be arranged so that entry to the premises is difficult or delayed.

Examples of properties falling into this category could be shops with all their front windows covered with sales posters or warehouse areas walled off with goods stacked from floor to ceiling to impede access. In extreme cases 'booby trapping' may be encountered. For example, it has been known for arsonists to leave hatches open so that firemen may fall through. This has reached such proportions in New York that Fire Marshals do not enter buildings alone or after dark.

Interference with Fire Prevention/Protection Measures

Most commercial properties have some measure of fire protection equipment; fire-resisting doors, fire extinguishers or, possibly, fixed systems such as sprinklers or fire detectors. Interference with these may be attempted so that the fire spread is substantially increased, specific high-risk areas become involved or the indications of an outbreak of fire are delayed.

(a) *Fire Resisting Doors.* On escape routes in properties subject to means of escape legislation, these doors are frequently designed to remain shut when not actually used, so that fire spread is restricted. The innocent propping open of smoke-stop doors in corridors is common practice, as they tend to impede traffic. Evidence of fire-resisting and/or smoke-stop doors having been systematically propped open, however, may be evidence of an attempt to aid fire spread.

(b) *Fire Extinguishers.* The arsonist may, on occasion, attempt to extinguish his own fire, and discharged extinguishers in an unoccupied building near to a seat of fire may be evidence of this. Alternatively, the removal of, or interference with, extinguishers so that they cannot be used is a strong indication of criminal intent.

(c) *Sprinklers.* Most fires can be controlled, if not actually put out, by a sprinkler system providing that the fire load and disposition of the contents matches its design. The failure of sprinklers to operate may be due to age, blockage by particles of rust or inadequate maintenance, and it must be remembered that after a fire, sprinkler heads will probably have the appearance of having operated even if no water came out. This is because each sprinkler head is a crude heat sensor (see Chapter 2, Effects of Occupancy). During fire fighting it will become apparent if sprinklers are not working, either because the sprinkler alarm gong is not sounding or because no water is being applied from the heads closest to the fire.

When the entire system has been turned off, this will be immediately apparent from an inspection of the main valve. Obvious situations such as these may well have a logical explanation (e.g. maintenance in progress or possibly disconnection because of cost). However, the coincidence of the removal of a major fire protection measure with a subsequent fire should not be ignored as this could provide valuable initial evidence of arson.

(d) *Fire Detectors.* Smoke detectors generally have a rapid response to fires. Ionising detectors have the fastest response to a flaming fire and the modern L.E.D. or photo-transistor, photo-electric detectors have the fastest response to smouldering fires. Heat detectors, whether rate-of-rise or fixed temperature, are less fast but are still faster than sprinklers. In well designed and well maintained systems, power failures are compensated for by stand-by batteries so that failure is highly unlikely. Further, the wiring to these systems is either fire resistant (M.I.C.C. cable) or, if plastic insulated, is incorporated into a fail-safe circuit so that short-circuits are treated as alarms.

The often quoted high failure rate of detectors is, in fact, not a failure to detect fires but an extreme sensitivity to heat, smoke or vibration resulting in a large number of false alarms. Systems ill adapted to their surroundings may be switched off, having become discredited, but a switched off system should bring to mind the possibility that it was done to delay discovery of the fire.

Persons Wrongly Dressed or Prepared
A person who, in a fire at night time, is fully clothed when normally he would have been expected to be in night clothes, is obviously suspect when a fire has developed rapidly. In this category also lies the person who appears to have had the opportunity to prepare for escape, when the circumstances make it seem improbable. Pets, livestock and other easily mobile and valuable chattels may well be capable of being rapidly evacuated but major, heavy or fragile articles require care and time to move. Checking on how and when such articles were moved may reveal group activity which could raise suspicion.

The Fire Appears to be Specifically Targetted
(a) This aspect of suspicious fires may arise because of the building itself; it may be a listed or scheduled historic building in an otherwise valuable redevelopment site, or the trade carried on may be the subject of gang warfare, protection rackets and 'take-overs'. Fires set for revenge purposes may exist in ethnic areas where also, for one reason or another, occupiers may resort to self help in a grievance rather than rely on the police. The extracting of the necessary background information may be very difficult because of non-cooperation by the owner or occupier. Revenge or gang 'discipline' fires are probably seldom disguised as accidental. As with terrorist activities, these fires are intended to show without any doubt to the local community that arson has been committed.

(b) Within a building a targetted fire may be seen where a specific item is damaged to the exclusion of others. Instances of this type could be company records conveniently damaged before an audit takes place, computer records destroyed together with their associated disc or tape storage (although efficient management should store duplicates remotely in fire-resistant cupboards). Specialist or vital machinery selectively destroyed, is another obvious factor for suspicion.

The Fire Would be Financially Advantageous
This factor could include the 'property development' fire indicated above but, more frequently, involves fires set for insurance gains.

When an owner finds he is overstocked on a falling market he may attempt to realise on his capital by having a fire. Therefore, every company fire where there is a suspicion of financial gain should really be investigated in the same manner as a suspected company fraud, by financial as well as technical experts. This is too much for a single police officer to perform as the special problems of proving financial gain, setting the fire and the probability of an arsonist having been employed by the principal require a multi-disciplinary team. It is possible that this type of 'arson' (frequently, as in R-v-Denton[1] not legally criminal damage because the property is owned by the perpetrator) occurs far more frequently than is currently believed.

Reasons for Suspecting Arson at or after the Scene Investigation

The rate of development of a fire does not necessarily indicate or eliminate arson. Fast or fierce fires may well be more likely to have resulted from the type and disposition of the contents, rather than from the method of ignition. Slow fires again, may well be due to the nature of the fuel or ventilation even if ignition has been deliberate. Of course, circumstances will exist where large quantities of a fire accelerant will considerably modify these characteristics. In the main, the recognition of suspicious fire seat characteristics will be the result of a logical deduction of the location of the seat or seats of fire, followed by a careful and complete excavation, and the application of sound fire science.

Multiple Seats of Fire

This is the most obvious reason for suspecting arson, and if several distinct and separated seats of fire can be seen without any reasons for them having resulted from natural fire development, then they must be regarded *prima facie* as having been ignited individually. Careful excavation of the remains present may show systematic preparation, (e.g. candles, papers or fire accelerants) and may show linking of several seats of fire with trailers made from easily flammable items or liquid fire accelerants. (See plate 15B.)

Unusual or Unnatural Disposition of Contents

In order to make the fire spread more surely the arsonist may make piles of furniture or make the contents of drawers or cupboards into a bonfire. A careful excavation of the seat, or

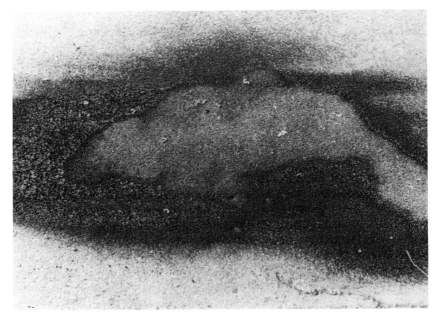

Plate 15A. An example of a pool burn on a carpet. Vapour ignition has scorched the surface beyond the confines of the liquid but the hard-edged burn can be seen where the fuel has been extinguished before burning completely away. Photo: M. J. Cooke.

seats, of fire, coupled with a knowledge of the correct original positions of the contents can develop this evidence.

Extraneous Materials at the Seat of Fire
These may be classical fire accelerants such as petrol, paraffin or diesel fuel, or materials brought in from outside. The presence of these is almost conclusive evidence of intent and preparation provided that they are not normal to the premises. If recognisable remains of a delayed action incendiary device are present no argument about intent is possible.

Unusually Severe Fire for the Known Circumstances
This could be because there should normally have been a very low fire loading in the area or because the fire had occurred in an unlikely place, for example, in a hallway where no stored materials should have been placed, or possibly, where no

accountable fire hazard can be found. Criminally started fires have occurred in these places because of the increased room-to-room fire spread which may occur.

Unusually Rapid Fire Development
When occupants have openly left a building only a few minutes before a well established fire is discovered, there are generally good grounds for suspicion if it is claimed that no smells, heat or other fire-related phenomena were noted prior to leaving.

It is obviously possible that on leaving, materials may have been dropped, heaters or lights left on or appliances switched on (e.g. security systems) which may have caused fire. It is also possible that a person has lit a small fire or even set a crude delayed-action device which has then operated much faster than expected. (See also page 249).

Untypical Fire Spread Patterns
These could indicate the presence of highly flammable substances which have not survived the fire. Fire involving these may, however, show specific burning patterns in unusual places, say in open floor areas. These could take the form of 'pool' burns from liquid fire accelerants (see plate 15A) or small concentrated burnt holes from chemical mixtures. On a larger scale untypical fire spread may be caused by propping open doors or hatchways. Care must be taken in interpreting these burning patterns. For example, 'pool' burns can be caused quite naturally in a fire, from melting and burning plastics or from burning polyols released from polyurethane foam. Their appearance can be distinguished from accelerant 'pool' burns particularly when residues of burnt plastics remain within the scorched pattern.

Evidence of Articles Missing from the Building
These could be genuinely stolen items, the fire resulting from an intruder setting the building on fire in order to try to hide evidence of his theft. It could also be the result of a fraudulent removal of stock or records, the fire being set to cover deficiencies. Fires of this sort may well involve specific high value but low fire risk locations. Combined with this feature, is the possibility that prior to the fire, an arsonist setting fire to his own property may have removed items of sentimental or particular value.

Plate 15B. An example of an accelerant assisted fire self-extinguishing because of lack of ventilation. The effects of a brief but smoky fire can be seen clearly. Photo: Courtesy of West Yorkshire Metropolitan Police.

Value of Stock Mis-matched with Claims

Here, there may be an indication that the occupier is in financial difficulties. Establishing evidence of this sort requires a comprehensive knowledge of market values. The average fire officer, forensic scientist or policeman would not be in a position readily to substantiate this and a chartered loss adjuster should, preferably, be consulted. A receiver of stolen goods may find it easier to destroy them by fire, (together with his 'records', which do not of course exist) than to resell them. In these cases there may well be an apparent insurance loss caused by lack of adequate cover. For this reason, fire-damaged goods should always be identified as far as possible. This may need a physical count of the remains, which indicates the necessity to establish all relevant details at a fire scene before clearing the debris away.

Plate 15C. Protected areas can be seen on the burnt floor surface where broken glass has been laying. This shows evidence of a window having been broken before the fire started. Photo: M. J. Cooke.

Evidence of a Further Crime

Many fires are set to hide evidence of a crime. Fires as a result of vandalism may well show further damage to items which can be traced back to having been caused before the fire. (See plate 15C.) There may well be target properties in this classification (e.g. public buildings). Crimes may be of greater significance, for example, murder, where there may have been an attempt to destroy the body or to damage it so badly as to hide homicide. This aspect is dealt with in Chapter 10, (Fires involving Fatalities).

No Recognisable Accidental Cause

This can only lead the investigator to *suspect* arson. Proof would, of necessity, require some substantial evidence, although this may be only circumstantially linked (e.g. a known burglary). It is possible that the findings at the scene may be ambiguous, particularly if the fire has been severe. From the legal point of view a limited corroboration of a suspect's confession by this kind of evidence, where the actual cause cannot be confirmed, may be acceptable but the investigator must be very careful indeed not to claim too much evidential strength or significance.

Technical Conclusions Failing to Match Witnesses Statements
There could be two basic reasons for this. Firstly, the interpretation of the findings at the scene could be faulty because of excessive damage. In such situations there could be so great a range of possibilities because of ambiguities in the findings, that any eye-witness report could fit, or not fit, depending on the investigators preference.

Secondly, it may be that the witness is not telling the truth. The investigator should not jump to this latter conclusion lightly because in all cases he must reconsider, in the light of what he has been able to find at the scene, his own competence in assessing the true cause of the incident. If the truthfulness of the witness is in doubt, a re-run of his alleged actions must be attempted to establish where, if possible, his account matches known or projected events.

One other reason for a witness' divergence from what is accepted as the truth is that he has not been questioned correctly and so has not been able to state fully what he has seen. This is distinctly possible if the questioner or interviewer is ignorant of what significance is to be placed on his observations. The interviewer is in a dangerous position, however, because pre-knowledge of what should be said could lead to prompting. Many witnesses will be able to sense what is to be the preferred answer from inadvertent signals from the interviewer.

Obstructive Behaviour by Occupier
An arsonist may have a very obvious objection to fire officers or investigators remaining on his property. In order to justify this, complaints may be made about the behaviour of the fire fighting team or the police. Accusations of unnecessary damage or even of looting have been made by this class of arsonist.

An alternative approach is the 'busy man' who wishes to remove items as fast as possible. This may be a genuine reaction by a person who wants to save as much valuable material as possible. Where the removal involves a loss of evidential materials it is quite possible that he is trying to cover up or remove incriminating evidence.

Recklessness in Fire-Raising

In the United Kingdom the legal definition of arson and the associate crime of criminal damage requires, not only that the property should belong to another, but that the person committing the act should do so deliberately or recklessly.

Recklessness has been considered by the Court of Appeal[2, 3] in criminal cases. The current situation appears to be that, if an obvious risk exists, then provided that the accused person is capable of recognising that risk, he will be culpable. In some ways this is the objective 'man on the Clapham omnibus' approach i.e. that if a reasonable person comprehends the risk then so should the accused. While in many cases deliberate fire raising can be deduced by the presence of cribs, accelerants or multiple seats of fire, a reckless act may be more difficult to establish. Many burglars who are accused of arson may admit breaking into the property but will deny the intentional starting of the fire; in English law a person may not be convicted unless it can be proved that he was at least reckless. 'Striking matches to see in the dark' is a frequently advanced suggestion as to why a burgled premises should catch fire. The investigator faced with this statement should examine the likelihood of, say, a carelessly (not, at this stage, recklessly) dropped match igniting things. If a room has been effectively ransacked and there are numerous piles of papers on the floor, dropping lighted matches at random on a paperstrewn floor may well constitute recklessness because most people would recognise the risk.

A successfully prosecuted case of arson by recklessness arose when a fire at a garage workshop clearly started against a safe which had been cut open with oxy-acetylene cutting equipment. The accused was, by trade, a trained oxy-acetylene cutter and was therefore well aware of the fire risks of sparks resulting from his work. He was convicted of burglary, theft and arson although there was no demonstrable intention to burn the place down.

An extension to the concept of recklessness has been decided in the House of Lords[4] that in the case where a person has caused a fire, even accidentally, and, being aware of it, has done nothing to prevent it from spreading, then he is reckless as to the damage caused and thus is guilty of arson. Such a situation requires the fire to have resulted from that person's act; a mere bystander would not appear to be criminally liable.

References
(1) R. *v.* Denton. (1981) Times Law Reports.
(2) R. *v.* Lawrence. (1981) 1 All E.R.874.
(3) R. *v.* Caldwell. (1981) 1 All E.R.961.
(4) R. *v.* Miller. (1983) Times Law Reports.

Chapter 16

Fire Setters

If it has been established that a fire had been deliberately ignited, the next stage in the investigation is the identification of the culprit. It would be very useful if the different types of fire setter shared common features of personality, background or appearance which would make them easily identifiable. However, whilst there is a tendency for certain types of fire setter to share some features, the characteristics described can only be generalisations based upon typical members of groups. Individuals differ widely and can behave in ways which do not at all resemble the expected behaviour of the type to which they belong.

It is the aim of this chapter to subdivide deliberately ignited fires into groups and to indicate the types of persons known in the past to have started fires in each group. The literature reviewed derives from Britain, Continental Europe and the United States, and it is apparent that experience in these different areas shows some features of agreement.

Many studies of groups of fire setters have been carried out, particularly in the USA, and in some of the more detailed investigations the groups have been sub-divided according to their motives.

If these studies are to be of any great value to the investigator, it is desirable that fires should be likewise classifiable.

Recognition of Motives
Whilst many deliberately ignited fires are lit to achieve particular aims, such as to defraud an insurance company or to handicap a business rival, some are started purely for their own sake. It is difficult for a normal person to comprehend the motives of pyromaniacs, and one suspects that the answers given by these individuals to psychiatrists are attempts to explain or justify irrational acts for which they have no real motive.

The Types of Fire Setter
Fire setters have, in this chapter, been classified into ten groups for convenience of recognition. Some of these groups may share

characteristics with others, whilst individuals may not necessarily exhibit all of the characteristics of the group to which they logically belong.

Psychologists divide mentally deranged fire setters into groups, including pyromaniacs, mental defectives, erotic fire setters and the psychotic group, which includes paranoid and catatonic schizophrenics. It would be dangerous for a fire investigator with limited knowledge of psychology to attempt to psychoanalyse a fire setter, when it is often the case that even the experts cannot agree. In this chapter, mentally deranged fire setters have been considered as one group, because many of the distinctions between the types would not be important to a fire investigator.

Insurance Fraud Fires

(a) *Ignited by the insured.* The property burned can vary considerably in value, from industrial premises costing millions of pounds, through domestic premises and cars, down to single items of furniture or articles of clothing. In fraudulent fires, the owner of the building or vehicle frequently has the opportunity to spend some time setting up delayed action devices, and these may be numerous and elaborately constructed. Trailers of flammable material, such as ropes of crumpled paper or trains of flammable liquid, may link separate flammable items or rooms.

In many cases, damage may be caused to make it appear that the building had been forcibly entered. Windows may be broken or doors forced. It may sometimes be apparent that this damage was intended to mislead investigators because either:—

(i) The window was broken from the inside.
(ii) It would not have been possible to enter the building through the opening produced.
(iii) Footprints, instrument marks or fingerprints associated uniquely with the damage can be linked with the owner or manager.

Flammable materials legitimately present in the premises may be arranged to facilitate fire spread, and this arrangement may have been carried out at the instigation of the owner some time prior to the fire. The burnt merchandise may have been specially purchased for insurance claim purposes, and is likely to be of low quality and readily flammable. Cheap fabrics, and clothing such as quilted anoraks are popular for this type of fraud. It is possible to draw a distinction between those who set up companies with the initial intention of starting a fire, and those who have found that economic pressures have caused their genuine businesses to lose money. Inquiries into the past history of the insured may reveal fires and allegedly costly burglaries in previous premises owned by him.

It is not unknown for well established fires to be discovered in buildings almost immediately after the owner or manager had locked up. Such fires are highly suspicious. It may be that the occupier had set a delayed action device which has operated prematurely. Alternatively, in ignorance of the speed with which fires can develop, he had ignited material hoping that the fire would not be discovered for several hours after his departure. However, the possibility that the fire was caused accidentally due to some omission in the shut-down procedure must also be seriously considered.

Occupiers setting fire to premises have, on occasions, been known to remove personal articles of sentimental value from their offices prior to the fire.

(b) *Ignited by a hired 'torch'*. Although probably more common in North America, professional fire raisers do exist in Britain. As in all other professions, standards vary greatly, and whilst some fire raisers are very expert indeed, others are as inept as the most inexperienced amateur.

In common with the owner of the premises, the hired fire raiser can make his preparations almost at leisure, confident in the knowledge that he is unlikely to be interrupted.

Efficient professional fire raisers plant delayed action devices in places from where the fire is likely to spread throughout the whole building, and set them to operate at times when the fire is least likely to be discovered, such as early on Sunday morning.

Most fire raisers in this group have a good understanding of the way fire spreads, and set fires which cause considerable damage. Having found a successful technique, the fire raiser may use it again and again as was the case in the Leopold Harris series of fires[1].

Just as it is possible to administer poisons which mimic the effects of serious natural illnesses, so it is possible to ignite fires which appear to have an accidental origin. However, fires started using indigenous materials in a building may not spread satisfactorily, and more than one attempt may be needed before the building burns to completion.

Many businesses are fitted with sprinklers, smoke detectors or self-closing fire doors. For a successful fire to occur, these systems must be rendered ineffective. Insurance fraud fire setters, more perhaps than any other group, take measures to nullify fire protection equipment.

Recognition of insurance fraud fire setters
If it is recognised that a fire has been set for insurance fraud purposes, there can be only a limited number of suspects. Any of the following indications may suggest an insurance fraud fire:—

(a) The property had been over-insured or recently re-insured.
(b) The contents of the building had been removed or changed just prior to the fire.
(c) The business had been in financial difficulties.
(d) Company records had been destroyed.
(e) The fire had occurred shortly before a stock-taking or audit.
(f) The owner had been trying to demolish, alter or sell the property.
(g) Fire prevention systems and alarms were inactivated prior to the fire.

If for these or other reasons insurance fraud is suspected, the most likely culprit is the person who will benefit most from the fire. He may give himself away by indications such as:—

(a) Behaving abnormally, for example by being particularly calm.
(b) Being well prepared and knowing details which he might not normally be expected to know, such as intimate details of the insurance.
(c) Being fully dressed in the middle of the night at the time of the fire.
(d) Arriving at the scene of the fire in a remarkably short time.
(e) Objecting to a full investigation.
(f) Destroying evidence under the pretext of tidying up.
(g) Removing items of real or sentimental value prior to the fire.

The hired professional fire setter is difficult to trace. Rider[2] drew a projected psychological profile of the American professional fire setter. He pictured a male of above average intelligence of any age, probably unmarried or living apart from his wife. The fire setter is likely to be unstable and impulsive, associated with criminal activities and a heavy drinker. Rider also noted that the fire setter often prepares the building for burning a day or so in advance, to ensure that it burns as intended. Hired 'torches' are most commonly traced either because of their previous history or because the hirer gives information to the police.

Fires Started by Business Rivals

Fires started by business rivals have much in common with insurance fraud fires. The main differences are that the fire damaged business is likely to have been thriving, otherwise it will not have seemed a threat to the rival concern, and the fire raiser is not likely to have spent so much time in the building setting up the fire. In addition it is possible that the fire-damaged premises may not be adequately insured.

The business rival may not know the exact lay-out of the target building and the fire may, for example, be started by means of flammable liquid poured through the letter box or by a petrol bomb. In some cases, however, the premises may be broken into and the fire may be set in a place most likely to damage the production of the company. After some fires of this type, the owner's dynamic drive, so feared by the rival concern, may show itself in getting the damaged company into limited production days or sometimes hours after the fire.

The owner of the damaged building may have suspicions that the fire was started by his rivals, and he will normally inform the police of his views. In some cases however, it has been known for the rival company also to suffer a fire within a fairly short time.

Fires Started by Employees

Particularly damaging fires in business premises may be ignited by an employee or ex-employee with a grudge. Employees, depending upon their depth of knowledge of the manufacturing process, may know how to start a fire which can disrupt the production for a long period. The employee may have free access to the premises and is likely to know his way about the building, even in the dark. It is possible that if the employee bears a grudge, it is not directed at the company as a whole, but against a particular individual. In such cases it is not uncommon for the fire to be ignited in the office, desk or work bench of the individual in question. There may also be evidence that property belonging to the disliked individual has been damaged or displaced prior to the fire.

Another possible motive for an employee to start a fire at his place of work is the concealment of long-term fraud or theft. In such cases, the fire will be intended to destroy company records or to damage the remaining stock sufficiently to conceal the fact that part of it is missing. Fires of this type are more common just before an inspection, stocktaking or audit, and may well be centred at the work area of the fire setter himself.

Recognition of employee fire setters
Employee fire setters share many characteristics with insurance fraud fire setters, since both are familiar with the premises and have legitimate access to them.

Any of the following guidelines may suggest that a fire was started by an employee:—

(a) The intruder had entered the premises with a key.

(b) The intruder had known his way around the premises and had started the fire at a point particularly damaging to the company.

(c) Valuables or items of sentimental value had been removed from the employee's desk before the fire.

(d) The fire had been started in the property of one particular employee, either the fire setter himself or the person against whom he bears a grudge.

During the nineteenth century, fire setting was particularly common among maidservants sent to work under harsh conditions away from home. Now that the social pattern has changed, only about 10% to 15% of fire setters are believed to be female and investigating officers tend to rule women out of their enquiries.

The modern equivalent of going into service, is work in the hotel industry. Employees in hotels still sometimes start fires, particularly in linen cupboards, airing cupboards and in beds. Fortunately fires in neatly folded fabric tend not to spread rapidly and they are often discovered before they get out of control.

Another type of fire setting employee who may rebel against the monotony of his occupation is the caretaker. Many school fires occur during the holiday periods. Whilst many of these fires are started by school children, ex-school children and youthful vandals, a significant number of school fires are ignited either by the caretaker or a member of his family. These fires are more likely to be in bags of waste paper, store rooms or the boiler room than in class rooms. It is possible that the caretaker may not have had the foresight to break a window or force a door to mimic forcible entry, and even if he has, it is possible that he has broken the window from the inside (see Chapter 9, Deductive Evidence at Fire Scenes).

Night watchmen also have monotonous jobs with little opportunity for them to excel. A nightwatchman who discovers a fire and speedily deals with it, is likely to earn praise. There have been cases of nightwatchmen starting fires and then 'discovering' them. Any employee who discovers a fire should at first be regarded with suspicion, particularly if he has been involved with a fire before. Employees who report fires which they themselves started may do so for one of two reasons:—

(a) They were seeking praise or reward.

(b) They started a fire intending it to remain small, and then panicked when it became apparent that the fire was developing more rapidly than expected.

Fires Started by Political Activists
Political activists are usually supposed to start fires for two reasons:—

(a) To destroy the property of the people or establishment that they hate and despise.

(b) To gain publicity for their cause.

It may also be that some acts of political terrorism are carried out because the terrorist enjoys the feeling of power that such destruction provides.

Political fires may be recognised from the type of target building. Terrorist groups may specialise in different types of buildings, such as airline offices, holiday cottages or army establishments. In addition, political terrorists do not shrink from publicity and may have made threats or given warnings before the fire, or even have claimed responsibility afterwards.

If an incendiary device is found, it may be of a design

characteristic of a particular organisation and it may be possible to ascribe it to a particular person in the organisation after detailed examination. It is not always the case however, that a politically motivated terrorist device was planted by the person who made it.

Fires Caused by Criminals Concealing other Crimes

Fires may be started by criminals in an attempt to conceal crimes ranging from attempted theft to murder. One interesting aspect of criminal psychology is, that when subsequently arrested, the criminal may freely confess the other crime (even murder) but is often reluctant to admit having caused the fire.

Fires started to conceal previous crimes may be recognised by the presence of evidence of the first crime. Drawers and internal doors forced open prior to the fire provide evidence that a search has taken place. Cash boxes may be displaced or forced. The charred contents of a closed cash box should be identifiable as a particular sum of money within close tolerances.

Items of particular interest to thieves include antiques and electronic appliances. Most of these items would be expected to leave recognisable residues if burnt in a fire. An absence of such residues would suggest that they had been removed prior to the fire.

The method of breaking into the building also may indicate that an experienced housebreaker has been involved. This may be indicated either by the general expertise, or by the fact that the method agrees with the modus operandi of a known criminal.

Fire started to conceal murder will be suspected when evidence emerges that the deceased had met his death prior to the fire, or that he had been drugged or constrained in some way at the time of his death (Chapter 10, Fires Involving Fatalities). There may also be evidence of a struggle, and bloodstains on the walls, articles of furniture or on items which could have been used as weapons.

Identification of the culprit

If it has been established that the fire was started to conceal evidence of a theft, the investigating officer is more likely to suceed in tracing the culprit than in an apparently motiveless fire. Records of criminals known to have committed similar previous thefts can be considered in association with eye-witness descriptions of people and vehicles. In addition, it is possible that the stolen property may be recovered, enabling the police to trace the criminal through his accomplices.

Fires started to conceal murder can be the least successful of all. The murderer may concentrate on trying to burn the body to the exclusion of other, far more flammable, items in the room.

Many murders are kept within the family, and as a result, the surviving spouse, lover or nearest relative is the first and most likely suspect. The police in Britain solve a very high percentage of the murders committed, and as a result, once the death has been recognised as murder, the culprit has little chance of escaping.

Fires Started by Children
Children commonly act irresponsibly and are frequently fascinated by fire. It is not surprising therefore, that many fires are attributed by fire investigators to 'children playing with matches'. This conclusion may be reached, however, as a result of a superficial examination and without any significant supporting evidence.

Fires caused accidentally by children
Children have very little understanding of the flammability of everyday materials, their experiments with matches, candles and home-made fireworks are part of their learning process. Unfortunately some children do not survive to benefit from their newly acquired knowledge. A number of children die each year in home-made dens and tents which they have made with sheets of fabric, cardboard or even bales of straw. Frequently they had lit candles or camp fires inside the dens. Dens of this type may be in the open air, but often they are constructed inside cupboards, wardrobes or under beds. Early smoking experiments can be another possible source of ignition. Home-made fireworks can result in fires or in explosions causing terrible injuries. Children lacking the knowledge or resources to make their own incendiary mixtures may use live match heads inserted into some type of container. Unexpected scattering of burning material from home-made fireworks can cause the ignition of flammable materials in the vicinity.

Principles of Fire Investigation

Fires caused deliberately by children
A popular activity amongst some children is to strike matches and throw them whilst the deflagrating head is still burning. Many of the matches go out immediately, others remain burning on the ground, whilst some land near enough to flammable material to set it alight. The presence of many spent matches with only the heads burnt, together with live matches and matches which have burnt whilst lying on the ground, is characteristic of this form of fire ignition.

Children do not normally bring liquid fire accelerants when they intend to start fires but they may use liquids present at the scene. In their use of fire accelerants children may show considerable lack of judgement; lighting fires with large quantities of petrol, or building bonfires under propane cylinders.

Types of fires most commonly caused by children
Out of doors, children may cause grassland fires and some fires in stored hay and straw. They also cause fires in rubbish tips, which although not otherwise serious, can result in children being trapped. Derelict cars are also a favourite target for children and adolescent fire setters. Building fires are mainly confined to schools and houses, although churches and factories have been targets.

The most extensive study of child fire setters was carried out by Yarnell[3]. She found that the majority of child fire setters were male, of average to superior intelligence, from a broken or unsatisfactory home environment and with some previous history of delinquency or truancy. Those who specifically set fires in schools tended to have learning disabilities and were unable to compete in the classroom. This group, unlike other child fire setters, tended to be of below average intelligence. Very few school fires were started by children under the age of ten. This contrasts with domestic fires in which half of the children who started them were between the ages of five and ten. Domestic fires started by children were often set on their own or on their parents' beds. Child fire setters, unlike adolescent vandals, preferred to be alone when starting fires.

Fires Started by Vandals
The number of fires attributed to vandalism in Britain has increased substantially during the past few years. This may, in

part, be a result of an increased awareness on the part of police and fire brigades that this is a serious problem. However, there is little doubt that vandals are causing an increasing number of fires. Vandalism fires may be recognised from the choice of target building, time and method of ignition, background information and the presence of associated damage. Vandals prefer as their targets, public buildings such as churches and schools. Lewis and Yarnell[3] found that the vandals that they investigated also set fires in factories, warehouses and barns. Most vandalism occurs in the late evening and is particularly common on the nights of Friday, Saturday and Sunday.

The fires are normally set on the spur of the moment and must therefore, be ignited using materials already available at or near the scene. Groups of vandals are often unimaginative creatures of habit, frequenting the same areas from week to week. Local enquiries may reveal that a group of youths regularly passed the building in question at about the same time each week. Fire setting is only one of the activities of vandals, and other damage in the same area may be linked with the group.

Although some groups of vandals start fires in buildings by introducing burning material through windows and letter boxes, other groups break into the target building. Once inside the building, the vandals may overturn furniture, tear up books, put items in a pile for burning, slash upholstery, break windows and set off fire extinguishers.

Identification of the culprits
Vandals often operate in groups or sometimes in pairs. The most common age group is from 14 to 18 years, and vandals are almost exclusively male. Lewis and Yarnell[3] found that most fire setting vandals as distinct from child fire setters, were below average intelligence, came from broken homes and lacked masculine drive (many would be regarded as effeminate).

Because of the rigid habits of adolescent groups of vandals, checks carried out on the weekly anniversaries of the fire can provide useful evidence in the investigation of the crime.

Fires Started by Attention Seekers and Enthusiasts
Fire setting attention seekers fall into two groups: those who wish to be regarded as heroes after their actions in discovering and fighting the fire and those who desire sympathy and protection.

Both types are likely to make themselves known to the investigator. Nightwatchmen, caretakers and other employees who start fires often fall into the 'hero' group, as do some firemen. Women who start fires in their own homes may come into the second category.

Fire enthusiasts also start fires, and are likely to be in the vicinity during fire fighting operations. Volunteer or retained firemen sometimes start fires motivated both by the desire to appear a hero and by financial considerations.

Identification of the culprits

Attention seekers start fires which will involve themselves. Either the fire will be at home or their own place of work, or they will themselves discover it. In the case of a retained fireman, he is likely to attend almost every one of the series of fires which he starts, often being at or near the fire station at the time of the call. He may give himself away to his colleagues by his restless demeanour when he is expecting a fire call. One characteristic feature of fires started by a retained fireman is that most of the fires in the series are likely to be ignited in a particular station area. The fires will be ignited at times which are convenient to the person responsible.

Attention seeking fire setters of all types tend to have several features in common. Many tend to drink heavily, a disproportionate number are single, many show intellectual defects and some have physical defects. Many show a particularly close attachment to their mothers and some are the sons of firemen or policemen.

Fires Started by Mentally Deranged Fire Setters

Mentally deranged fire setters are the hardest group of all to comprehend and to catch. Their fires are apparently motiveless and they may have had no previous association whatsoever with the target building. Their fires are often unplanned, and simple materials such as newspaper and matches may be used. However, some fire setters in this group have been known to bring containers of paraffin or petrol with them.

Individual fires started by the mentally deranged are normally difficult to recognise as such, but they are likely to form part of a series of fires in the same area. It is possible that many of the fires in the series may be attributed wrongly to accidental causes.

Characteristics of mentally deranged fire setters
The most widely known of this group are the pyromaniacs. These tend to be male, adolescent, of poor educational performance (although not necessarily below average intelligence) and from broken homes. Physical defects are frequently present and pyromaniacs tend to be sexually maladjusted, heavy drinkers and unmarried (or unsuccessfully married).

Pyromaniacs normally set fires alone at night, frequently starting several in rapid succession. When caught, many pyromaniacs admit the crime and quietly co-operate with the police. Some go so far as to ensure that they will be arrested, or go voluntarily to the police to confess, finding it a relief to be prevented from starting more fires.

Magee[4] found that what he called 'the excitement fire setter' can obtain satisfaction by mingling with the crowd and watching the fire-fighting operations.

Psychotics form another part of the mentally deranged group of fire setters. One particular feature of fires which they set is, that whatever the motive for the fire, a suicidal aspect is often apparent. A major proportion of the psychotic group is schizophrenic. Schizophrenic fire setters suffer from hallucinations and delusions and many act in the belief that God wants them to start particular fires. Most schizophrenic fire setters are middle-aged or older.

It is believed by some workers (Lewis and Yarnell[3]) that certain types of schizophrenics start fires against their own family. Virkkunen[5] believes that schizophrenics start fires against outsiders and unoccupied structures whilst those who start fires at home tend not to be schizophrenic. There is therefore, a considerable amount of research required in this field.

Mentally deranged fire setters may show sexual abnormalities including effeminacy, homosexuality and flagrant sexual perversions. One of the sexual abnormalities common to many fire setters is exhibitionism, and a number of fire setters were found to have had previous convictions for indecent exposure.

Contrary to popular belief, only a small percentage of fire setters obtain sexual gratification from the setting of fires but erotic fire setters have on certain occasions been apprehended whilst watching the fire, behaving in a characteristically anti-social manner.

When an educationally subnormal (ESN) person claims to have

started a series of fires, he may be telling the truth or he may simply be seeking attention. It may even be the case that although he had not started any fires, he genuinely believes that he had.

It will be difficult to find detailed evidence to support his claims. Details which he claims to have observed may have been gleaned from news coverage or may have been given unwittingly to the suspect by the Police Officer carrying out the interview. It is required by the Judges Rules that questioning of the ESN person should be carried out in the presence of a witness such as a parent, guardian or solicitor.

The suspect may be able to provide small pieces of seemingly irrelevant fine detail, which can sometimes be verified independently by examination of the scene or the questioning of another witness. It is desirable that at the time of the interview, the interviewing officer should not know too many details relating to the fire in question because the ESN are often quick to pick up clues from the interviewer's behaviour, and give the answer which they think he wants.

General Characteristics of Fire Setters

Sex

In all surveys considered, male fire setters greatly outnumbered the female. Figures from Britain, Continental Europe and the United States suggest that male fire setters comprise about 90% of the total, although the percentages reported vary between 85% and 98%.

Age

Fire setting is often regarded as a crime most often committed by adolescents, and figures published by the F.B.I.[6] seem to support this view.

It is of course true that statistics of this nature can only be based on the cases in which the fire setter has been caught. This may to some extent bias the statistics in favour of young, inexperienced, mentally subnormal criminals since these form the groups most likely to be caught.

Use of alcohol

A disproportionately large number of adult fire setters were found to have some sort of drinking problem, and descriptions range

Fire Setters

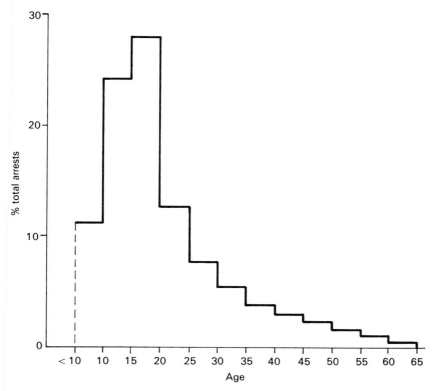

Figure 16·1.   Age frequency of Fire Setters.

from 'heavy social drinking' to 'often alcoholic'. It is by no means always the case that the fire setter will have a drink problem, but many do, and it is not uncommon for a fire setter to have been drunk at the time that he started the fire.

Intelligence
Many workers report that the adult fire setters that they have investigated are predominantly below average intelligence or are educationally subnormal. Again, there are exceptions and fire setters with intelligence quotients up to genius level have been reported. It is difficult to envisage how a genius who applied himself to fire setting would ever have allowed himself to be caught.

Marital status
A high percentage (often as much as 70% or 80%) of adult male fire setters were found to be either single or separated from their wives. Those still living with wives often had poor marital relationships. About 40% to 60% of female fire setters were married.

Sexual abnormalities
Some fire setters show sexual abnormalities such as homosexuality and exhibitionism. However, many of the fire setters investigated have shown no particular sexual abnormality. As might be expected, attention seeking fire setters include the highest proportion of sexual exhibitionists.

Childhood
Many fire setters originated from broken homes and had received inadequate parental supervision. There is often a history of truancy and petty crime such as stealing and malicious damage.

References
(1) H. Deardon. The Fire Raisers.
(2) A. O. Rider. The Fire Setter a Psychological Profile.
(3) N. D. C. Lewis and H. Yarnell. Pathological Fire setting (Pyromania) Nervous and Mental Disease Monographs No. 82 New York Coolidge Foundation 1951.
(4) J. H. Magee. Pathological Arson Scientific Monthly Vol. 37, 1933, p. 361.
(5) M. Virkkunen. ACTA Psychiatrica Scandinavia. Vol. 50, 1974, pp. 152–160.
(6) Crime in the United States. Annual US Government Printing Office 1969–1978. F.B.I.

Chapter 17

Physical Processes in Fire

To understand the reasons for the effects that fire can have in a building, it is necessary to consider some of the relationships that have been found to exist between fire growth and building contents, geometry, ventilation, etc. Thus, the quantity of fuel, its thermal output on combustion, the effects of ventilation, temperature and radiation each have their effects, and an appreciation of these is needed if one is to develop a theory of how and where a fire started. In this chapter, some general relationships will be examined and consideration of their significance in fire investigation will be made.

Heat, Temperature and the States of Matter
In the conventional world about us there exist three states of matter; solids, liquids and gases. The differences between them depend on the spacing and movement of their component molecules.

Molecules are held together by attractive forces which operate strongly in solids, holding them close-packed so that each molecule vibrates about a fixed point. In liquids the forces act more weakly so that, though still close, the molecules move randomly about. In gases, the attractive forces are weak and allow considerable space and motion to exist between molecules.

All molecules are constantly in motion irrespective of the state of matter. Only at Absolute Zero (approximately −273°C) does all motion theoretically cease.

There is a further state of matter called 'plasma'. This occurs only when gases are so highly energised, that electrons are stripped away from the atoms. Plasmas are not normally encountered except in high energy physics.

If we have a solid material, we can increase its internal energy by raising its temperature (that is, by putting heat energy into it). This will have the effect of making the vibrating molecules vibrate faster. Eventually the energy supplied will exceed the energy of the forces holding the molecules together and they will cease to occupy the 'fixed' positions of a solid and move randomly about. The substance has melted.

Applying further heat energy raises the temperature until at a sufficiently high level, the boiling point is reached and the molecules move so far away from each other that they become a vapour and eventually a gas. A vapour exists when the gaseous state can condense back to a liquid if there is a sufficient increase in pressure without a decrease in temperature. Examples of vapours are, steam, butane and propane. The so-called 'permanent gases' which include oxygen, hydrogen and nitrogen cannot be liquefied by pressure alone.

Heat energy is measured in Joules (J). One Joule is equivalent to the heat produced by one watt of electricity in one second. It is important to realise that it is the *level* of heat energy (that is, the measure of molecular vibration that has been produced) that we call temperature. This level of heat energy depends, among other things, on the mass of material present. Thus, the same *quantity* of heat can raise the *temperature* of a *large object* by a *small amount* or a *small quantity* of the same material by a *large amount*.

A concept of temperature is that, if heat energy can flow spontaneously from body 'A' to body 'B' then body 'A' is at a higher temperature than 'B'.

The concepts of heat and temperature are very important. For instance, the reason why some bulk materials are not ignited by sparks is that, although the spark temperature may be very high and above the spontaneous ignition temperature of the material, its mass is low and, consequently, its total heat energy is low. Therefore, the quantity of heat transferred to the material is below that which is required to raise its temperature to its ignition point. Further, the reason that, say, vapours or dusts *can* be ignited by sparks, is that a high temperature with a low quantity of heat energy may well be capable of starting an exothermic reaction in a few isolated molecules, which can then contribute further heat to the reaction system, forming a chain reaction.

Conversely, sustained heat at lower temperatures may eventually provide heat energy sufficient to overcome any cooling effects and may cause spontaneous heating within a mass of material. This aspect is discussed later.

Putting the same quantity of heat into equal masses of different materials, will cause their temperatures to rise by different amounts. As an example, one kilogram of water requires 4.2 kilojoules (i.e. 4.2 kJ) of heat energy to raise its temperature by one degree Celsius but one kilogram of concrete requires only about 0.75 kJ to raise its temperature by the same amount. The quantity of heat required to raise the temperature of 1 kilogram of the substance by one degree Celsius is termed the 'Specific Heat Capacity' of that substance. This is measured in Joules per kilogram per degree Celsius.

From the fire investigator's point of view the effects of increasing the heat energy of a substance are of profound importance, for they are responsible for a number of phenomena, many of which will be apparent at the fire scene.

The disturbance and progressive weakening of the forces between molecules as the temperature rises, is the reason for the progressive weakening of many materials. An example of this is the reduction to approximately one half of the original load-bearing strength of a steel beam, when its temperature rises from 100°C–510°C.

The increasing amplitude of the vibrations of the molecules in a solid substance and the consequent greater space occupied by them when the temperature is raised, causes thermal expansion. For example, a heated steel beam can expand against a wall sufficiently to push it down. The expansion of heated plaster on a cooler substrate can result in the plaster surface spalling off.

The linear expansion of materials with respect to a change in temperature can be expressed by the relationship:—

$$L_t = L_0(1 + \alpha t)$$

where L_0 = the length of the specimen at 0°C
L_t = the length of the specimen at temperature t°C
and
α = the coefficient of linear expansion with temperature (i.e. the ratio of the change of length per degree °C to the length at 0°C)

Generally speaking, metals have a higher coefficient of linear expansion than non-metals, such as brick or glass. Some examples are given below. It will be noticed that over extreme temperature ranges the coefficient for any one substance will not be constant. Calculations which are attempted should always use the coefficient for the appropriate temperature range.

Bulk materials have thickness and depth as well as length and consequently expand in all dimensions. The coefficient for volumetric (cubical) expansion for a material is three times its respective coefficient of linear expansion.

COEFFICIENTS OF LINEAR EXPANSION

Substance	Temperature range °C	Coefficient ($\times 10^{-6}$)
Aluminium	20–100	23.8
	20–300	25·7
Brass	25–100	19.0
Cast Iron	Up to 15°	8.5
Mild steel	100–200	11.5
	200–300	13
	300–700	15
	Greater than 900	29
Brick	—	9.5
Glass (soda)	0–100	8.5–9.0
(borosilicate)	0–100	3
Concrete	—	10–14
Porcelain	20–800	4.13

The volumetric expansion of liquids can cause the build up of hydrostatic pressure in sealed containers (for example, LPG containers) which may rupture with considerable force. The phenomenon known as a 'BLEVE' (boiling liquid expanding vapour explosion) may occur if the liquid is well above its boiling point when this happens. (See Chapter 11, Explosives and Explosions.)

The large volumes of vapour which result from a boiling liquid can be seen in the following table.

EXPANSION OF LIQUIDS INTO VAPOUR

Substance	B.PT,°C	Vol. of vapour for one vol. liquid
Water	100	1,300
Methane	−161.5	650 (at 20°C)
Propane	−42	274
Butane	−10	233

The further expansion of gases or vapours due to increasing temperature is seen in the buoyancy effects which develop in a fire. The physical rules which govern this expansion, although only strictly valid for a perfect gas, can be used in general cases. The permanent gases:— oxygen, nitrogen, helium, etc. obey the laws closely, vapours, such as butane or propane, do not.

The laws governing the changes in the volume of gases with changes in temperature differ from those for solids and for liquids.

The coefficients of volumetric expansion vary little from gas to gas under constant pressure. However, the fact that a gas is much more compressible than a solid or liquid means that the pressure must be taken into account.

The general expression covering the change in volume with temperature is as follows:—

$$\frac{P_1 V_1}{T_1} = \frac{P_2 V_2}{T_2}$$

where

P_1 is the original pressure and P_2 is the new pressure

V_1 is the original volume and V_2 is the new volume

T_1 is the original temperature (in degrees Kelvin) and T_2 is the new temperature.

(N.B.) Degrees Kelvin means the temperature above absolute zero (minus 273°C). Therefore, 0°C = 273° Kelvin.

It can be seen from this equation that any increase in temperature causes an increase in volume, or, in a sealed system, causes an increase in pressure. The pressurising of a hot room in a fire can play a part in causing smoke to be forced out of windows and doors or via ducts and cavities.

Density

The density of a material is the mass per unit volume, therefore any increase in its volume results in a reduction of its density. Hot, less dense gases rise and cause buoyant thermal convection currents over a fire. This is the cause of smoke spread over the highest points of the room before cooling occurs. Calculations of smoke production and spread, with respect to fire size are complex and beyond the scope of this book.

Heat Transfer

The way in which heat is transferred from a fire to its surroundings will affect fire growth. Thus, materials with a high mass, conductivity and specific heat will be effective 'heat sinks', absorbing large quantities of heat before their temperatures rise to a dangerous point.

Materials which can transmit heat easily can allow heat to pass from one place to another sufficiently well to cause a dangerous temperature rise in an otherwise apparently separated area. This could give the effect of a separate seat of fire, or modify the fire spread pattern within a building.

The ability of a substance to conduct heat is quantified by the coefficient of thermal conductivity, (K), which is calculated from:—

$$K = \frac{W}{A} \times \frac{d}{(T_1 - T_2)}, \text{ where,}$$

W = Rate of heat passing in watts (Joules per second),
A = Area of the surface (in square metres),
d = Thickness of material (in metres),
$(T_1 - T_2)$ = Temperature difference across the faces of the material (in degrees Celsius).

The thermal conductivity of a material influences the temperature difference across it when one surface is heated. Metals have a high value and consequently can allow a lot of heat to pass, which, for any given value of the thickness and area would also indicate a small temperature difference $(T_1 - T_2)$. This obviously means that the face of a metal panel opposite the fire would be at almost the same temperature as that on the fire side and so indicates an increased ignition hazard.

Thermal conductivity influences ignitability because, if a flammable material has a very low coefficient of thermal conductivity, heat imparted to its surface is not easily dissipated. If the surface temperature reaches the spontaneous ignition temperature (SIT) of the substance then ignition will occur. Other factors are involved, namely the density, expressed as the term 'ρ' (kg/m^3) and specific heat capacity, expressed as the term 'c'

THERMAL PROPERTIES

Substance	Thermal conductivity (K) W/m/°C	density (ρ) kg/m^3	Specific heat (c) kJ/kg/°C	K.ρ.c.
Aluminium	0.206	2,710	0.895	500
Concrete	1.6×10^{-3}	2,400	0.75	2.88
Brick	8.0×10^{-4}	2,600	0.8	1.66
Chipboard	1.5×10^{-4}	800	1.25	0.150
Plasterboard	1.6×10^{-4}	950	0.84	0.127
Aerated concrete	2.6×10^{-4}	500	0.96	0.125
Fibre insulation board	5.3×10^{-5}	240	1.25	0.016
Fibreglass insulation	3.7×10^{-5}	60	0.08	1.78×10^{-3}
Expanded polystyrene	3.4×10^{-5}	20	1.5	1.02×10^{-3}

(kilojoules per kg). The product of these three values (K.ρ.c.) will characterise not only the ignitability of the material surface but will influence the behaviour of coatings upon it.

Thus, the combined factors of (K.ρ.c.) for a plaster wall are sufficient to inhibit the ignition of wallpaper pasted onto it and, probably, also the ignition of well fixed polystyrene insulating sheet.

Any combustible sheet material on an insulating underlayer is an inherent surface spread of flame hazard. A layer of paint on expanded polystyrene sheet is well known for this.

Low K.ρ.c. values also considerably shorten times to flashover. (Flashover is the stage in a fire when all combustible surfaces ignite). A room lined with plasterboard on timber studding may take only about a quarter of the time to reach flashover when compared with a room with walls made from traditional plaster on brick, given that the quantity and type of fuel and the ventilation are the same.

Radiation

Heat transfer by radiation is an important factor in fire spread; the downward radiation of the extended flames spreading across a ceiling is a major influence on flashover. Similarly, heated objects may radiate sufficient heat to ignite susceptible materials, provided they are reasonably close.

Heat flux is a term used to describe the quantity of heat received by a body and is usually measured in kilowatts per square metre (kW/m^2). If the received heat flux is greater than the quantity of heat conducted from or re-radiated away from the receiving surface, then the surface temperature will rise and may reach the temperature at which a small flame can ignite vapours given off by the pyrolysing material (pilot ignition). At higher levels of irradiation, the surface may spontaneously ignite.

The quantity of heat radiated from a hot object is dependent on the fourth power of its absolute temperature and its emissive power. For radiating objects Stefan's Law of Radiation states that the quantity of heat radiated per second is expressed as

$Q = e. \sigma. T^4$, where
Q = Joules per square metre per second (i.e. watts per square metre),
e = Emissivity (see below),

269

σ = Stefan's Constant = 5.67×10^{-8} Joules per (degree)^4 per square metre per second,

T = Temperature (degrees Kelvin) of the radiating (hot) object.

For a so-called 'perfect' black body the emissivity will be equal to 1. This term is used to describe an object having the ability to radiate all of its heat energy. In practical terms a 'black' body is one which also *absorbs* all radiated energy. An everyday example is a small hole in a closed tin can. When looking at such a hole it appears to be a dense black colour because light entering it is repeatedly reflected and is absorbed on the insides of the can so that virtually no light gets out again. If the can is heated to incandescence, the interior seen through the hole, now appears brighter, as there is a higher emissivity of radiated heat through the hole than from the outer sides. Radiant surfaces, such as panels, are not black bodies and have lower values of emissivity which depend upon their surface characteristics.

An example of this is seen when the heat from a flame, from burning materials is compared with the heat emission from a burning room via an opening. The opening now approximates to a 'black' body and emits much higher radiation per unit area than the flame.

The emissivity of a material is lower when it is light coloured or shiny, and increases with increasing roughness or darkness. Additionally, increasing the temperature of the surface usually increases its emissivity.

Just as the physical characteristics of the radiating object are important, so its shape, angle and distance, as viewed from the irradiated object, must be considered. These characteristics are cumulatively termed the 'configuration factor' (f) and heat received by the object is governed by the relationship:—

Quantity of heat received = f × (quantity of heat radiated) or, bearing in mind Stefan's Law,

Quantity of heat received = f.e.σ.T^4

where f = the configuration factor. (This ranges in value from 0 to 1).

In the worst situation of radiation exposure, where an infinitely long and broad flame closely confronts the receiving object, the factor would be unity. In other situations the calculation of the factor is difficult, but examples of various configuration factors are available[1,2,3]. They show, for example, that for a surface

Substance	Surface type	T°C	Emissivity (e)
Aluminium	Polished	50–500	0.04–0.06
	Oxidised	50–500	0.2–0.3
Brass	Polished	200	0.03
	Tarnished	200–600	0.60
Chromium	Polished	500–1,000	0.28–0.38
Copper	Polished	50–100	0.02
	Oxidised	50–500	0.6–0.8
Steel	Polished	750–1,050	0.52–0.56
	Oxidised	200–600	0.8
Stainless steel	Polished	500	0.35
Carbon (lamp black)		20–400	0.94
Fire brick		1,000	0.75
Glass		250–1,000	0.87–0.72
Flames (dependent on enclosure)			0.3–1.00

Notes (1) The higher the emissivity of the material, the more radiant heat will be given off for any specific temperature and, conversely, if the material is subjected to thermal radiation from another source at a higher temperature, the more heat it will absorb. (2) Non-luminous flames, such as from alcohols, have very low emissivities.

exposed to a hot flue pipe 20 cm in diameter, the configuration factor changes from 1, immediately adjacent to the pipe, to 0.5 at 20 cm distance and 0.17 at 50 cm distance from the pipe.

If the radiator was a point source, the radiation would obey the inverse square law so that doubling the distance between the radiator and the receiver would reduce the heat falling on the surface of the receiver to one quarter. From flat surfaces the relationship is more linear[4].

Examples of Radiation Effects
Flames of 1,000°C in a building fire emit heat at a rate of about 15×10^4 Joules per square metre per second. This means that a one metre square opening, say a window fully involved in a fire, emits about 150 kilowatts energy. Bearing in mind the configuration factor (about 0.2) of a 1 m^2 surface about a metre away this would result in radiation of the order of 30 kilowatts per square metre being received by the surface.

Radiation of the order of 12.5 kilowatts per square metre incident on a timber surface can cause charring with pilot ignition (the ignition of released vapours by a small flame). Values of 28 kilowatts per square metre can cause radiation induced spontaneous ignition[5, 6]. Thus, in the example above, the radiation from the one square metre window would be sufficient to cause ignition of the exposed surface.

As the radiation is proportional to the fourth power of the temperature, doubling the temperature (in degrees Kelvin) gives a sixteenfold increase in the radiation. Langdon-Thomas (1972)[7] indicates the relative intensities of radiation from plane surfaces. For example, a change from 900°C (about 1200°K) to 1100°C (about 1400°K) nearly doubles the intensity of radiated heat.

The limit of safe exposure of skin is generally considered to be about 5 kilowatts per square metre. 10 kilowatts per square metre will cause injury after about 30 seconds.

Radiation from sources such as sunlight may occasionally be the cause of fires. Natural sunlight in the United Kingdom (Latitude 52° North) may reach one kilowatt per square metre. Anything which can concentrate this by twenty or thirty times could cause direct radiation-induced ignition of cellulosic materials. A concave mirror or a bulls-eye glass may possibly produce a focussed spot having a heat flux well in excess of 28 kilowatts per square metre. (See plate 14D.) Further aspects of this are discussed in Chapter 14, (Recognition of Types of Fires).

Spontaneous Ignition

When exothermic reactions proceed in a mass of materials, the temperature will rise, provided that the heat produced within the pile exceeds the heat losses.

The rate of heat loss by radiation, etc., is proportional to the surface area, whereas the quantity of heat produced in a reaction, (which depends upon the mass of reactants present) is proportional to the volume. The rate at which chemical reactions proceed generally increases by a factor of two for every ten degrees Celsius rise in temperature.

Figures 17.1, 17.2 and 17.3 each represent, in simplified form, the heat balance in a pile of materials which is capable of undergoing some internal reaction.

In Figure 17.1, the rate of heat loss by cooling (represented by the dotted line A–A') is, from point (x), greater than the gain in heat (represented by the solid curve) which results from any internal reactions. Self-heating does not develop and the mass is stable.

In Figure 17.2, the line B–B' representing the rate of heat loss

Physical Processes in Fire

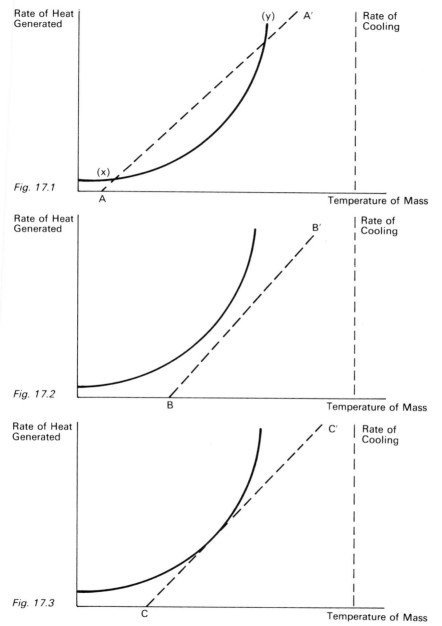

Fig. 17.1

Fig. 17.2

Fig. 17.3

Figures 17.1, 17.2, 17.3.   Heat gain/Heat loss Relationships.

does not cut the curve representing the heat of reaction. This could arise because either the ambient temperature is higher or because the stack of materials is larger or more insulated. In this situation, the rate of heat production by the reaction always exceeds the rate of cooling and the materials undergo self heating which may result in ignition. This is termed thermal runaway.

In Figure 17.3, the meeting point of the two lines represents the point at which the rate of heat production is balanced by the rate of cooling. This is an unstable condition and any change which adversely affects the rate of cooling will result in self heating.

This is the principle utilised in laboratory tests on materials suspected of being capable of self heating. Thomas and Bowes[8] indicate that in a test cube of material capable of spontaneous heating, the relationship,

$$\log_e \delta_c \frac{T_c^2}{r^2} \text{ varies as } \frac{1}{T_c}, \text{ holds, where,}$$

δ_c is a factor which depends on shape. Specimen values are quoted by Beaver (1982)[9]. (For example, a cylinder, radius 'r', has a value of 3.32 and an infinite slab thickness 2r, has a value of 0.88.)

T_c is the lowest ambient temperature (in degrees Kelvin) at which ignition is observed.

r is a characteristic dimension of the mass (e.g. the radius of a cylindrical bin).

In testing a material suspected of being capable of spontaneous heating, small cubic samples within a range of sizes (for example, cubes of side 5 cm, 7.5 cm, 10 cm, (etc.)) can be heated in an oven at constant trial temperatures until the lowest temperature leading to ignition in the cube is found. Beever[9] gives a worked example. The critical ambient temperatures (in deg. $^\circ$K) can be plotted against their cube size according to the above relationship. The curve can then be extrapolated to the known stack size. This will give an indication of the critical ambient temperature for this quantity of material. Frequently such extrapolations are large and can give sizeable cumulative errors. Calculations based on such data should therefore be treated circumspectly, as only general indications are possible.

An interesting calculation on this problem regarding the possible spontaneous ignition of stacks of resin-bonded fibreglass has been performed by Morgan (1966)[10].

274

References

(1) Heat Transfer by Radiation. 1953. Fire Research Special Report No. 2. H.M.S.O.
(2) Hottel, H. C., Sarofim, A. F. 1967. Radiant Heat Transfer. McGraw Hill.
(3) Drysdale, D. 1983. Fire Dynamics (in press).
(4) Lawson, D. I., Hird, D. 1953. Radiation from Burning Buildings. Fire Protection Association.
(5) Griffiths, L. G., Hesselden, A. J. M. 1967. F.R.N. 648. Fire Research Station.
(6) Ashton, L. A. 1970. Fire and Timber in Modern Building Design. T.R.A.D.A.
(7) Langdon-Thomas. 1972. Fire Safety in Buildings. A. C. Black.
(8) Thomas, P. H., Bowes, P. C. 1961. British Journal of Applied Physics.
(9) Beever, P. 1982. B.R.E. Information Paper, I.P.23/82.
(10) Morgan, H. D. 1966. Quarterly Journal of I.F.E. (26) 2, 91.

Chapter 18

Electricity

In this chapter it is assumed that the reader has some knowledge of circuitry and the associated physics of electricity. Readers wishing to pursue the theory and practice of power generation and transmission are referred to suitable sources[1, 2, 3].

The heating effect of a current
When a current flows in an electrical circuit, the heat produced (measured in watts) is proportional to the current, according to the relationship

$$\text{Power} = \text{Voltage} \times \text{Current or } W = e.i$$

This relationship only holds strictly for direct current but can be broadly assumed for alternating current.

The energy of an electrical current can be transformed into heat as well as light, motion, magnetism, sound or a combination of these. The first is the most important to the fire investigator.

Referring again to the relationship, watts = voltage × current, an electric fire of 1 kilowatt consumes (or converts) about 4 amperes of current at 240 volts. Doubling the heating required to 2 kilowatts, the current needed is also doubled to about 8 amperes.

If we remember Ohms Law (voltage = current × resistance) we can derive the relationship

$$\text{Watts} = (\text{Current})^2 \times \text{Resistance or } W = i^2 r$$

Again this is strictly correct for direct current only. Alternating current circuits possess 'IMPEDANCE' which for practical purposes can be considered to be identical to resistance.

Ohms Law has significance to the fire investigator, because it explains much about the problem of localised heating in circuits possessing poor connections, which have high resistances. If, in our first example we double the current by doubling the heat requirement of the electric fire, the heating effect at a resistance in a joint or connector will be increased by a factor of four.

Specific instances of uncontrolled heat production in circuits nearly all result from practical applications of this effect.

Ways of Achieving Heat in a Circuit

Quite apart from the normal heating effects seen in appliances (which, of course, constitute a fire hazard themselves if they are misused) the following are some of the more frequent problems arising from damaged or ill-used circuit wiring.

Overload

This, the classic misuse of a circuit, arises quite simply when appliances of a higher power consumption than the designed circuit capacity are allowed to operate. For instance, a domestic circuit intended for lighting only, cannot cope effectively with applied loads of 2 kilowatts or more and the inherent resistance of the finer gauge wiring significantly increases the heat developed in the circuitry. Fuse or circuit-breaker protection of these circuits is frequently only of 5 amperes rating. A 2 kilowatts load will use a current of about 8 amperes at 240 volts. After a short time the fuse will melt or the circuit-breaker, which frequently has closer protection limits, will operate. If repeated fuse or circuit-breaker failures are experienced, there may be a temptation for the consumer to up-rate the fuse or jam the circuit-breaker. This, in itself will not necessarily start a fire although the cable will become hot and suffer accelerated insulation breakdown. Charring and smouldering may eventually develop but the more significant effects of a continual overload may well be short-circuiting and arcing when the insulation finally breaks down.

Older wiring in many cases will originally have been intended for lighter loads. The 'topping-up' of circuits by spurs, extensions and accumulations of adaptors in plugs, as more appliances are brought into use, can accelerate insulation ageing. Again, with older circuits the insulation could well be 'T.R.S.' (Tough Rubber Sheath) or even rubberised cotton. Both are far more combustible and susceptible to spark or pilot ignition than modern PVC insulation.

Short-circuits

Assuming that the earth loop impedance (the resistance of the earth wire in an alternating current circuit to its earth connection) has a value of, say, about 2 ohms or less, a direct short-circuit to the earth from a live conductor on a 240 volt circuit will develop a fault current of at least 120 amperes. This is clearly enough to melt a normal main domestic 60 ampere fuse wire very rapidly, within seconds, but there will also be a momentary power dissipation of (120×240) watts (nearly 29 kilowatts), particularly noticeable at the short circuiting point. Although this is sustained for a very short time it may be more than enough to raise the temperature locally to well over $1,000°C$ and may cause the destruction of even robust copper fittings. Incandescent particles may well ignite flammable dusts, fluff, insulation, etc. As there is an explosive ejection of material from the area of short-circuiting it may, however, be difficult to ignite any more robust substances.

Poor earthing, possibly by bad jointing in conduits or from poor connections at screwed junctions may raise the earth loop impedance to rather high levels of, say, 10–20 ohms. A fault current from a direct short-circuit in these circumstances may reach only 12–24 amperes and point sources of heat at the short-circuit position may achieve, say, 2,500 watts. This type of failure may require several minutes before fuse failure occurs, by which time high resistance connections in the circuit may heat up to incandescence. This probably constitutes a higher fire risk than the more spectacular direct short-circuit, as the sustained heating is more likely to ignite susceptible materials. The fire growth however, is more likely to be of a smouldering nature in this case. Circuits prone to this type of failure are those in which imperfect continuity of the earth conductor is present, such as older screwed metal conduit, where the conduit is used as the earth return path, or where the bonding of the earth conductor to an earth connection is corroded. A fault current, say, 10 amperes, may well go undetected for indeterminate periods if reliance is placed upon fuse failure, for example, in a ring-main circuit protected by a 30 amp fuse (see Figure 18.1).

Current operated circuit-breakers, in which the device senses whether the currents flowing in the live and neutral circuits are significantly different, are valuable in preventing fires and personal injury by electric shock. Such devices detect a short-circuit to earth or a dangerously low value of insulation between conductors. These are, at the time of writing, rare in domestic properties but are becoming more frequently used in commercial premises.

Localised resistances in circuits
As the heating effect of a current is proportional to the product of the square of the current and the resistance, (i^2r), then any joints

278

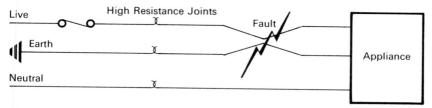

Figure 18.1. A fault between live and earth will, if the earth has a high resistance path, allow a fault current to flow which does not immediately blow the fuse. Excess heating can occur at the joints. Alternatively, even normal but heavy load currents can cause resistance heating at these joints.

in a circuit which have not been correctly bonded will, if a sufficient current flows, heat up. The current need not be a fault current but may well be an ordinary load to an appliance. Faults of this nature may well make themselves known by smoke or smouldering and a classic case of this fault is the insecure cartridge fuse which heats up and burns a hole in the plastic plug casing.

Of more serious concern is the case where an ordinary short-circuit may spark and cause a fire. The high fault current could cause localised heating at each poor junction, which, under dirty conditions, can cause separate fires at each position. These could be misinterpreted as a multi-seat arson although, in most cases, the origin or burning will be behind fascias or under floors and clearly associated with the remains of the wiring.

In-line arcing

If breakages in the conductor occur, momentary separation of the broken ends while a current is flowing can cause sparking. High currents may, on occasion, cause actual arcing although it is fairly hard to set up a stable, continuous arc with alternating current. The temperatures achieved can be higher than 1,000°C and can be capable of igniting insulation, etc. Generally speaking this condition will only be found in parts of circuits subject to movement, for example, wandering leads, temporary wiring, etc.

Electric blanket fires are frequently caused by this fault; insulation and conductor breakdown can occur at the junction where the flex joins the heating elements. Blankets made to good safety standards are especially reinforced here.

As indicated above, it is generally easier to maintain a stable

Principles of Fire Investigation

arc in direct current circuits than with alternating current. Thus, both as a combination of this, and of the high currents which can flow, battery leads from heavy electrical equipment such as fork-lift trucks have, if damaged, been found capable of starting fires in the vehicle. Flexible battery-charging leads used in recharging electrical fork-lift trucks at the end of the workday may well suffer from insulation damage as a result of indifferent working conditions. Insulation failure from this cause can allow electrical heating to cause fires external to the vehicle.

Static Electricity
As a cause of fire, static electricity requires very special conditions to be satisfied. It may be difficult to prove that static electricity was the cause of fire because the conditions which led to the collection of a static charge probably will not exist after a fire. As an example, static electricity was, at one time, thought to be responsible for the sudden explosions in oil tankers which had discharged their fuel. Several experiments indicated a distinct possibility that static charges could be built up on the water droplets in sprays used during tank washing but no research appeared to give unequivocal results. It is now alternatively believed that other conditions, including unstable oxidation states of iron and iron sulphides could be the cause of these accidents. The research involved indicates the uncertainty surrounding the determination of electrostatic charges and their properties.

The development of electrostatic charge
The ability of electrically insulating materials to build accumulations of electric charge on their surfaces, gives rise to the term 'static' electricity[4]. Unless the surface is connected by a conductor to earth or to an oppositely charged object, the charge will only gradually leak away if the air surrounding the surface is dry and non-conductive. If forces acting on the surface keep supplying an electrical charge, the density of charge will increase to the point where the electrical potential is great enough to produce a spark. Readers wishing to go further into the theory and production of static electricity are referred to any competent textbook on the subject.

The important aspects of static charges so far as the fire investigator is concerned, are the conditions under which it will collect and the fire hazard which static discharges represent.

Under the extreme conditions of a lightning flash, several million volts potential between the storm cloud and earth are discharged and currents of, on average, 20,000 amps resulting in energies of the order of 10^{10} joules[5] are present in each flash. Clearly, lightning striking combustible materials will pose an ignition problem[6]. Fortunately, such strikes are relatively rare in the United Kingdom. Usually, ample evidence is available, visibly, audibly and physically that such an event has occurred (see Plates 18A & 18B).

Static electricity as an ignition problem in industry always involves the collection of charge by moving and separating components which are insulated from earth and are in the vicinity of flammable gases, vapours or dusts. These last, unlike solid

Plate 18A. Lightning strikes can produce dramatic effects on some equipment. In this case, several small fires had been started in other electrical equipment in addition to the characteristic damage seen below. Photo: L. Summerscales.

Plate 18B. Further evidence of the destructive power of a lightning strike. The ceramic fuse to the television plug has ruptured. This phenomenon could be expected to be found in areas other than those where fires have started. Photo: L. Summerscales.

objects, can be ignited by low energy sources. A gap of 1 cm of dry, non-ionised air requires a potential difference between a charged body and earth of 30,000 volts to allow a spark to pass. Dependent on the capacitance of the discharging object (that is its ability to hold a given quantity of charge), the energy in such a spark may reach that required to cause ignition of gases or dusts. Ignition may take place more easily if the frequency of the spark discharge is high. (See Table of Minimum Ignition Energies for Gases, Vapours and Dusts).

Situations where static electricity may be built up are frequently recognised in industry and measures are usually taken. These can be, for example, 'brush' contacts to earth from moving belts, small ionising sources which make the air conductive and allow lower potentials to discharge to earth, or the inclusion of conductive materials in non-conducting flammable liquids.

An uncontrolled static electricity discharge may occur when people, wearing synthetic fibre clothing and who are insulated from the ground by rubber soles, approach an earthed object associated with flammable vapours (e.g. a petrol container). Ignition of petrol vapour in an earthed dish by the discharge from a pointed finger of a person who has collected a charge merely by sliding off a plastic covered seat has been reported[7]. Spark energies from a charged human being may be of the order of 20 mJ[8]. This can be compared with the energy of a photographic flash gun which is about 50–200 J[9]. These quoted values can all be seen to be well within the critical range of ignition energies for many dusts and vapours.

The investigator's problem is usually that the physical evidence has probably been destroyed in the resultant fire and the conditions for static electricity build-up are hard to recreate. He

MINIMUM IGNITION ENERGIES FOR GASES, VAPOURS AND DUSTS

Substance	Approximate Minimum Ignition Energy (mJ)
Gases and Vapours	
Hydrogen H_2	0.02
Methane CH_4	0.6
Acetylene C_2H_2	0.2
Ethylene C_2H_4	0.5
Propane C_3H_8	0.5
Butane C_4H_{10}	0.5
Petrol	0.5
Dusts	
Aluminium (6 μ)	13
Benzoyl Peroxide	31
Capralactam	60
Carbon	45
Coffee	140
Epoxy Resin	12
Grain	128
Melamine Formaldehyde	68
Methyl Methacrylate	13
Nitrocellulose	30
Nylon II	32
Paper Tissue (1400 μ)	39
Polythene	38
Soap	25
Soya Meal	330
Sugar	48
Urea Formaldehyde	34

Source: Explosibility tests for industrial dusts. Fire Research Technical Paper 21. 1974. H.M.S.O.

will then be forced to rely primarily on the known conditions, and relate them to the probability of a dangerous accumulation of charge.

Examples of possible static collectors
Gases—High velocity leakages from valves, joints, etc. Discharge of carbon dioxide from fire extinguishers.

Liquids—Pumping of non-conducting liquids, e.g. petroleum (at velocities greater than three metres per second).

Solids—Non-conducting surfaces sliding against and separating from one another, e.g. moving belts. Separation of Non-conductive materials. Movement of synthetic clothing on bodies. Discharge of non-conductive powders or granules from hoppers, etc.

If these or similar conditions apply, ignition may possibly occur when flammable dusts, vapours or gases exist within their appropriate flammable limits. Discharges of these magnitudes would not normally be expected to ignite a solid object unless its temperature had been raised to pilot ignition point.

The Recognition of Electrical Causes of Fire

An electrical cause of a fire is possibly the most difficult of all causes to detect, for in any live circuit involved in fire a time comes when insulation breakdown causes short-circuiting. Additionally, electrical apparatus involved in fires frequently receives so much damage that an accurate assessment as to whether it was on or off is impossible.

Tracing circuits
At the scene, one will almost invariably find electrical wires. An uncritical approach may possibly lead to a suggestion that the fire was of electrical origin without any adequate investigation as to the credibility of the proposition. Many fires, thought at first to be of electrical origin have, on fuller investigation, been found to be from other sources.

Therefore, wiring which has been found must so far as is possible, be traced to determine its electrical status before and during the fire. This is difficult and at times impossible, the normal problems of broken wires hanging down and intermixed with debris being, in older premises, worsened by the presence of obsolete wiring left in by the electrician after rewiring has taken place.

The copper conductors of electrical wiring may melt for one of three reasons:—

(a) Damage to insulation allowed arcing which caused the fire.
(b) Fire damage to the insulation of live wires allowed arcing.
(c) The heat of the fire melted the wires.

Copper melts at 1083°C, which is a relatively high temperature for many fire environments. However, copper conductors used for normal mains wiring can attain this temperature as a result of the heat of the fire. For melting to occur, the copper wires must normally be situated in a high part of the room, and materials capable of producing a high heat output in a short time must normally be involved. Such materials include polyurethane foam, bituminous felt, large quantities of structural timber and most fire accelerants. Because of the temperature gradient in burning rooms, it is extremely improbable that the copper wires of a flex leading across the floor to an electrical appliance could melt as result of the heat of the fire, unless the floor has been destroyed by a fire at a lower level.

A number of studies have been carried out to investigate the appearance of wires heated electrically and by external heat[10,11,12]. External or overload heating produces a general and widespread effect to a considerable length of the wire, characterised by blistering of the copper. This effect occurs throughout the length of an overloaded wire, but is confined to the exposed regions when the cause is external heat. External heat also produces 'necking' and 'beading' effects and the melted ends of the wire or wires are often pointed.

Crystal structure analysis by the use of the scanning electron microscope appears to be able to detect differences between fire damaged conductors which have carried current and those which have not[11].

Copper wiring which comes into contact with certain other metals, particularly zinc, whilst heated, may form an alloy of lower melting point in that region. The locally melted zone which results, is normally of a strikingly different brassy colour, and is unlikely to be confused with the other types of melting.

Overload heating may result in 'offsets' due to partial separation of the wire. There may be evidence of arcing at the final point of failure, and where there is insulation present, it is likely to show evidence of heating from the inside, the so called 'sleeving' effect.

Mineral insulated cable

In the construction of mineral insulated copper cable (MICC), the copper conductors are insulated with compressed magnesium oxide and contained inside a seamless copper tube. This outer tube acts as the earth conductor.

Its fire resistant properties are well known, and because of the non-combustible nature of its construction, the insulation remains effective even if the surface copper cladding is damaged. However, when fire fighting water comes into contact with a live, damaged cable a current flows between the conductors, and fuse failure typical of that which can be expected from an overload (when normal wiring is considered) occurs. Penetration of this type of cable by nails can also give rise to high resistance short-circuiting due to moisture from the atmosphere entering at the punctured point. The resultant 'hot-spot' may cause fire and an example of this can be seen in Plate 7G. The damage to the copper jacket shows that the localised temperature must have been over $1083°C$ (the melting point of copper) whereas the adjacent cable, exposed to the same external heat from the fire, of, possibly, only $850°-950°C$, has suffered only the expected surface damage.

Fuses and circuit protection

The re-wirable fuse (as found in the majority of circuits in the United Kingdom) and the circuit-breaker are each designed to protect a circuit from excessive current. It must be realised that fuses rated at, say, 3 amps or 5 amps, etc., do not fail specifically at these ratings. Momentary high loads (surges) occur quite normally in circuits when motors are switched on. Peak currents can be quite high, in excess of about two and a half times the rated current, and very close protection could result in frequent fuse failures. The wide range of currents acceptable momentarily by fuses and well designed circuit-breakers, increases the safety of the circuit by removing the temptation to over-fuse in such circumstances.

Fuses in live circuits will generally have been found to have blown during or at the ignition of a fire which effects a circuit.

286

Exposure to fire will also cause fuses to fail by general heating. The investigators' problem is to determine the type of failure.

Re-wirable fuses

Direct short-circuits will cause the fuse wire to spatter, frequently leaving little behind but short stubs in the fixing screws. As these fuses are re-wirable the signs of scorching and vaporised copper condensate on the porcelain fuse holder may relate to past conditions and not to the current problem. Examination of the wire remains must always be performed.

A general over-load, beyond the carrying capacity of the fuse wire will melt the wire, often in just the central section. Distinct 'blobbing' of the ends will be noticed and frequently, long remains of fuse wire will be seen. In such cases the rating of the fuse wire is critical, as damage of this sort may take several minutes to develop at currents of about $2-2\frac{1}{2}$ times the fuse rating. Therefore, if the fuse is heavily overrated it is possible that the wiring may have overheated to incandescence, particularly at a poor, high-resistance joint.

If fire has externally heated the fuse box to the extent of causing the fuse wires to melt, then generally speaking there will have been sufficient damage to the external wiring insulation to cause short-circuiting and fusing, before the internal fuse carrier temperature reached its melting point. An externally heat melted fuse is therefore, a reasonably precise way of showing that the circuit was *not* live during the fire. Fuse wires in such situations often collapse onto the fuse carrier showing an overall melting without the 'spot' heating and failure seen in overloaded fuses.

Cartridge fuses

Similar effects to those described above can be seen in cartridge fuses but here either careful dismantling or radiography will need to be performed.

Small, domestic cartridge fuses (found in fused plugs) conforming in the United Kingdom to B.S.S.1362 : 1973 are sand filled and have a silver wire, or silver wire with a soldered bead in the centre, running through the filler material and connecting the two end caps. Non-standard designs may have no filler and the fuse wire may be tinned copper wire.

As with re-wirable fuses a direct short-circuit causes complete disintegration of the fuse wire. This ejects the metal into the filler

Plate 18C. Radiographs of cartridge fuses. The fuse on the left is intact, the other fuses show the effects of short circuiting. The right-hand fuse is sand filled whereas the centre fuse has no filling. Photo: L. Summerscales.

and close microscopic examination may reveal sand grains coated with metal or metal oxide.

Overloads cause a channeling along the sand grains which are loosely held in place by the deposited metal. This effect is concentrated at the solder bead in that type of fuse, one end of the free wire usually showing a higher concentration of metal than the other.

External heat gives a rather more complex effect. If no current has been flowing, breakage frequently occurs near one of the end caps and the solder bead type generally fails at the bead. The appearance of the melted bead is usually smoother than that found when an overload has occurred as no momentary arcing has taken place.

If external heating by fire has occurred through a fuse in a live circuit, the same problems as with re-wirable fuses apply, in that it would be expected that insulation failure could well cause short-circuiting before the external fire could affect the fuse itself. Therefore, interpretation of these results calls for a careful consideration of the known conditions.

Highly rated fuses may fail while lower rated fuses in the fault circuit may remain intact. This phenomenon can be a result of the fuses having unmatched current/time characteristics. At a particular overload current the highly rated main fuse may operate more quickly than the lower rated fuse. Cheaply produced low current cartridge fuses may not have been manufactured to a high standard and may exhibit a particularly slow response time (see Figure 18.2.)

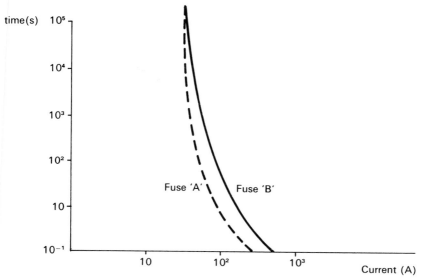

Figure 18.2. Time/current characteristics of fuses. Both have the same nominal 30 amp rating but at a heavy fault current, fuse 'A' will fail before fuse 'B'.

The Examination of Electrical Apparatus
Items of electrical apparatus are frequently blamed, (often unjustly), for fires. The remains of television sets, heaters, electric blankets, lights and motors are from time to time submitted to laboratories for examination. Such appliances are often too badly damaged to determine whether they have been the cause of the fire, particularly when they have been removed from the scene and the examiner has not seen them in place.

When investigating a particular electrical appliance as the possible cause of the fire, the following points should be considered:—

(a) Had the appliance been located at the seat of the fire?
(b) Had it been connected to a supply of electricity?
(c) Had the appliance been switched on?
(d) Had there been a fault which caused part or all of the appliance to be live even if the switch had been off?
(e) Had there been any material in the vicinity of the appliance capable of being ignited and of passing on its own heat of

Plate 18D.   Short-circuits hidden from sight by insulation may be non-destructively revealed by X-radiography. This photograph shows where a short-circuit has occurred at a grommet. Photo: B. R. G. Roberts.

combustion to other materials?

(f) Would the appliance have been capable of generating temperatures above the ignition temperature of the materials in the vicinity, either in normal operation or if it had been faulty?

(g) Is there any evidence that the appliance had been hotter inside than could be explained by the effects of the fire?

(h) Had the appliance been used incorrectly?

For the laboratory to provide worthwhile evidence, it is necessary that the whole appliance, including the supply flex, plug and, if possible, the relevant wall socket should be submitted. In addition, photographs and plans of the appliance in its original position provide background information which may be essential for a full investigation in the absence of a scene visit.

Plugs
Many appliances in homes and industrial premises are left in an unplugged state when not in use. This may be a result of safety

consciousness or, more probably, a lack of available plug sockets. When any electrical appliance suspected of having caused a fire is examined, its plug should be examined also.

A plug which had been in a socket at the time of the fire will show smoke protection on the surface which had been flush with the socket (see Plate 9D). The pins will also have been protected from smoke-staining to a large extent.

Most plugs include a 13 ampere or lower rating cartridge fuse. Failure of this fuse indicates that the socket had been live, and that there had been a fault in the appliance or in the flex leading to it, before or during the fire.

Fire damaged flexes may break during fire fighting operations, and it will then be necessary to establish which of the plugs in the room were attached to which appliances. Eye witnesses are often unreliable when questioned about mundane articles such as plugs, and it may be necessary to link plugs with appliances by the comparison of the short lengths of flex attached to each. In the absence of a remaining connection, the number of strands in each multistranded conductor remaining in the terminal screws can help to indicate whether a particular plug was connected to a particular item.

Equipment

For an item of electrical equipment to cause a fire, it must either contain combustible materials which ignite and cause flames to be emitted, or it must reach a temperature capable of igniting external objects. Fire seat location logic can sometimes be applied to determine whether the casing of an electrical appliance had been hotter inside than outside. Depth and severity of char, temperature indications from melted materials, and the extent of burning to paint surfaces can all give guidance. In addition, plastics which have melted as a result of the fire and have come into contact with a metal surface of the casing can be used. If the casing was hotter than its surroundings, the plastic in contact with the metal may be more charred and degraded than the plastic more distant from the contact surface.

It is also necessary to establish whether the apparatus had been 'live' at the time of the fire. Examination of the plug and fuse may provide part of the answer. Switches should also be examined. Even if the external control lever or knob has burnt away, sufficient of the mechanism may remain for a conclusion to be

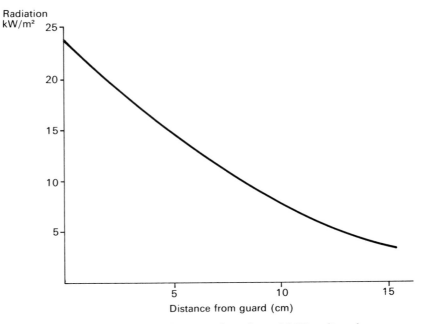

Figure 18.3. Typical radiation values from 1 kW radiant heater.

reached. Heat damaged control knobs may sag downwards, indicating their exact position at the time of the fire. Even in the event of switched sockets having the switch lever burnt, an examination of the contacts within the switch may show whether it was on or off; sometimes the copper blades of modern cam switches 'set' in position when heated by an external fire. It is almost impossible to determine the position of the older type of sprung tumbler switch should the switch supports be damaged by fire.

The following items are frequently blamed for starting fires.

(a) *Radiant heaters.* It is difficult, if not impossible, to set materials on fire if they are more than about 5 cm (2 inches) from a radiant heater grille. Typical radiation from a one kilowatt heater at varying distances is shown in Figure 18.3.

(b) *Electric blankets.* Electric blankets, now subject to B.S.S. 3456 (1971), may have a maximum power of about 85 watts per square metre (9 watts per square foot). Double or triple folding, which may occur under well insulated conditions beneath the bed covers can cause charring within an hour or so, but it is probable that no free burning will take place. It is extremely hard to cause any fire merely by folding the blanket over once.

A more frequent electric blanket fault can be found at the joint where the flex joins the blanket. Repeated bending and pulling may strain the reinforcing materials, and cause an in-line arc on the conductors.

The crossing over and resulting short circuiting of the heating elements is nowadays relatively rare, because of the effective bonding of the heating element into the body of the blanket.

(c) *Television sets.* While it appears that there was a possibility in earlier television sets for the electron gun to overheat if it was left on while no signal was being received, more possible causes nowadays might be insulation breakdown on resistors or capacitors, or localised heating of poor or damaged connections.

Fire spread characteristics from a television set may well involve an early implosion of the tube, in which case screen glass (characteristically thick, curved and coated) will be on unburnt flooring below fire debris. It must be appreciated that even with an implosion there will be much scattering of glass. The usual position of a television set against curtains and close to a window, could give rise to the belief that it may have been responsible for the fire, merely because of the localised fuel loading and ventilating effects which could mimic an original fire seat. Proper excavation techniques can clear up doubts, particularly if plastic which has melted from the cabinet and components is examined for directional heating effects.

(d) *Electric motors.* Motors working in dusty conditions may suffer a lack of cooling air and overheat. Very severe overheating of electric motors is said to result in the seizing up of the motor bearings. The test of attempting to rotate the armature of an electric motor should be regarded as a rough and ready guide only, and if there is any reason to suspect that the motor had caused the fire, it should be dismantled and examined in the laboratory.

Tests
It is sometimes possible to test electrical appliances in the laboratory. However, any piece of apparatus which has caused a serious fire is likely to be so badly damaged that no meaningful electrical test can be applied to it. It may however, be possible to

acquire a similar appliance, for example from an undamaged part of the building and carry out tests on this. It will be necessary to modify the test appliance so that it shows any defects known to have been present in the suspected appliance. This procedure carries obvious evidential as well as physical risks.

References

(1) Regulations for Electrical Installations. 15th Edition. 1981. Institute of Electrical Engineers.
(2) J. F. Whitfield. Guide to the 15th Edition of the I.E.E. Wiring Regulations. 1981. Peregrine Ltd.
(3) W. E. Steward and J. Watkins. Modern Wiring Practice. 1982. Newnes.
(4) C. L. Davids. The Problems of Static Electricity. 1975. Fire Engineers Journal. September.
(5) R. H. Golde. 1973. Lightning Protection.
(6) The Chances of Being Struck by Lightning. Fire Prevention, 143 12–15.
(7) H. Hughes. 1958. Institute of Fire Engineers Quarterly XVIII (30).
(8) H. J. Yallop. Explosion Investigation. 1980. Forensic Science Society.
(9) C. R. Arnold, P. J. Rolls and J. C. J. Stewart. Applied Photography. 1971. Focal Press.
(10) E. H. Ling. Electrical Wiring in Structural Fires. 1975. N. W. Fire and Arson Seminar.
(11) D. A. Gray, D. D. Drysdale and F. A. S. Lewis. Identification of Electrical Sources of Ignition in Fires. 1983. Fire Safety Journal (6) 147–150.
(12) D. W. Levinson. Copper Metallurgy as a Diagnostic Tool for the Analysis of Building Fires. 1977. Fire Technology (13) 211.
(13) W. Fordham Cooper. Electrical Safety in Industry. 1970. I.E.E. Reviews. Vol. 111 (8).

Chapter 19

Chemistry and Fire

Fire is an associated series of chemical reactions which releases energy stored in the fuel as heat. The chemical reactions involved in burning are exothermic oxidations.

Fuel + oxygen ⟶ products + heat

The oxygen is normally supplied by the surrounding air, although in certain cases an oxidising agent may be present in or associated with the fuel.

The products are likely to include inert solids, which remain as ash, gases such as carbon dioxide, together with pyrolysis products which can give smokes their characteristic smells. A large amount of water is normally produced and this, together with other volatile liquid combustion products, is lost as vapour. Much of the heat is lost to the surroundings, but for a fire to continue to burn, sufficient of the heat generated must act on the unburnt fuel.

The fire triangle
The fire triangle is a simple representation of the requirements for ignition to take place.

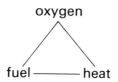

Removal of one of the three components will cause a fire to be extinguished. In common with all simple representations, the fire triangle has limitations.

Some materials can burn without any external supply of oxygen, other elements such as halogens can act as oxidising agents. Furthermore an oxidising agent may already be present in the compound or mixture. In addition, it is evident that this simple representation does not take into account other requirements for burning, such as the ability of the system to form free radicals.

When considering a possible cause of a fire, the fire triangle forms the basis of a common-sense approach, and in almost all cases fuel, air and a source of ignition are necessary before a fire can occur.

Stoichiometric Mixtures

The French chemist, Gay-Lussac, carried out ignition experiments with gases and he summarised his results in his law of gaseous volumes:—

'When gases react, they do so in volumes which bear a simple ratio to one another and to the volumes of the products formed if gaseous.'

This led Avogadro to put forward his hypothesis:—

'Equal volumes of all gases under the same conditions of temperature and pressure contain equal numbers of molecules.'

It can be shown that the molecular weight of an ideal gas in grams (gram molecular weight) occupies 22.4 litres at standard temperature and pressure (STP).

When methane burns, its reaction with the oxygen in the air can be represented:—

$$CH_4 + 2O_2 \longrightarrow CO_2 + 2H_2O + heat$$

$$\begin{array}{ccccccc} \text{1 molecule} & & \text{2 molecules} & & \text{1 molecule of} & & \text{2 molecules} \\ \text{of methane} & + & \text{of oxygen} & \longrightarrow & \text{carbon dioxide} & + & \text{of water} \end{array}$$

It follows that one volume of methane mixed with two volumes of oxygen is the perfect mixture for a methane explosion. Mixtures of chemicals in their exact reaction ratios are called stoichiometric mixtures.

Since air contains only 21% oxygen, the stoichiometric mixture of methane in air is about 9.5% methane in 90.5% air. For most purposes it can be assumed that the most violent explosion will occur on ignition of a flammable gas at or near to its stoichiometric concentration.

Flammability Limits

Whilst a concentration of 9.5% methane in air can easily be ignited, it is common experience that smaller proportions of the gas in air can also burn. The lowest concentration of methane which can be made to burn in air is about 5%. This is the lower flammability limit (FLl) for methane. The equivalent upper flammability limit (FLu) is about 14% for methane in air. Above this upper limit there is insufficient oxygen available for ignition to take place. A familiar example of a mixture above its upper flammability limit occurs when a motorist 'floods' his carburettor, and is unable to start his car, even though in the cylinders high energy sparks are being produced in an atmosphere of petrol vapour.

TABLE 19.1

Material	FL.l	FL.u	Range
Methane	5.3%	14%	8.7%
Propane	2.4%	9.5%	7.1%
Butane	1.5%	8.5%	7%
Petrol	1.4%	5.9%	4.5%
Hydrogen	4%	74.2%	70.2%
Acetylene	2%	82%	80%
Carbon monoxide	12.5%	74.2%	61.7%

There is, as can be seen from the table, a wide variation in the flammability limits and ranges of different compounds.

Flash Point and Fire Point
The flash point of a liquid is defined as the lowest temperature at which it gives off sufficient vapour in air for it to be momentarily ignited on the application of a small flame.

Several standard pieces of apparatus have been designed to measure this property, including the Abel, Pensky-Martens and Cleveland devices. All techniques involve raising the temperature of the liquid until the head space vapour can be momentarily ignited by a small flame. Closed cup methods, in which the flame is introduced at intervals through a shutter opening, yield lower results than open cup techniques. The result obtained will also depend upon the type of apparatus used.

When a liquid is heated, its vapour pressure increases and consequently the concentration of vapour in the headspace goes up.

In the case of a liquid such as paraffin, as the temperature rises the concentration of vapour will eventually reach the lower flammability limit. When this occurs, the vapour can be ignited by the flame of the flash point apparatus. The flammable vapour burns away and self-extinguishes. This is the 'flash'.

At a slightly higher temperature (the fire point) the vapour continues to burn.

It is evident that the fire point is a very much more significant property of a liquid than the flash point.

Radiation Induced Flashover
When the flames from burning furniture in one part of a room spread horizontally at ceiling level, a considerable amount of heat is radiated downwards. As the radiated heat approaches about 30 kW/m², many materials in the room will be decomposing producing flammable pyrolysis products visible as smoke. Shortly after this, individual items in the room will burst into flames. The transformation from a situation with flames reaching the ceiling at one end of a room to ignition of all flammable items occurs very rapidly. This phenomenon, radiation induced flashover (flameover) results in widespread, almost uniform destruction throughout the area involved.

Flames
Most burning takes place in the gaseous state in the form of flames. For flames to occur, sufficient concentrations of flammable gases or vapours must be produced by the effect of the heat on the fuel[1].

Flames can be regarded as belonging to two main groups: diffusion and pre-mixed.

Diffusion flames occur when a flammable gas or vapour is released or produced steadily in relatively still air conditions. The gas mixes with the air by diffusion and, when ignited, the combustion zone occurs in the region where diffusion has lowered the gas concentration to a level between the two flammability limits. No reaction occurs in the central region of the flame where the gas is above its upper flammability limit, and as a result, the luminous reaction zone is a thin hollow shell.

Pre-mixed flames are normally produced deliberately in a specifically designed device such as a Bunsen burner. Pre-mixed flames burn more fiercely than diffusion flames and can attain higher temperatures.

At pressures above 1 bar, it is possible for certain organic compounds, such as ether and carbon disulphide, to burn

Chemistry and Fire

incompletely in the form of cool flames. Cool flames occur at vapour concentrations above the normal upper flammability limit and are virtually invisible. It is possible in a chemical plant for an ignition source in a part of the system above the upper flammability limit, to cause cool flames which could travel to a more oxygen-rich area, resulting in a fire or explosion.

Smouldering Combustion

Smouldering is a form of flameless combustion which can occur in cellulosic and similar materials capable of charring. Smouldering can occur at very low oxygen concentrations, and proceeds at a very slow rate.

A common example of smouldering combustion is the burning of a cigarette.

Heat from the glowing combustion zone (which is normally at a temperature of 600°C or more) chars adjacent tobacco, releasing distillation and pyrolysis products.

As the combustion zone progresses down the cigarette, compounds are released from the tobacco in any particular region, in a sequence which depends upon the volatility and ease of production of each compound. The tobacco immediately adjacent to the glowing front becomes almost pure carbon. If air is drawn through the cigarette, the temperature of the combustion zone rises and the rate of progression of the smoulder along the cigarette increases.

Most experiments on the phenomenon of smouldering have been carried out using sawdust. Typically, sawdust smoulders at a rate of about 5 cms/hour in still air, but the rate of smouldering is affected by the prevailing conditions. The rate of smouldering increases with decreasing particle size and decreasing moisture content. The presence of an air flow can substantially increase the smoulder rate, perhaps by up to ten times. As the air flow is increased, flaming may result except in very fine dusts which blow away before this state is reached. The greatest increases in smouldering rate occur when the air flow and smouldering are in the same direction[2].

Spontaneous Combustion

Most chemical reactions are accelerated by a rise in temperature. A typical increase would be a doubling of reaction rate for every rise of about 10°C.

In the case of exothermic reactions a doubling of reaction rate

299

would also double the rate of heat production. Since an increased rate of heat production will raise the temperature of the reacting system, all exothermic reactions might be expected to react faster and faster until they resulted in explosions.

Fortunately, heat is lost from exothermic systems to their surroundings and the rate of heat loss is proportional to the excess temperature above ambient. An object at a very high temperature loses heat to its surroundings very much faster than one at a temperature slightly above its surroundings. Another factor which influences rate of heat loss is the size of the object concerned. Large objects have a relatively small surface area in proportion to their mass, and lose heat more slowly than small objects of similar composition. For this reason large piles of any material likely to self-heat are very much more likely to ignite than small portions of the same material. Hay stacks can spontaneously ignite, single bales of hay do not. The principle is discussed in more detail in Chapter 17, Physical Processes in Fire.

Since the most common form of exothermic reaction likely to lead to spontaneous ignition is oxidation, the phenomenon most commonly occurs in piles of material which incorporate minute air spaces and channels.

The low temperature oxidation of a solid by oxygen from the air, occurs as a surface phenomenon. For this reason, materials may show a greater tendency to self-heat when finely divided. Certain materials such as coal have an enormous internal surface area, which can play an important part in this effect[3].

Spontaneous ignition of hay

The most well known example of spontaneous ignition is that which occurs in damp hay stacks[4]. For the hay to ignite it must be sufficiently moist for vigorous bacterial action to take place, but dry enough to limit the amount of heat lost by water vapour migration. Initial heating occurs as a result of bacterial action, and temperatures in the region of about 70°C can be achieved before the bacteria become inactive or die.

As the temperature rises, non-biological oxidation mechanisms take over and the temperature can continue to rise until ignition occurs. Spontaneous ignition of hay stacks occurs most commonly between 5 and 13 weeks after stacking, typically after about 8 weeks. It is generally believed that spontaneous ignition is confined to first crop hay. Hay in a baled form is less susceptible to spontaneous ignition because of the opportunities for heat loss provided by the inevitable narrow gaps between bales. Farmers are very much aware of the causes of spontaneous combustion, and with modern equipment it is possible to dry hay effectively even when the weather is unfavourable. This type of ignition is therefore becoming an increasingly rare event.

Spontaneous ignition of hay stacks may be recognised by the geometry of the burning (hay deep within the stack being charred from the earliest stages of the fire), from the tobacco-like smell and by chemical analysis. During the self-heating process, organic acids are formed. The quantities of these found would normally be several times as great as those in sound hay. However, since organic acids can be formed in the burning process and also as a result of the water used in fire fighting, considerable caution is required in the interpretations of such results.

Other materials susceptible to spontaneous ignition
Materials which can readily be oxidised, such as fats and oils of unsaturated fatty acids, can spontaneously heat under certain conditions. Fires have occurred in heaps of rags soaked in linseed and similar oils. However, materials which are normally very much less easily oxidised can spontaneously ignite if they are present in sufficiently large quantities, or if they are for some reason subjected to higher than normal temperatures.

Laundry removed in commercial quantities from tumble driers and left in a large pile whilst hot, has been known to ignite. The lagging of steam pipes, though not necessarily itself combustible, can cause fires if it becomes soaked with oil[5][6]

Beever[7] lists materials known to have a tendency to self heat to ignition (table 19.2).

Some oils and fats are readily oxidised and become hazardous if dispersed on a porous medium such as cloth or powder.

Spontaneous ignition temperature
Defined as 'the minimum temperature at which the self-heating properties of a substance lead to ignition', the spontaneous ignition temperature (SIT) cannot be regarded as an absolute constant for any particular substance. Factors such as specimen size and geometry, moisture content and particle size can cause wide variations in the SIT.

The measurement of the SIT of a solid material can be carried

TABLE 19.2 SELF-HEATING MATERIALS

Animal feedstuffs	Laundry
Beans	Maize
Bone meal	Manure
Brewing grains, (spent)	Milk products
Carbon	Monomers for polymerization
Celluloid	Oils
Coal	Palm kernels
Copper ore concentrates	Peat
Copra	Plastics, powdered
Cotton	Rags
Cottonseed	Rapeseed
Distillers dried grains	Rice bran
Fats	Sawdust
Fertilizers	Seeds
Fishmeal	Seedcake
Flax	Silage
Foam and plastic	Sisal
Grains	Soap powder
Grass	Soybeans
Hay	Straw
Hemp	Varnished fabric
Hides	Wood fibreboard
Iron filings/wool	Wood flour
Iron pyrites	Wool
Jute	Zinc powder
Lagging	

out in an oven comparing the temperature in the midst of the sample with that surrounding it. When the temperature of the sample exceeds its surroundings, it is then generating heat faster than it can be lost. At this temperature, although smouldering may not have developed, in a sufficiently large sample the temperature would continue to rise until ignition occurred. Spontaneous ignition temperatures for cellulosic materials such as sawdust, paper and cotton tend to be in the region of about 200°C.

Autoignition Temperature

The study of the ignition properties of flammable liquids and gases is normally carried out in glass apparatus. Minimum ignition temperatures are measured under these conditions. These measurements take no account of catalytic and other effects which may occur and it is possible for a flammable gas or vapour to ignite at a temperature significantly different from the figure quoted in the literature.

Measurements made in this way are of considerable value in attracting attention to particularly dangerous substances, such as diethyl ether (AIT 180°C) and carbon disulphide (AIT 125°C)[8]. However, when subsequently investigating a fire involving these substances it is not safe to assume that the vapours must have been heated to either of these respective temperatures. The AIT for petrol is widely quoted as 246°C, but it is a matter of common experience that petrol does not necessarily ignite when spilt upon a hot exhaust manifold at a temperature of perhaps 400°C. At the other extreme, hydrogen (AIT 585°C) can be ignited apparently at room temperature by means of a catalytic gas lighter.

Discussion

It is important to recognise that many of the quoted properties of materials such as flash points and spontaneous ignition temperatures have been measured under carefully controlled laboratory conditions. While these figures provide valuable background information regarding the dangerous properties of materials, they should not be interpreted too literally. The conditions prevailing in the situation under investigation may have been significantly different from the ideal laboratory conditions. For this reason, it may be necessary for a scientist to investigate ignition properties in laboratory tests designed specifically to model the conditions prevailing at the time of the fire[9]. It can be dangerous for an investigator with limited scientific knowledge to attempt to interpret his findings using published data.

References

(1) D. J. Rasbash. Fire Factors Sources of Ignition. FEJ 41 32.
(2) K. N. Palmer. Dust Explosions and Fires. Chapman and Hall.
(3) C. A. Couper. How spontaneous combustion occurs. FEJ 38 18.
(4) H. P. Rothbaum. Spontaneous combustion of hay. J. Appl. Chem 13 291.
(5) P. C. Bowes. Fires in oil soaked lagging. BRE CP 35 74.
(6) P. C. Bowes and D. Langley. Spontaneous ignition of oil soaked lagging. Chemical and Process Engineering 1968.
(7) P. F. Beever. Understanding the problems of spontaneous combustion. FEJ 42 38.
(8) M. Sheldon. Understanding autoignition temperature. FEJ 43 27.
(9) H. L. Malhotra. Fire testing and fire hazard assessment. Fire Prevention. 144 21.

Chapter 20

Chemistry of Flammable Materials

Most materials present in fires in domestic and industrial premises are altered by, or make some contribution to the fire. This chapter considers the chemical properties of materials of particular significance in fires. Almost all of these materials are organic compounds or mixtures, i.e. they contain compounds based on the element carbon.

A limited background knowledge of basic chemical terms is assumed. This background information is given in any elementary chemistry text book or in the Manual of Firemanship—Book 1. More detailed information is available in books such as the excellent IFE publication by D. M. Wharry & R. Hirst[1]-[5].

It is evident that mixtures such as petrol and paraffin, commonly used as fuels, are of significance in a fire investigation. However, many plastics burn as freely as paraffin and together with wood, they make up the greater part of the fuel in building fires[6][7]. Less flammable materials such as PVC are also of interest.

Flammable Gases
The flammable gases most commonly involved in fires are methane, butane, propane, acetylene and hydrogen. Other flammable gases may be encountered, particularly in the chemical manufacturing industry, but many of these other gases share properties with the five under consideration.

Methane
Compounds containing hydrogen and carbon only, form the group known as hydrocarbons. All hydrocarbons are flammable and all tend to burn with a yellow, often smoky flame.

Methane is the simplest of all hydrocarbons. Its molecule consists of a single carbon atom with four hydrogen atoms attached in a symmetrical manner.

Methane is a colourless, odourless gas which burns readily. It is less dense than air and is the main constituent of natural gas. It is found in association with the fossil fuels oil and coal, and its presence in the galleries of certain coal mines, where it was known as 'fire damp', has been the cause of many serious explosions. Methane is also known as 'marsh gas' because it can be formed in marshes under anaerobic (oxygen free) conditions by the action of certain bacteria on cellulose. It can even be produced in this way in the rumens of animals such as the cow. Sewage sludge can be made to produce methane by fermentation and some local authorities utilise limited quantities of gas produced in this way as a fuel. Devices constructed to propel motor vehicles by the use of poultry droppings or similar materials also depend upon the generation of methane. Methane forms a valuable fuel resource and is found in substantial quantities mixed with other gases trapped in geological formations, the mixture is known as 'natural gas'. It is transferred from sources such as the North Sea Oil fields, in pipelines under pressure. Methane can also be liquefied by cooling, and transported in tankers.

Liquefied methane has a boiling point of $-162°C$ at atmospheric pressure and its safe transport demands sophisticated technology. The consequences of an accident involving the release of large quantities of liquefied natural gas (LNG) could be extremely serious.

Natural gas supplied as a fuel to consumers contains small proportions of other gases besides methane and stenching agents are deliberately added to facilitate the detection of any leakages. Despite this precaution, a number of buildings are destroyed by gas explosions every year. The recognition of gas explosions is discussed in Chapter 11, Explosives and Explosions.

Propane and Butane

Propane and butane are members of the same chemical series as methane. They have similar chemical properties, both are more dense than air and both are normally present in small quantities in natural gas. They are important products of the refining of oil and can be stored in large quantities under pressure or at reduced temperatures. Because of their convenient physical properties these two gases are the most commonly liquefied of the fuel gases. When liquefied petroleum gas (LPG) is referred to, it is probable that one or both of these gases is involved, although quantities of other flammable gases such as propylene and butylene are likely to be present. Propane (C_3H_8) has a boiling point of $-42°C$, whilst butane (C_4H_{10}) boils at $-0.5°C$. Because of its lower boiling point, liquid propane is more suitable for applications where it may be necessary for the cylinder to be stored out of doors. It is predominantly used for industrial heating, flame cutting and for large industrial blow torches. At temperatures below −0.5°C liquid butane is below its boiling point and no effective gas pressure is produced.

Butane is preferred for applications in which the storage cylinder is kept reasonably warm, such as cooking, heating or lighting in boats, caravans or rural dwellings. It has been used increasingly as a convenient source of fuel in self-contained cabinet gas heaters. Increasing use is also being made of butane as a propellant in aerosol containers. Butane has the advantage over Freon, the other commonly used propellant, in that it is not believed to interfere with the formation of ozone in the upper atmosphere (a possible disadvantage of Freon, which has caused concern amongst conservationists). Butane does, however, constitute a fire risk, and fatal accidents have occurred when aerosol sprays have been ignited accidentally. This danger is exacerbated by the fact that many liquids sprayed in this manner (for example hair lacquers) are themselves flammable. Mixtures of butane and propane, formulated to provide particular desired physical properties, can be used as fuels for suitably modified motor vehicles. Storage of liquefied petroleum gas in a motor vehicle can present problems and a number of explosions have occurred. In general, explosions involving LPG occur as a result of misuse of equipment. Since the consequences of an accident involving several kilogrammes of LPG are likely to be serious, concern has been expressed regarding the increasing use of these fuels by the general public.

Acetylene
In common with methane, propane and butane, acetylene is a hydrocarbon gas. It is however, very much more reactive since the molecule contains more energy. For this reason it is a useful fuel gas for applications where high temperatures are required. The oxyacetylene flame can reach a temperature of 2700°C and is commonly used for welding and flame cutting steel.

Acetylene (C_2H_2) owes its high energy content to the triple bond between its two carbon atoms.

$$H—C \equiv C—H$$

It is notoriously unstable and can explode if it is stored alone under pressure. The gas is therefore stored in specially constructed cylinders in which the void space is entirely filled by a porous ceramic. The ceramic is soaked with acetone in which the acetylene is dissolved under pressure. Acetone can dissolve approximately 300 times its own volume of acetylene. Even when stored in solution, acetylene can decompose. Careless handling of the cylinder, exposure to heat or a flash back can cause the acetylene in the cylinder to heat up. The ensuing decomposition reaction may continue with a progressive rise in temperature until an explosion results. Compressed acetylene is very much less likely to explode when it is present in a limited volume, such as in the narrow bore of the fuel line to a welding torch. However, explosions occur even in this situation, but these explosions are normally the result of mixture with oxygen rather than direct decomposition of the acetylene.

Acetylene has a wide explosive range (2.5%–80%) and is slightly less dense than air.

A further hazard peculiar to acetylene is that it can react with certain metals such as copper and silver, forming explosive acetylides.

Hydrogen
Unlike the other gases discussed, hydrogen is an element. It is the lightest gas, having a vapour density (relative to air) of 0.07 and because of this it was used widely for the filling of airships and balloons. It has now been largely replaced in this role by the inert gas helium.

Hydrogen burns with a nonluminous, blue, very hot flame producing water.

$$2H_2 + O_2 \longrightarrow 2H_2O.$$

The reaction of a stoichiometric mixture of hydrogen and oxygen takes place with explosive violence at 550°C. However, if the gases are dessicated, reaction will not take place even at 1000°C, because a trace of water is necessary for the reaction to be initiated. In the presence of finely divided platinum which can act as a catalyst, the reaction will initiate at room temperature.

Hydrogen is used in the manufacture of ammonia, in the hardening of fats and in other chemical processes. Air/hydrogen and oxyhydrogen flames are used in welding, and a significant quantity of the gas is used in many laboratories.

Petroleum Products

Natural petroleum or crude oil is a viscous dark brown or greenish oil, formed by the partial decomposition of prehistoric organic material. It collects in pockets of porous rock from which it can be recovered by drilling operations.

Since petroleum oil normally occurs in association with natural gas, it is not uncommon for the oil in an oil well to be forced to the surface by gas pressure for a time. When a considerable quantity of oil has been taken, the loss of oil and the associated gas may result in a drop in pressure, necessitating further removal of oil by artificial means.

Crude oil consists of a complex mixture, predominantly hydrocarbons, and the various fractions of commercial value are separated from each other by distillation.

The principal fractions are as follows:—

Boiling range °C	Fraction	Uses
Below 20	Natural gas	Fuel
20–60	Petroleum ether	Solvent
60–100	Light naphtha	Solvent
25–190	Petrol (gasoline)	Motor fuel
165–255	Paraffin (kerosene)	Heating fuel
180–340	Diesel fuel (gas oil)	Motor fuel
Vacuum distillation	Heavy oils	Lubrication
Vacuum distillation	Greases	Lubrication
Vacuum distillation	Asphalt or petroleum coke	Road surfacing

Petrol

Petrol (gasoline) is a volatile, mobile, colourless or straw-coloured liquid having a boiling range of between 25° and 190°C. Because of its volatility, it has a very low flash point (below −30°C).

More than 200 major hydrocarbons can be detected in petrol by the use of capillary column gas chromatography (Chapter 23, Laboratory Analysis) and as techniques of analysis have become more discriminating, better comparisons can be made between questioned and control samples. The hydrocarbons in petrol include branched and straight chain alkanes from butane upwards. The aromatics include benzene, toluene, the three xylenes, methyl ethyl benzenes and trimethyl benzenes.

Petrol currently contains small proportions of anti-knock additives such as tetraethyl lead and tetramethyl lead. Scavengers such as 1,2-dibromomethane and 1,2-dichloroethane may also be present. These compounds can easily be analysed by electron capture detection gas chromatography q.v., and are of some value in characterising samples of petrol[8].

Petrol is a valuable product of the distillation of crude oil. For this reason methods have been developed to convert some of the less valuable higher boiling point oils into lower molecular weight compounds sufficiently volatile to fall within the acceptable boiling range of petrol.

At first, all petrol produced by refineries was 'straight run' petrol separated from the crude oil by simple distillation. Later, a cracking process was developed by Burton of Standard Oil, in which the heavier, higher boiling range fractions were heated under pressure forming lower molecular weight compounds. Subsequently, the more efficient and economical process of catalytic cracking was developed by Eugene J. Houdry. In this process the higher boiling range fractions are, in the presence of a catalyst, subjected to a temperature of about 500°C at a pressure of 2 bar.

Behaviour of petrol in fires

Petrol has a high vapour pressure at normal temperatures and therefore produces considerable quantities of vapour at concentrations above its lower flammability limit (1.4%) very rapidly. When petrol is used as a fire accelerant, various unexpected effects may result. If petrol is poured onto an absorbent material in a fairly open situation and is ignited immediately, it will normally burn fiercely but relatively safely. If it is scattered around a room and ignited after a delay, a violent explosion may result.

Large quantities of petrol and a long delay before ignition may result in an initial flame which depletes the oxygen in the room to such an extent that the fire self-extinguishes. Cases have been reported in which rooms heavily saturated with petrol have been ignited through an open door which has then slammed shut as a result of the explosion, causing the fire to self-extinguish. This effect has been confirmed experimentally[9].

Petrol vapour is substantially heavier than air (vapour density about 2.5) and as a result, there may be a tendency for the burning due to a petrol vapour explosion to be at a low level. However, turbulence effects during the explosion can alter the distribution of the flammable vapour.

Ignition of petrol by cigarettes
Petrol vapour cannot normally be ignited by glowing cigarettes, a fact which has been verified by many experiments. Tests have been carried out under a wide variety of conditions, but petrol, in common with many other flammable liquids and natural gas, cannot normally be ignited in this manner. A possible explanation is that the rather low value of the upper flammability limit for petrol (5.9%) indicates a high oxygen requirement for the ignition of petrol vapour. In the vicinity of the glowing tip of a cigarette, it may be that insufficient oxygen is present for the petrol to ignite.

Paraffin
Paraffin (Kerosene) consists of the distillation fraction having a boiling range between about 165°C and 255°C. It is very much less volatile than petrol and has a flash point above normal ambient temperatures. Paraffin contains predominantly alkanes between nonane (C_9H_{20}) and pentadecane ($C_{15}H_{32}$).

There can be significant differences between the ratios of component alkanes even between different batches of paraffin of the same nominal type. Detectable differences occur in the proportions of the minor constituents particularly those which occur chromatographically between undecane ($C_{11}H_{24}$) and tridecane ($C_{13}H_{28}$).

In addition, most manufacturers add mixtures of oil-soluble dyes to paraffin intended for the domestic market. These dyes can be identified by thin layer chromatography (qv). Several techniques are therefore available for the comparison of paraffin recovered from debris with paraffin taken from the possession of a suspect (see Chapter 23, Laboratory Analysis).

Liquids such as paraffin, white spirit and diesel fuel which have flash points above ambient temperature, cannot normally be ignited by a flame or spark without the liquid having been pre-heated to a temperature above its fire point.

The burning of paraffin at a wick or in the form of an atomised spray would seem to be exceptions to this rule. However, in both cases, small amounts of the fuel which can be quickly heated to a temperature above the fire point, are presented to the flame. In the case of an absorbent material acting as a wick, the flame vaporises and burns the fuel which has been brought to the combustion zone by capillary action up the wick. In oil lamps or paraffin heaters with wicks, control is achieved by adjusting the length of wick which protrudes above the metal shielding. It is only this part of the wick which is affected by the heat of the flame to produce flammable vapour. The greater the length of wick protruding, the greater the amount of vapour produced and the larger the flame.

When an absorbent item such as a carpet soaked in paraffin is ignited, the larger the flame the greater the area of fuel-soaked carpet that will be heated. As a result there is a rapid lateral spread of flame across the fuel-soaked carpet. The surface tension of an oil falls when it is heated and, consequently, hydrocarbon fire accelerants migrate away from the heat both laterally and vertically. Residual fire accelerants are most likely, therefore, to be detected at the edges of the burnt area of the fuel-soaked carpet or in the floor boards below the burnt region.

White Spirit
White spirit is similar to paraffin except that no dye is added to it, and it is a fraction with a narrower boiling range (150°C–200°C). White spirit consists predominantly of alkanes between nonane (C_9H_{20}) and dodecane ($C_{12}H_{26}$). White spirit is defined by a British Standard. However, the solvent sold as 'turpentine substitute' may be indistinguishable from undyed paraffin.

Diesel Fuel Oil
Diesel fuel oil (DERV or gas oil) is a mixture of alkanes between decane ($C_{10}H_{22}$) and pentacosane ($C_{25}H_{52}$). It is less volatile than petrol, paraffin or white spirit. Diesel fuel burns in a similar manner to paraffin but there is a tendency for the flames to be significantly more smoky.

Ethanol
Ethanol (ethyl alcohol) is the only common water-miscible liquid fire accelerant. It can be produced by the fermentation of sugars by yeasts, and it is by far the most commonly encountered of all the alcohols.

The most alcohol tolerant of the yeasts can only produce concentrations up to about 14% w/v and as a result, alcoholic beverages produced only by fermentation cannot exceed this concentration.

Spirits are produced by a two stage process of fermentation followed by distillation. Fortified wines such as some sherries and ports have their alcohol concentration enhanced by an addition after the fermentation.

ALCOHOL CONTENTS OF VARIOUS BEVERAGES

Beverage	% w/v Ethanol
Shandy	1½
Beer	3
Cider	3½
Wine	5–12
Sherry	16
Vodka 65° proof	30
Whisky 70° proof	32
Schnapps	34
90° proof spirit	41

It is common experience that beer and wine cannot burn but that under certain conditions, spirits can.

The traditional ignition of brandy on a Christmas pudding is technically difficult unless the pudding is already hot. The fire point of a 32% solution of ethanol in water is significantly above normal room temperature. For this reason it is difficult to start a fire using 70° proof spirit unless the item to be ignited is already hot or there is present a porous material which can act as a wick. Once ignited, the ethanol burns for a short time and then extinguishes, leaving a considerable quantity of watery residues. It is evident that irrespective of other considerations, 70° proof spirits are not recommended as fire accelerants.

Absolute Alcohol
Ethanol can be produced from a fermented mash by distillation and dehydration, or chemically, by the hydration of ethylene. The pure product is known as absolute alcohol. It is a colourless, mobile, pleasant-smelling, water-miscible liquid which is easily ignited, burning with a blue, scarcely visible flame. Although absolute alcohol has desirable properties as a fuel and a solvent, it is subject to considerable excise duties. For this reason, ethanol intended for use as a fuel is deliberately contaminated in order that it cannot be drunk.

Methylated Spirit

Methylated spirit consists of a mixture of about 90% ethanol 9.5% methanol and 0.5% pyridine together with traces of naphtha and methyl violet dye. This mixture has burning characteristics closely similar to those of absolute alcohol. Related mixtures include industrial methylated spirits and surgical spirits, both of which are water white and consist predominantly of ethanol with a small percentage of methanol.

Plastics

Plastics are high molecular weight compounds which are formed by the process of polymerisation and they are therefore known as 'polymers'. A polymer is a substance formed by joining together a very large number of simple molecules (monomers). Two molecules of the monomer linked together are known as a 'dimer', and three linked in this way are called a 'trimer'.

When the plastic has been formed predominantly from only one type of monomer, it is termed a 'homopolymer'. When two or more different types of monomer are present in the plastic, it is called a 'co-polymer'.

Polymer molecules are frequently written $(R)_n$ where n is the degree of polymerisation i.e. the average number of monomer molecules present in a polymer molecule.

The physical properties of a plastic depend not only upon the type of monomer or monomers present but also upon the way in which they are linked together. Polymers can be in the form of straight chains, resulting in plastics which tend, in general, to be flexible and capable of being stretched.

In order to alter the properties of a plastic, molecules may be introduced which cause links to form between the chains. This process of cross-linking renders the finished plastic less flexible, less soluble in organic solvents and possibly more brittle.

Plasticisers

Plasticisers are substances incorporated into plastics to improve their properties, for example, to increase flexibility, workability or distensibility or to reduce brittleness. Plasticisers effectively lower the glass transition temperature to below the ambient temperature, changing the material from a hard, brittle solid, to a soft, flexible, tough material.

Most plasticisers are oily liquids present in solid solution in the plastic. For the plasticiser to be effective, it must be permanent, having a low vapour pressure and a low rate of diffusion in the plastic at normal temperatures. It must also be compatible with the plastic and must therefore have similar intermolecular forces. It is difficult to find plasticisers compatible with non-polar plastics such as polyethylene and polypropylene.

About half of all plasticisers used today are phthalate esters. These are high molecular weight oily liquids which have a very low vapour pressure at normal temperatures. At elevated temperatures in the vicinity of a fire, the vapour pressure of the plasticisers increases and can enhance the ignitability of the plastic. In recognition of this problem, phosphate ester plasticisers were developed. These esters (particularly tricresyl phosphate) impart a flame-proofing characteristic to the plastic.

It is possible for primary plasticisers to migrate out of a plastic resulting in increased brittleness. The PVC insulation of wiring buried in expanded polystyrene granules can lose plasticiser in this way over a period of time.

Fillers

Inert substances are often added to a plastic to improve its physical properties and to reduce its overall cost. Fillers can be organic or inorganic but both types, in general, tend to make the plastic less flammable.

Organic fillers, such as wood flour, cotton flock, keratin, leather dust, sisal or paper, though themselves flammable to some extent, tend to impede the melting and decomposition of plastics. This can inhibit the formation of flammable volatile decomposition products which are essential for the ignition of the plastics.

Inorganic fillers, such as asbestos, calcium carbonate, china clay, silica, talc, titanium dioxide, zinc oxide or slate dust are non-flammable and inhibit the burning of the plastic. Solid residues after the melting and burning of inorganically-filled plastics remain as misshapen, coke-like, fused masses, which may incorporate fragments of charred wood and other materials from the fire. These coke-like residues bear no resemblance to the original plastic items which had been burned, but comparison may be made between the composition of the 'coke' and specimens of unburnt plastic. Inorganic analysis and X-ray diffraction studies may well show that the charred residues could have originated from plastic items of the same composition as the control sample.

Thermoplastics and thermosets

Thermoplastics melt at temperatures below their decomposition temperature. If allowed to cool, they re-solidify forming a material having very similar properties to the original unmelted plastic. This property is utilised in the moulding of such thermoplastics as polyethylene, polypropylene, polystyrene and poly(vinyl chloride) (PVC).

Thermoplastics have molecules which could untangle and separate from one another when heated. At higher temperatures the molecules decompose, forming a mixture of volatile, flammable, low molecular weight compounds in which the monomer may be one of the major constituents. For a plastic to burn, it is necessary for flammable pyrolysis products to be produced because, in common with most other materials, the burning of a plastic takes place as a gas reaction.

Thermoplastics have the additional disadvantage in fires that they may cause fire spread by the dropping of burning melted material from elevated positions.

Thermosetting plastics (thermosets) such as urea formaldehyde are normally heavily cross-linked, and when heated decompose before melting. These rigid materials characteristic of cross-linking are often filled, and thermosetting plastics are often less flammable than thermoplastics.

The burning of melted thermoplastics and of flammable liquid decomposition products of thermosetting plastics, can produce burning patterns similar to those caused by the burning of liquid fire accelerants such as paraffin or petrol. Subsequent chemical analysis of the residues will normally establish which of the alternatives was involved.

Polyethylene and Polypropylene

Polyethylene (Polythene) is normally encountered as a soft, flexible, translucent thermoplastic with a waxy texture. Because of its good properties in the form of a thin film it is commonly used for the manufacture of plastic bags.

Two main types of polyethylene are manufactured, low and high density. Low density polyethylene is produced at high temperatures and pressures, high density polyethylene is formed at lower temperatures and pressures in the presence of catalysts. High density polyethylene is similar in properties to the closely related plastic polypropylene. Both are tough, somewhat flexible and rather water repellent, especially when new.

All forms of polyethylene together with polypropylene are moderately easy to ignite and burn with yellow flames which may be blue at the lower edges. When the flames are very small, the yellow part disappears leaving small almost invisible blue flames. All three materials melt producing flaming droplets which may remain burning in a pool where they land. A characteristic of all three materials is the wax-like smell which occurs immediately after flames have been extinguished. The pyrolysis products of polyethylene and polypropylene include straight chain and branched alkanes together with the equivalent alkenes. Gas chromatography of pyrolysed polyethylene reveals that the C_6 and C_{10} peaks are enhanced due to preferential formation of compounds of these two chain lengths.

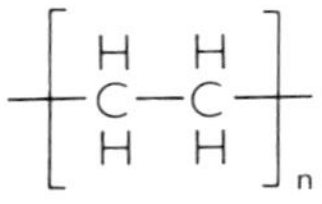

Polyethylene

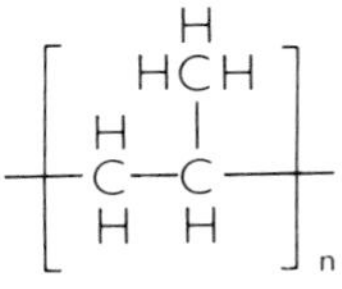

Polypropylene

Poly(Vinyl Chloride)
Another commonly used thermoplastic is poly(vinyl chloride) (PVC)

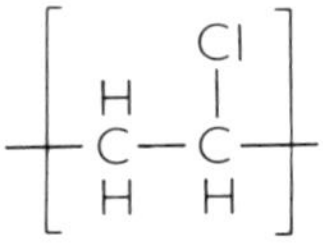

Poly(Vinyl Chloride)

The physical properties of PVC can be modified by variations in the manufacturing process and the addition or omission of plasticisers. The wide variety of uses of the plastic reflect its versatility. It is used in the form of a semi-rigid corrugated transparent sheet for roofing and other building applications. It is also widely used in plumbing and in the manufacture of drain pipes and guttering in the form of tough, opaque, rigid extrusion mouldings. In its flexible plasticised forms, it is used for the electrical insulation of wires and as an upholstery covering in the furnishing industry.

Apart from its inertness and resistance to weathering, one of the most valuable properties of PVC is its resistance to ignition. When heated in a flame, a sample of PVC will melt and burn with difficulty producing a characteristic acrid smell and a yellow and green flame. On removal of the heat source, the plastic tends to self-extinguish. The behaviour of PVC in fairly large quantities in a well developed fire, however, illustrates a danger of drawing conclusions from small scale tests. In situations where there is already a very high ambient temperature such as in a well developed fire, PVC burns fiercely and can make a significant contribution to the fire loading in the area. When PVC burns, the volatile products can include hydrogen chloride, carbon monoxide, phosgene, vinylchlorides and various other chlorinated hydrocarbons. It can, therefore, present serious toxicity problems in fires.

Polystyrene

Polystyrene is produced by the polymerisation of the aromatic hydrocarbon styrene. It is a hard, rigid, colourless thermoplastic with a tendency towards brittleness.

Polystyrene

Polystyrene articles are fabricated by injection moulding and by extrusion techniques. They are fairly tough, lightweight, relatively free from taste or odour and can be either transparent or opaque. Polystyrene lends itself to detailed moulding and separate mouldings can be strongly glued together.

Another major use for polystyrene is in the manufacture of rigid plastic foam. Pellets of polystyrene, including traces of a volatile hydrocarbon such as pentane, are heated in a mould. The polystyrene softens and the pentane turns to vapour causing the pellets to expand after the fashion of 'popcorn'. The expanded pellets press together to fill the shape of the mould, and the hardness of the final expanded polystyrene moulding depends upon the number of pellets present in the mould initially. Expanded polystyrene is used in the manufacture of ceiling tiles, packing and insulating materials and for other applications where its low density or good thermal insulating properties are required.

Polystyrene burns readily with a yellow-orange, sooty flame. It melts and burning droplets may fall. If the plastic is extinguished the characteristic odour of the pyrolysis products may be smelled; the smell of the monomer styrene is predominant.

Expanded polystyrene is not particularly easily ignited by a small flame as there is a tendency for the plastic to shrink away from the source of heat without ignition. Obviously, in a developing fire, expanded polystyrene ceiling tiles can easily be ignited and can make a significant contribution to fire spread.

Poly(Methyl Methacrylate)
Poly(methyl methacrylate) (Perspex) is a tough transparent thermoplastic with good optical properties and high impact strength which has been used in the manufacture of aircraft canopies and light fittings. Side, rear and indicator lamp covers of vehicles are commonly constructed of this plastic. Poly(methyl methacrylate) burns with a yellow flame which may be blue at the bottom and which may spurt a little black smoke. The plastic melts but remains fairly viscous during the burning process.

It has the formula:—

$$\left[\begin{array}{c} H \quad CH_3 \\ | \quad | \\ -C-C- \\ | \quad | \\ H \quad | \\ COOCH_3 \end{array}\right]_n$$

Poly(Methyl Methacrylate)

The degree of polymerisation 'n' is normally between 5,000 and 10,000. Poly(methyl methacrylate) is soluble in most aromatic and chlorinated hydrocarbons, and esters. It dissolves slowly in

318

acetone and is decomposed by concentrated and oxidising acids and by alcoholic alkalis.

Pyrolysis products include the monomer methyl methacrylate, and formaldehyde.

Cellulose Acetate

Cellulose acetate is a tough thermoplastic with good impact resistance, and good electrical properties. It is made by treating cellulose with acetic acid and acetic anhydride. It has the formula:—

$$
\left[
\begin{array}{c}
CH_2R \\
| \\
CH\!-\!O \\
/ \qquad \backslash \\
-CH \qquad HC\!-\!O- \\
\backslash \qquad / \\
CH\!-\!CH \\
R \quad R
\end{array}
\right]_n
$$

The degree of polymerisation 'n' varies according to the intended application for the plastic. When cellulose acetate is used in lacquers, n is 200 or less, in the form of plastic it is about 300, and in the case of cellulose acetate fibres, it may be up to about 400.

Groups R are hydroxyl (OH) in the case of cellulose but these are partially or completely replaced by acetyl groups (OOC CH_3) in cellulose acetate. The completely esterified triacetate polymer has very good electrical properties but is rather brittle for many applications, and therefore the partially esterified diacetate is often preferred.

The properties of cellulose acetate depend to some extent upon the degree of esterification and the degree of polymerisation. The triacetate is slightly soluble in certain chlorinated hydrocarbons but is insoluble in most other solvents. The diacetate is soluble in many common solvents including acetone, many esters, halogenated hydrocarbons and dioxan.

Cellulose acetate burns fairly readily with a yellow flame with a blue base leaving an irregularly shaped black charred bead. The pyrolysis products include acetic acid and therefore a vinegar-like smell may be apparent on extinction of the flames.

Cellulose Nitrate

Cellulose nitrate (Celluloid) is one of the earliest plastics to have

319

been produced in quantity. Its widespread uses have included the manufacture of photographic and cine films, the manufacture of paints, varnishes and lacquers and such varied applications as knife handles, billiard balls, piano key sheaths and bicycle pumps.

Because of its very high flammability, cellulose nitrate has been replaced in most applications by safer plastics but it is still used in the manufacture of nitrocellulose paints, table tennis balls and explosives.

The general formula of the simplest fundamental unit of the molecule is the same as that for cellulose acetate except that the groups designated R are either OH or NO_3. For most applications the average degree of substitution is approximately two, but in the case of explosives the glucose residues are predominantly tri-substituted.

Polyurethane

Polyurethane is one of the most versatile of the thermosetting plastics. Its applications include flexible films, resilient mouldings such as footwear soles and both flexible and rigid foams.

Flexible foam is the form of polyurethane of most interest to fire investigators since it can burn extremely fiercely and rapidly producing dense toxic smoke[10].

Urethane is the product of the reaction between an isocyanate and an alcohol.

$$\underset{\text{isocyanate}}{RNCO} + \underset{\text{alcohol}}{R'\ OH} \longrightarrow \underset{\text{urethane}}{R-\overset{\overset{\textstyle H}{\textstyle |}}{N}-\overset{\overset{\textstyle O}{\textstyle ||}}{C}-OR'}$$

Di-functional materials (compounds with two reactive groups) yield straight chain polyurethanes. Cross-linked polyurethane can be produced by the use of multi-functional alcohols.

Foams are produced by the addition of a blowing agent which causes the production of bubbles during the polymerisation process. If water is added to the mixture, it reacts with isocyanates generating carbon dioxide and an amine.

Volatile liquids such as the halon fluorotrichloromethane ($CFCl_3$) and the hydrocarbon pentane are now also used as blowing agents. Considerable heat is generated by the polymerisation reaction and this is sufficient to vaporise the blowing agent.

320

The use of a blowing agent of this type has several advantages:—

(a) Isocyanates are not destroyed as would be the case if water was used as a foaming agent.
(b) The presence of a halon lowers the viscosity of the components, facilitating mixing.
(c) The vaporisation has a cooling effect which may help to prevent scorching or discoloration at the centres of large blocks of foam.

The isocyanates commonly used in the manufacture of polyurethane foams include tolylene diisocyanate (TDI) and methylene bis (4-phenyl isocyanate) (MDI).

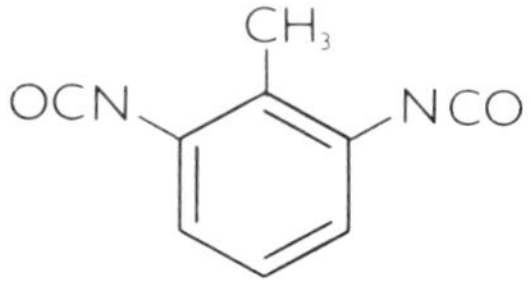

Tolylene diisocyanate
(TDI)

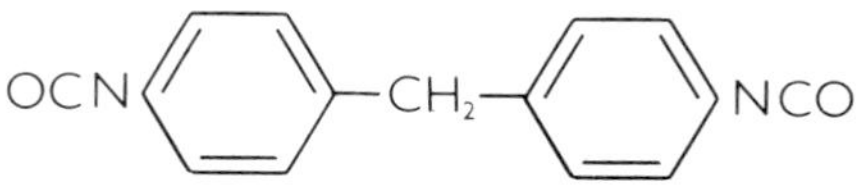

Methylene bis
(4-phenyl isocyanate)
(MDI)

Polyols
The alcohols used in the manufacture of polyurethane foam have many hydroxyl groups, and are therefore known as polyhydric alcohols or polyols. A wide variety of polyols is available and it is largely the type of polyol selected which determines the properties of the final foam. Flexible foams are produced by the use of high molecular weight polyols with a relatively low number of hydroxyl groups (i.e. a low functionality). Rigid foams are formed when high functionality polyols are used. Two types of polyol are used in the manufacture of polyurethane; polyester polyols and polyether polyols. Polyester polyols are exactly analogous to triglyceride fats (q.v.), and in fact, the natural triglyceride castor oil has been used for the manufacture of certain polyurethane foams.

Polyether polyols are cheaper and more versatile than polyesters and are produced by reacting propylene oxide with poly functional alcohols such as glycerol, pentaerythritol, sorbitol or even sucrose (cane sugar).

The burning of flexible polyurethane foam
Polyurethane does not melt in the true sense, and as a result, it is rather more easily ignited than some thermoplastic foams which show a greater tendency to shrink away from the source of heat.

Polyurethane foam most commonly burns fiercely with smoky flames producing gaseous and liquid flammable decomposition products. In common with most nitrogen-containing materials, polyurethane can produce cyanides when it burns. However, the most serious threat to life is posed by carbon monoxide which can be produced rapidly and in large quantities. Many volatile pyrolysis products have been identified. The flammable liquid pyrolysis products which are also formed, can burn at ground level beneath the article of furniture involved. The burning of these liquids can, on a preliminary examination, give the impression that liquid fire accelerants had been used. Chemical analysis can be used to differentiate between the two alternatives.

Flexible polyurethane foam can, under certain circumstances, smoulder. This smouldering is normally confined to situations where the polyurethane foam is associated with a cellulose fabric (such as cotton or rayon) and where the material was ignited by a non-flaming source such as a cigarette. However, it is conceivable that furniture ignited by a flame could revert to the smouldering state, under certain circumstances. (See Chapter 1, Effect of Structures and Contents).

When polyurethane foam smoulders, flammable gaseous pyrolysis products are formed and the residual foam changes to form a fragile black meringue-like material. After a period of an hour or more, a deep seated, smouldering fire in polyurethane foam can suddenly switch to flaming combustion. This change may be triggered by a sudden draught.

Spontaneous combustion of polyurethane foam
The reactions between isocyanates and polyols are exothermic, and because the foam is a good thermal insulator, the rate of dissipation of heat is slow. The heating effect is greatest in large blocks of foam and in mixes which generate most heat. One factor which influences the amount of heat generated is the equivalent weight of the polyol. Polyols having a low equivalent weight (a large number of hydroxyl groups in proportion to the rest of the molecule) generate most heat of reaction.

The self-heating properties of polyurethane foam are well understood by manufacturers and freshly made foam is stored in a cooling area for at least eight hours. The highest temperatures are developed in the centres of the blocks and this sometimes results in discoloration of the finished foam. The temperatures of the stored blocks are monitored with temperature probes, in order that any found to be dangerously overheating can be removed before they ignite[11].

Once it has cooled, properly formulated polyurethane foam is not susceptible to self-heating and tests have shown that foam-filled furniture is fairly resistant to ignition by radiant heat. (See Chapter 1). The work of Woolley et al indicates that the ease of ignition of polyurethane foam by a small flame depends substantially upon the nature of the fabric covering the foam[12].

Fire Resistant Foams

Flexible polyurethane foam has rightly been recognised as a serious fire hazard. The particular problems are:—

(a) The foam by its very nature incorporates air spaces.
(b) Polyurethane is flammable.
(c) Normal polyurethane foam retains its shape during the initial stages of burning.
(d) Polyurethane produces many toxic pyrolysis products.

Manufacturers of polyurethane foam have been aware of this problem for many years and have dedicated a considerable research commitment to its solution. Unfortunately, many of the modified foams available had in the past sacrificed other desirable properties, particularly cheapness, to achieve greater fire resistance.

Modifications to the foam include formulations which decompose and shrink away from the heat source before ignition (neomorphic foams). The incorporation of bromine into the molecule also causes the foam to be less prone to ignition but this advantage is bought at the expense of increased smoke toxicity.

Foams incorporating fire retardant materials such as aluminium trihydrate may provide satisfactory resistance to ignition although the manufacturing costs are likely to be higher than those for normal foam.

Rubber
Natural rubber is a polymer of the hydrocarbon isoprene,

$$\begin{array}{c} CH_3 \\ \diagdown \\ CH_2 \end{array} \!\!\! > C\!\!-\!\!CH = CH_2 \text{ isoprene.}$$

and is produced from the latex exuded from incisions deliberately cut into the bark of the rubber tree, Hevea brasiliensis. Rubber exhibits a characteristic elasticity, a property which is conferred by the convoluted shape of its long molecules. The rubber molecule is formed from about 5000 isoprene molecules, giving a total molecular weight of about 350,000. Raw rubber is elastic but has undesirable properties such as a tendency to become sticky with age or in hot weather. The process of vulcanisation greatly improves certain properties. This process, devised by Goodyear and Hayward, involves heating the rubber with sulphur (usually 1–3%). Cross-links are formed between the isoprene chains, which improve the durability of the finished rubber at the cost of the loss of some flexibility. The addition of inert fillers such as clays, whiting or silicas in light coloured rubbers, and carbon black in dark rubbers, further improves the wearing qualities.

The main volatile pyrolysis products of natural rubber are the monomer isoprene and the dimer dipentene, both of which are flammable.

Synthetic Rubbers
The first synthetic rubber developed, was Neoprene, a polymer of chloroprene.

$$CH_2 = CH\!\!-\!\!\underset{\underset{Cl}{|}}{C} = CH_2$$

Chloroprene

Neoprene can be vulcanised by heat alone, but normally zinc oxide is added as a vulcanising agent. Neoprene is more expensive than natural rubber but it is considerably more resistant to solvents, oils and oxidative degradation. Its uses include industrial hoses and belts, wire and cable coatings and shoe heels.

The other important group of synthetic rubbers are formed by the polymerisation of butadiene.

$$CH_2 = CH\!\!-\!\!CH = CH_2$$
Butadiene

Although a polymer of butadiene with a certain amount of cross-linking produces synthetic rubber having relatively good properties, the most important rubber of this type contains styrene as a co-polymer. This material, (SBR or GRS) contains butadiene and styrene in the ratio of about 3 : 1.

SBR is vulcanised with sulphur compounds, resulting in cross-linking between the chains. The extent of the cross-linking determines the properties of the final rubber. Pyrolysis products of this material include butadiene, styrene and toluene.

Natural and synthetic rubbers, with the exception of neoprene are highly flammable. When heated, or when they smoulder, they can produce dense white smoke containing high concentrations of flammable volatile pyrolysis products which can be ignited elsewhere, causing rapid spread of fire or an explosion.

Rubber fires are notoriously difficult to extinguish for two main reasons. Rubber has a very high calorific value and it is also inherently waterproof.

Carbohydrates

The widely distributed group of biological chemicals known as carbohydrates includes the sugars, starches and cellulose. Carbohydrates, as their name implies, contain carbon, hydrogen and oxygen. The hydrogen and oxygen are normally in the same ratio as in water. Carbohydrates are produced by green plants by the process of photosynthesis, in which the energy of sunlight is converted to chemical energy.

Photosynthesis is a complex series of reactions catalysed by the green leaf pigment chlorophyll, but in terms of end results the reaction can be represented as:—

$$6\ CO_2 + 6\ H_2O + energy \longrightarrow C_6H_{12}O_6 + 6\ O_2$$

| carbon dioxide | water | | glucose | oxygen |

Glucose is one of the simplest of the single ring (monosaccharide) sugars.

Glucose

325

Cane sugar or sucrose, the most commonly encountered of the sugars is a disaccharide, that is, it consists of two linked monosaccharide sugars, glucose and fructose.

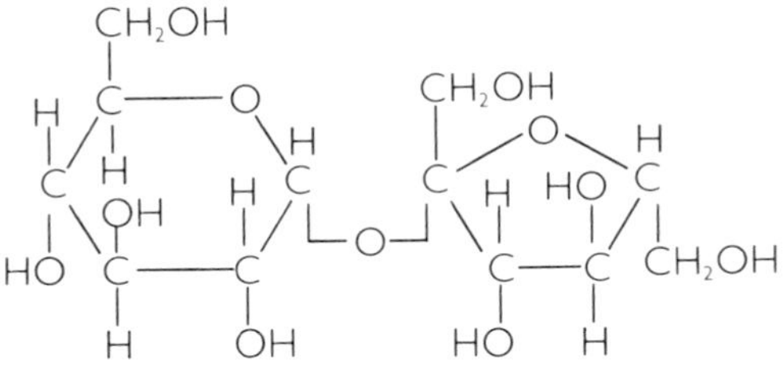

Sucrose

Sugars contain a great deal of energy, hence their misuse in certain home-made incendiary mixtures. However, because of their extreme solubility in water, sugars are not necessarily the most convenient energy storage compounds for plants, and carbohydrates are stored in large quantities in the form of polysaccharides such as starch. Starch is a natural polymer of glucose which is, in general less soluble in water. It is however, easily broken down to glucose, which can then quickly be utilised by the plant's metabolism when required.

Cellulose

Cellulose is an insoluble natural polymer of glucose which forms most of the structure of plant cell walls. Cotton is almost pure cellulose, and it is also the major ingredient of paper. Wood consists of cellulose, hemi-celluloses of related structure and lignin.

Cellulose is of significance in fires because many traditional materials contain it in large quantities. Almost all flammable solids of a vegetable origin owe much of their flammability to cellulose or to related carbohydrates. However, although natural vegetable materials such as wood, cardboard, paper, straw, hay and cotton are all cellulosic and flammable, their behaviour in fires depends to a large extent upon a) water content and b) surface area. Not only is the burning behaviour of, for example a baulk of green elm wood totally different from that of finely divided cotton fibres, but the end products will differ too.

Proteins

The proteins are another large group of naturally occurring polymers. Although proteins occur in plants, they are most likely to be encountered in the form of items manufactured from animal tissue. Leather, ivory, wool, silk, fur and feathers are all predominantly protein.

Proteins are generally not particularly flammable and tend to self-extinguish when subjected to limited heating. However, they may be associated with other more flammable materials, particularly fats, which may modify their burning behaviour. Proteins consist of mixed polymers of amino acids which have the general formula:—

$$R-\underset{\underset{NH_2}{|}}{\overset{\overset{H}{|}}{C}}-C\overset{\diagup O}{\diagdown_{OH}}$$

Amino acids link together in chains by means of peptide links, in which the amino group of one molecule links to the carboxyl group of the next molecule.

Nineteen or twenty different amino acids are normally present in each type of protein. There are between thirty and several thousand amino acid residues linked in a specific sequence in each protein molecule.

Proteins form much of the muscle tissue of the body and are also encountered as enzymes. However, it is the fibrous proteins such as keratin, fibrin and collagen which form the basis of most of the protein artifacts encountered at fire scenes.

Keratin

Keratin, the protein of wool and feathers, can be regarded as typical of all the fibrous proteins. It does not burn freely, but decomposes with a characteristic smell when subjected to limited heat. Under the conditions of a well established room fire, keratin burns fairly well, and in conditions of limited ventilation, a complex mixture of pyrolysis products is formed.

Nitrogen is present in the molecules of the constituent amino acids and nitrogen-containing pyrolysis products, including hydrogen cyanide are produced. There is evidence that more hydrogen cyanide is produced by burning wool than would be produced by an equivalent weight of the notorious polyurethane.

Fats

The third major group of biological chemicals is the lipids (fats). These are soluble in solvents such as ether and are relatively insoluble in water.

The lipids most commonly encountered in fires are the neutral fats or triglycerides. This group includes cooking fats and oils, linseed oil and human body fats. Triglycerides are the esters of glycerol and fatty acids.

| Glycerol | Fatty acid | Monoglyceride |

A natural triglyceride is normally esterified with three different fatty acids:—

The three fatty acids in this compound are palmitic acid, oleic acid and stearic acid respectively.

The soap manufacturing industry uses natural triglycerides which are split or saponified, releasing glycerol (which is subsequently used for the manufacture of explosives), and the fatty acids in the form of their sodium or potassium salts.

Triglycerides from vegetable sources, particularly the seed oils, tend to esterify with a predominance of unsaturated fatty acids. This has two effects upon the properties of the oil; (i) it tends to have a low melting point and (ii) it tends to be more susceptible to oxidation. Oils of this type are known as drying oils because of their tendency to undergo oxidative polymerisation forming a solid polymer. This property of oils such as linseed oil, has been

Chemistry of Flammable Materials

Saturated fatty acids (no double bonds)

		Source
Butyric	C_3H_7 COOH	Mainly animal fats such as butter and lard
Caproic	C_5H_{11}COOH	but also some vegetable oils such as
Caprylic	C_7H_{15}COOH	peanut oil.
Capric	C_9H_{19}COOH	
Lauric	$C_{11}H_{23}$COOH	
Myristic	$C_{13}H_{27}$COOH	
Palmitic	$C_{15}H_{31}$COOH	
Stearic	$C_{17}H_{35}$COOH	
Arachidic	$C_{19}H_{39}$COOH	

Unsaturated fatty acids

One double bond		Mainly vegetable oils, particularly the
Oleic	$C_{17}H_{33}$COOH	drying oils such as linseed, rapeseed and
Two double bonds		cottonseed oil.
Linoleic	$C_{17}H_{31}$COOH	
Three double bonds		
Linolenic	$C_{17}H_{29}$COOH	
Four double bonds		
Arachidonic	$C_{19}H_{31}$COOH	

known to the paint and linoleum industries for many years. An unfortunate property of drying oils is their ability to self-heat. Linseed oil absorbed in a porous material such as cotton waste or polishing rag, can steadily oxidise, and the consequent rise in temperature can result in self-ignition under certain circumstances (see Chapters 17 and 19).

Cooking fats and oils

These triglyceride mixtures are of interest to the fire examiner because they are frequently the first materials to be ignited in accidental domestic fires. Cooking oils are used at temperatures of about 200°C and they ignite at temperatures between about 310 and 360°C. Hot cooking fats and oils burn fiercely and fires and personal injuries frequently occur in this type of fire, due to improper first aid fire fighting measures. Despite well publicised warnings, many people are injured each year because they attempt to extinguish burning fat with water which flash vaporises, scattering burning oil with almost explosive violence. Other injuries have been caused by accidents resulting from attempts to carry burning cooking utensils out of the house.

References

(1) D. M. Wharry and R. Hirst. Fire Technology, Chemistry and Combustion. 1974 IFE.

(2) Manual of Firemanship. Part 1 HMSO.

(3) A. M. Hughes. Chemistry in balance. University Tutorial Press 1981.

(4) A. Atkinson. Certificate Chemistry. Longman 1977.

(5) Holderness and Lambert. A New Certificate Chemistry. Heinemann Educational Books. 1977.

(6) J. F. Flynn. Plastics, how they increase fire losses. FEJ 1977. 7.

(7) E. G. Butcher. Plastics and fire and increasing risk. FEJ 1975. 24.

(8) H. A. Frank. Lead alkyl components as discriminating factors in the comparison of gasolines. JFS Soc. 20, 285.

(9) D. F. Nelson. Petrol fires in closed rooms. JFS Soc. 10, 3.

(10) P. Smith. Polyurethane foam hazards. FEJ 1976, 40.

(11) G. J. Bibby. Industrial fires involving polyurethane foam. FEJ 1973, 29.

(12) W. D. Woolley, S. A. Ames, A. I. Pitt and K. Buckland. The ignition and burning characteristics of fabric covered foams. BRE CP30, 78.

Chapter 21

Laboratory Examinations

The laboratory can provide valuable evidence to substantiate or refute theories formed at the scene, but laboratory examinations and analyses are meaningless unless adequate background information is obtained. For this reason, any investigator who carries out a half-hearted search and then sends a bag-full of debris to the laboratory is wasting his own and the scientists' time.

To make the most effective use of any laboratory facility available to him, the investigator must:—

(a) Know exactly what he is trying to establish and make this clear in his submission form or letter.

(b) Take the questioned sample from the correct place. If the sample is supposedly from the seat of the fire, totally misleading information will result from the analysis if the exact seat of fire has not been located.

(c) Provide one or more meaningful control samples. These can be particularly important when analysis is required. (Chapter 23, Laboratory Analysis).

(d) Label and package the samples adequately and unambiguously.

(e) Provide background information, plans and photographs. If a particular appliance is suspected of having caused the fire, photographs showing it in position are valuable and sometimes essential for an effective laboratory investigation.

Fire Debris Samples

Debris from the supposed seat of the fire is normally submitted for analysis for volatile fire accelerants but, where appropriate, the samples are searched under laboratory conditions for items of significance. If the seat of the fire is known, it follows that whatever caused the fire must be in the debris from that area, unless it has been removed. It is not normally possible to make a detailed examination of the debris at the fire scene because of limited lighting and other problems. It might be supposed that a detailed laboratory search of the debris from the seat of the fire

331

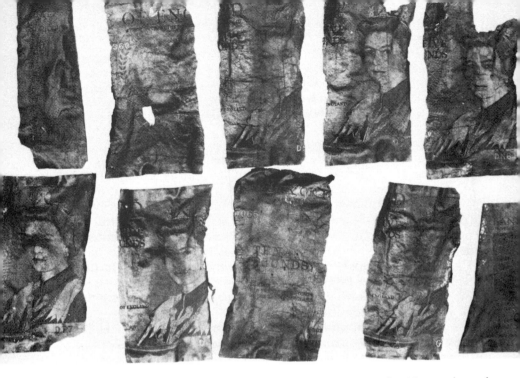

Plate 21A. The original print or writing may remain legible on charred paper. Print on good quality paper tends to remain more legible than that on cheap paper which has a lower inorganic dressing content.

Bank-notes can remain recognisable after severe fires. Photograph B. R. G. Roberts.

should always establish the cause. This is not the case, partly because many items which cause fires are flammable or fragile and partly because the debris is disturbed during the sampling process. Therefore any information which might have been obtained from the relative positions of items, is lost.

Examination of debris

Debris samples from fire seats are normally analysed. After analysis, the debris may be searched if there is reason to suppose that a useful purpose will be served by this. If it is known that the items being sought are fairly robust, e.g. articles of jewellery, coins, fragments of glass, or cartridge cases, then sieving can be employed. However, sieving has the serious disadvantage that it causes fragile items to break up and since most materials become fragile when burnt, sieving can destroy evidence.

An alternative to sieving is to spread the debris carefully and thinly in shallow dishes with an instrument such as a spatula, putty knife or pointing trowel. Searching is carried out under bright, uniform, white illumination and items are often more recognisable and somewhat less fragile if the debris is allowed to dry prior to the search. However, the opposite approach of washing the debris, either by decantation or by means of a steady stream of water on a post mortem table, can prove useful.

Debris may be searched for particular items whose presence may confirm or refute the statement of a witness. In such cases the particular physical properties of the items being sought can be used to locate them. For example, glass fragments reflect light and can be best located if the debris is illuminated by a powerful oblique beam of light, small iron and steel items are best recovered with a magnet and small pieces of unburnt paper fluoresce in ultraviolet light.

In most debris examinations, the search is for anything which could possibly have caused the fire or have been concerned in its spread. Matches, cigarette ends, parts of incendiary devices and charred, crumpled paper can be identified in quite burnt debris.

Incendiary Devices

The laboratory involvement with incendiary devices is at three possible levels:—

(a) To identify the questioned item as part of an incendiary device.

(b) To provide information of the mode of action and possible source of the device.

(c) To link the device with others from similar incidents or with materials taken from the possession of a suspect.

Incendiary devices normally consist of three parts:—

(a) *A delayed action device.* Clocks, watches, parking meter timers, modified spring clothes pegs and electronic circuits have been used, and the remains of such timers are normally easily recognisable as such. Timers can, however, be constructed of materials which are likely to be consumed in the fire, but fortunately these timers are notoriously unreliable and are unpopular with survival-conscious arsonists.

(b) *An igniter.* Mechanical devices involving mousetraps and cartridges or elaborate spring-loaded mechanisms, are sometimes encountered, but normally igniters are electrical. A typical electrical igniter consists of a battery wired in series with the timer, and with a hot wire filament such as a gas lighter element or a light bulb, with the glass envelope removed. The filament of the igniter is in close proximity to the incendiary material.

(c) *The incendiary material.* The incendiary material is normally a mixture of solid oxidising and reducing agents. Methods of testing for the residues produced after ignition of typical incendiary mixtures are described in Chapter 23, Laboratory Analysis.

Recognition of incendiary devices

Successful incendiary devices can sometimes be difficult to recognise because they have been subjected to considerable heat. However, this heat damage can form one basis of recognition, since it is likely that the device will have been subjected to higher temperatures than its immediate surroundings. A successful device will also be located at the exact seat of the fire, and this should draw attention to it. Timing devices of all types, particularly if they are associated with wires, should be regarded with suspicion. Residues of incendiary mixtures, if detected, provide categorical evidence in most cases, that an incendiary device had been present.

Molotov Cocktails

Molotov Cocktails consist of glass bottles partially or wholly filled with a flammable liquid, with a means of ignition such as a porous wick inserted into the neck. The wick of the device is ignited and the bomb is thrown violently to smash against the target.

Fragments of the bomb are scattered by the combined effects of the impetus and the blast effect of the fire ball. For this reason it may not be possible to find all of the fragments of a successful device but in general, sufficient fragments are found for identification purposes.

In the laboratory the fragments and the associated debris are analysed to establish which flammable liquid had been used. The bottle may then be partially reassembled in order to identify the type, and possibly to provide linking evidence with bottles taken from the suspect.

The material inserted into the neck is normally cloth, and it may be possible to identify the type of material used and to link it with a control sample from the suspect. In many severe fires it has been found that the fabric inserted into the neck of bottles used as petrol bombs is unburnt in the region where it is tightly packed. Since in most cases the wick has been torn from a larger piece of fabric, it can be possible to link the two uniquely by means of physical fit evidence.

When not all of the bottle is available, useful evidence can still be obtained from the two regions most commonly found; the neck and the base. From the neck it can be established whether the bottle had been screw-capped or crown-corked, and the ubiquitous milk bottle can be recognised instantly. The neck size may also provide identification evidence. The base of the bottle bears the manufacturer's code marks, and it is possible to calculate the circumference from very small fragments of the edge of the base.

Containers

Extraneous containers found at fire scenes are frequently submitted to laboratories for examination. The containers are in the first place subjected to analysis in an effort to establish the original contents.

The containers most popular with arsonists are five litre and one gallon rectangular cans. These cans are commonly used for the retailing of motor oil and are painted with designs and slogans characteristic of the particular oil. In the case of cans which have remained upright throughout the fire it is normal for all of the paint on the outside of the can to have charred to an almost uniform grey colour. Under different lighting conditions such as ultraviolet, infra red and laser illumination, the original inscription can sometimes be discerned. On occasions when writing is not visible, parts of the pattern may be seen, enabling the scientist to identify the can against a reference collection held in the laboratory. More specific identification may be possible if price labels, or labels referring to the place of purchase or manufacture remain. Many paper labels, particularly those on bottles, bear along the edge a code of slits which specifically identifies the place where the container was filled, the date, the machine involved and possibly additional information. These

Plate 21B. Petrol can. Containers involved in fires may show lines indicating the volume of liquid originally present. The geometry of the lines indicate the orientation of the container at the time of the fire. This can had contained some petrol and had been horizontal at the time of the fire. Photograph R. H. Ide.

codes are specific to each particular manufacturer, and can be interpreted by certain employees of the company involved.

Other information from containers

By examination of the char patterns on a container it is often possible to establish how full it had been at the time of the fire, whether it had been upright or lying on its side, and whether it had been sealed during the fire. (Plate 21B).

The fullness of a metal container prior to the fire can often be estimated from a horizontal line which divides the upper, heavily heat damaged part of the can (light grey) from the lower, somewhat less heat damaged part (a darker grey). If the liquid has remained in the container throughout the fire the lower section of the container may bear undamaged paintwork. The orientation of the container can also be deduced from this liquid line.

Other evidence of orientation can be obtained from sides of the container protected by the floor during the fire and from the direction of liquid trickles of plastic or melted metal.

Clocks and Watches

Estimates of times of burning are notoriously unreliable, and one approach in the estimation of ignition times is to take account of the times shown by stopped clocks and watches. However, if such evidence is important, the clock or watch in question should be examined in order to establish exactly why it stopped. For example, it has been of significance in a number of murder enquiries to establish whether the victim's watch stopped as a result of shock during the violence of the murder, or as a result of high temperatures when the murderer attempted to destroy the body by burning. It is also important to establish that the watch or clock was wound and, therefore, likely to have been running at the time of the fire.

Plate 21C. Care must be taken when attempting to read any significance into the time shown by a stopped clock. This clock did not stop at 6.30, the hands have dropped to that position because the concentric spindles have partly melted. Photograph M. J. Cooke.

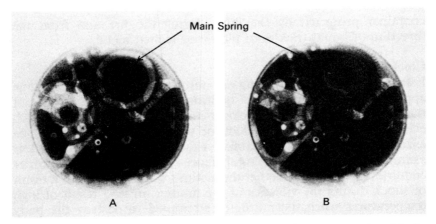

Plate 21D. These two X-ray photographs show the same watch, with the mainspring fully wound in A and fully run down in B.

It is not always desirable to dismantle items for examination and X-ray techniques can be invaluable. Photographs B. R. G. Roberts.

Reasons for failure of clocks and watches in fires

Fires tend to cause short circuits in buildings resulting eventually in the failure of the main fuse, causing all mains electric clocks to stop at the same time. This can be a very useful indication, particularly if it can be established where in the electrical wiring the short circuit had occurred.

Watches and some clocks often stop as a result of the softening of the face lens which collapses onto the hands. The part of the internal mechanism of a conventional clock most sensitive to heat is the balance spring. This fine spring can lose its elasticity at elevated temperatures and the clock or watch will stop.

It is important to establish whether the main spring is fully or partially wound in the stopped clock or watch. This examination can be carried out by partially dismantling the clock or watch, or by taking X-ray photographs.

Electrical Apparatus

The examination of electrical apparatus has been dealt with in detail in Chapter 18, Electricity.

Examination of Hair and Clothing for Scorching

In cases of arson, particularly when liquid fire accelerants have been used, it is possible for the culprit to scorch his hair and clothing during the ignition of the building.

Hair

Human hair consists mainly of the protein keratin, which decomposes when heated. During the decomposition, gases are produced which cause the affected part of the hair filament to swell forming a brittle hollow cinder. Parts of the cindered hair may fall off, but portions recognisable by microscopical examination are likely to remain attached for several hours or more.

It is normal for a person in the vicinity of a large indoor fire to bend forwards to protect his face from the heat. As a result, hairs on the back of the head are more likely to become singed under these conditions. Singeing to hairs at the front of the head may occur during the initial heat flash on ignition of a volatile liquid fire accelerants, such as petrol, although there are many possible innocent explanations.

The hairs on the backs of the hands can also be scorched by proximity to flames but sampling of these hairs for laboratory examination can present difficulties.

Because of the fragile nature of singed hairs, it is common for some of them to break off and remain on the jacket, jersey or shirt of the criminal. Examination of the outside of the collar and the insides of the cuffs of the garment may provide valuable evidence of recent proximity to heat.

Scorching of Clothing

The outer garments of a person who has been in the proximity of severe heat may show evidence of scorching. Synthetic materials such as nylon, Acrilan and Terylene show evidence of heating effects much more clearly than do natural fibres such as cotton.

Most fabrics when examined under a microscope show many loose protruding fibres. These fibres are very vulnerable to heat damage. Regions of the garment which have been in or close to flames show evidence of melting of the protruding fibres which may shrink, distort or form blobs on their ends.

More severe heating of synthetic fabrics will result in localised shrinking, stiffening and possibly discolouration. Contact with sparks or small flying brands of burning material can cause small holes to be melted into the material. Natural fabrics such as

339

cotton do not melt but evidence of charred fibres may be found by microscopical examination.

Legitimate heat damage

Articles of clothing can be scorched by ironing or other heat treatment processes. The damage caused by careless ironing can normally be recognised by its position on raised or thickened regions of the garment and possibly by its characteristic shape showing the outline of one side of an iron.

Other fabric heat treatment processes normally affect the whole of the article of clothing and for this reason suspected fire damage to the fabric should be compared with fabric from other regions of the garment. Protected fabric such as that under collars and lapels and inside the garment should always be compared with the region of supposed fire damage.

Damage similar to that caused by sparks from the fire can be caused by carelessly discarded cigarette ends. Spillage of acids too can cause damage which may mimic burns. When possible, tests should be carried out on similar material, or on an agreed region of the article of clothing involved.

When a building fire has been started by low-level ignition of liquid fire accelerants, scorching may be observed on the stitching or laces of the shoes of the criminal. Scorching may also be seen on the under surface of the shoes but this should not be confused with the marks caused by the treading out of cigarette ends.

Examination of Clothing for Trace Evidence

Criminals, including arsonists, who break into buildings, normally do so either by breaking a window or by forcing a door. During these processes, minute fragments of glass or flakes of paint may be deposited on their clothing. In addition, fibres, footprints, instrument marks and blood stains may be left at the scene of the crime.

Clothing examined in the laboratory is normally drawn or photographed, and detailed notes are made. The presence of any smears, stains or visible particulate material is recorded. Loose particulate material is then collected from the garment under laboratory conditions. The surface debris and pocket sweepings are placed in petri dishes for microscopical examination. Material which appears to be of evidential significance, such as glass fragments, paint flakes or anything else which might help to establish guilt or innocence, is recovered from the bulk of the debris for subsequent detailed examination.

Evidence from glass
Sheets of glass, although indistinguishable by normal examination, exhibit wide variations in refractive index. Even the rigorously controlled float glass process produces glass whose refractive index varies significantly between acceptable limits.

Refractive index is a measure of how much a transparent material bends light and is defined as:—

$$\mu = \frac{\text{sine } i}{\text{sine } r}$$

Where μ is the refractive index, i is the angle of incidence and r is the angle of refraction.

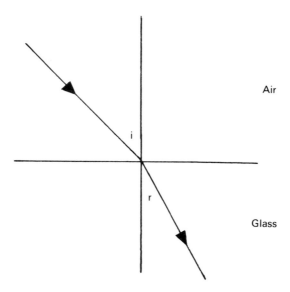

The refractive index of minute fragments of glass recovered from the clothing of the suspect can be measured by a technique, which depends upon the fact that glass is invisible when immersed in a liquid of exactly the same refractive index[1].

The refractive index of a liquid falls as its temperature rises. The fragments of glass are immersed individually in a suitable liquid under a hot stage microscope and the temperature is raised until the glass disappears. The refractive index of the glass can then be calculated by consideration of the optical properties of the liquid involved. For increased accuracy the disappearance and reappearance temperatures of the glass are measured.

The method is accurate, non-destructive and can be used to measure the refractive index of fragments of glass about one hundredth of the size of a pin's head. Control fragments of glass from the window at the point of entry are measured by the same technique. If glass from the two sources agrees in refractive index, it is evidence that the glass on the clothing could have originated from the window in question. The strength of the evidence depends upon the rarity of the glass. Additional discrimination can be obtained by chemical analysis, fluorescence measurements and interferometric surface curvature comparison.[2-3]

Evidence from Paint

Small flakes of paint may be recovered from the clothing or possibly from an instrument such as a screwdriver, which had been used to force a door or window frame.

Flakes of paint which appear to be of significance are selected for examination. Paint flakes often show a layer structure which is indicative of the history of the object from which they originated.

This layer structure can be clearly seen by cutting a section of the paint flake, and viewing the sectioned edge through a microscope with top illumination.

The flake is compared with a flake from a control sample taken from the door or window in question.

A paint flake from a domestic door may include many layers of paint of widely varying colours. It is unfortunate that many householders choose to paint their window frames white. A paint flake from this source would show successive layers of white or cream, often interspersed with layers of dirt.

Microscopy using straight-forward white light illumination can provide much evidence about the paint structure. Layer colours and thicknesses can easily be determined; inclusions will be observed in particular layers and small splashes of paint of a different colour may sometimes be present at a layer interface. Illumination using different visible colours and ultraviolet light, strengthen the discriminating power of the comparison technique, and stains or chemical reagents are also commonly used.

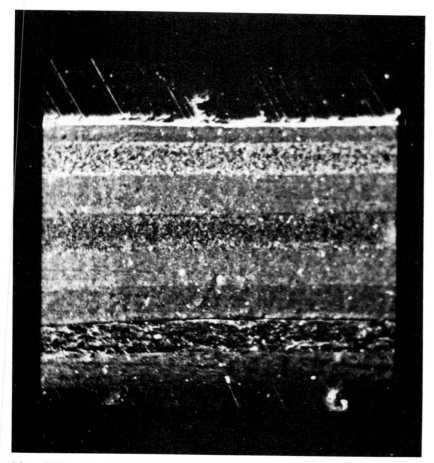

Plate 21E. Seen from the edge, the layers of paint in a paint flake record the painting history of the object from which the flake originated.
Using a scanning electron microscope, differences can be seen even between successive layers of white paint. Photograph J. M. Dubery.

If the recovered flake of paint has several characteristic layers which agree in all tested respects with flakes of paint from the control sample, then the microscopical techniques described may be more than adequate to establish that the two flakes had originated from the same source. However, the forensic chemist has a whole battery of techniques available to him, and in cases where the recovered paint is less characteristic, he may choose to carry out one or more methods of analysis or measurement[4]-[6].

Other Examinations
Other examinations carried out in the laboratory include:—

Comparisons of footwear impressions
Marks left at scenes of crime may be enhanced electrostatically or by means of laser photography[7]-[9]. Footwear impressions may be identified or compared with test impressions made using shoes or boots taken from the suspect. It is possible for the laboratory to provide conclusive evidence linking suspected footwear with the scene of a crime.

Examination of instrument marks
Imperfections in the edges of instruments, such as screwdrivers used to force entry into buildings, can result in unique marks to the door or window frame. Casts of the instrument marks can be compared microscopically with laboratory test impressions made by the suspected instrument. A comparison microscope is necessary for this type of work which can again provide conclusive evidence to link the suspected article with the scene of the crime[10],[11].

Examination of vehicle traces
Vehicles used during the commission of crimes are frequently damaged in the process. Pieces of trim, paint, filler, glass or plastic left at the scene can provide evidence to identify the model and age of the vehicle involved. These same materials can later be compared with samples from a suspected vehicle to provide linking or elimination evidence.

Blood
Blood stains left at scenes of crime can be grouped by any combination of a number of systems to provide evidence to implicate or eliminate a suspect. It is sometimes possible to establish the sex of the donor from a small stain.

Fibres and hairs
Fibres and hairs are commonly found at scenes of crime and are of particular significance in cases of murder and assault. Valuable

identification and linking evidence can be obtained by the examination or analysis of fibres. Hairs can be of particular evidential significance if they have been dyed, or are in some other way abnormal.

Handwriting

Examples of handwriting relating to a crime can be compared with control samples properly taken from suspects. In addition, sophisticated methods can be used to recognise or decipher alterations and erasures in documents of all types.

Conclusion

Much physical evidence can remain at a scene of crime, even when the greater part of the building has been destroyed by fire. If properly sampled, materials and items of evidential value can sometimes link the criminal conclusively with the scene. However, by its very nature, trace evidence tends to be transient and can easily be destroyed or rendered valueless during a preliminary examination of the scene, or by well intentioned cleaning up procedures. On more than one occasion, office cleaners have arrived at the scenes of safe breakings and have swept up all traces of safe ballast, polishing the furniture and removing fingerprints and footprints.

It is important for firemen to be aware of the potential value of various types of physical evidence. While in certain cases it may be necessary to destroy evidence for strategic fire fighting reasons, the decision to destroy it should be made in knowledge rather than ignorance.

References

(1) S. M. Ojena and P. R. De Forest. Precise refractive index determination by the immersion method using phase contrast microscopy and the Mettler hot stage. J. For. Sci. Soc 1972. V.12.315.
(2) J. Andrasko and A. C. Maehly. The discrimination between samples of window glass by combining physical and chemical techniques. J. For. Sci. 1978.V.23.250.
(3) R. J. Dudley, C. R. Howden, T. J. Taylor and K. W. Smalldon. The discrimination and classification of small fragments of window and non-window glasses using energy dispersive X-ray Fluorescence Spectrometry. X-ray Spectrom 1980 V9.119.

(4) D. Crown. The Forensic examination of paints and pigments. pub Thomas.

(5) Paint Testing Manual. ASTM Tech Publication.

(6) P. M. Fisk. Advanced Paint Chemistry. pub Leonard.

(7) J. S. Brennan. The visualisation of shoemarks using the Electrostatic Detection Apparatus. MPFSL Report 10.

(8) K. G. Barnett and B. R. G. Roberts. The use of the electrostatic document analyser for the detection of latent footwear impressions. HOCRE Tech Note 88 1978.

(9) K. E. Greer. Some applications of an argon laser in Forensic Science. For. Sci. Intern (1982) 20 179.

(10) S. J. Butcher and P. D. Pugh. A study of marks made by bolt cutters. J. For. Sci. Soc. 1975.15.115.

(11) R. O. Andahl. The examination of saw marks. J. For. Sci. Soc. (1978) 18 31.

Chapter 22

Matches

From the point of view of the fire investigator, the main aspect of interest in the study of matches, is the comparison of those recovered from the scene with matches taken from the possession of a suspect. However, a knowledge of their physical and chemical properties can be of value in establishing the causes of some fires.

Matches are sold either in books or in boxes, and can be made of wood, cardboard, or waxed paper. Whilst book matches dominate the market in the USA and Canada, boxed matches retain their widespread popularity in Europe.

Matches consist of a deflagrating head borne on a stick or splint. The head consists of a solidified paste of a composition of low spontaneous ignition temperature. This is ignited by abrasion on either a rough surface in the case of strike-anywhere matches or on a chemically active friction paint for safety matches.

The stick
With the exception of book matches, most match sticks are constructed of wood. The wood used almost universally in most countries of the world is that from one of several species of aspen. Aspen wood is white, straight grained and relatively free from knots. It also has good burning properties.

The match sticks or splints can be made most economically from the tree trunk by a spiral planing or peeling process. The tree trunk is rotated in contact with a sharp blade which planes the trunk into thin layers of veneer. The veneer which is usually about 2–3 mm thick, is then chopped into splints.

Careful examination of most match splints will indicate which surfaces resulted from the peeling and which from the chopping process. Most match splints made by this process tend to be slightly rhomboidal in cross-section. The 'peel' surfaces tend to be smooth and perfectly parallel whilst the chop surfaces may bear transverse striation marks, and will not be perfectly flat.

From the point of view of linking wood splint matches dropped at a fire scene with those found in the possession of a suspect, identification of the species of wood is unfortunately seldom likely to be of value because of the popularity of aspen wood in this application. There is considerable variation in splint lengths used and it is therefore possible for relatively unburnt matches to be tentatively identified from their splint length and thickness.

The splints are normally subjected to an automatic sorting process which removes small fragments and broken splints. This process and the subsequent transportation to the match machine, tends to shuffle the splints making it highly improbable that matches cut from adjacent areas of veneer will end up in the same box.

Afterglow prevention
From the point of view of fire prevention it is important that the splint should not continue to smoulder after the flame has been extinguished. To this end all British and American matches are impregnated with a fire retardant such as phosphoric acid or diammonium hydrogen phosphate.

Insertion marks
The splints are punched into lines of holes in the dipping chain of the match machine.

The insertion mark in the undipped end of the match normally remains clearly visible and the length of the insertion mark may be characteristic of the manufacturer.

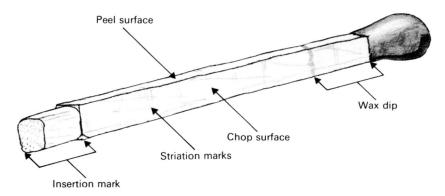

Figure 22.1. Machine-made wood splint matches show features imposed by the method of manufacture. Increasingly standardised techniques are leading to greater uniformity between manufacturers, but significant differences exist. Figure D. S. Loxley.

Wax dip

The heat of the burning match head would not normally ignite an untreated wood splint, and to ensure that proper ignition will occur, the splints are dipped in wax. The dipping takes place on the match machine and adjacent matches on the same bar of the match chain are dipped to precisely the same depth and finally end up in the same box.

The depth of wax dip is typically about 15 mm but considerable variation can occur even between matches made by the same manufacturer on the same machine.

Match head dipping

The splints are dipped into a water-dispersed paste of head composition to a depth of about 3 mm and the route of the match chain causes the splints to invert to allow the paste to run down the splints slightly. The match chain then doubles backwards and

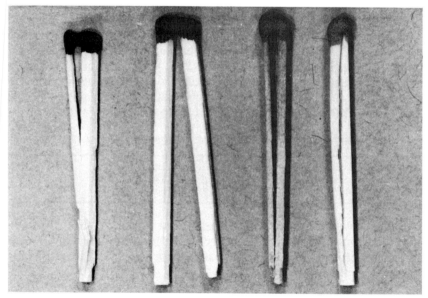

Plate 22A.   Bent or split splints can result in defective match sticks in which abnormally shaped double heads may be formed.

Abnormally shaped heads can be more prone to accidental ignition by head to head friction than normal match heads. Photograph B. R. G. Roberts.

forwards allowing the match heads to harden somewhat, before the matches are punched out from the bars of the chain into match boxes.

During the dipping process it is possible for distorted or misaligned splints to come into close proximity to adjacent splints, causing paste to bridge between two match heads. Such defective matches, predictably known as 'doubles' in the industry, can have undesirable properties such as a greater tendency to ignite as a result of head-to-head friction inside the match box. (Plate 21A).

Another fault results from unduly rapid drying of the match head paste. If this occurs, match heads can be formed which have a hard outer layer. Matches having this fault may spit or explode when struck, scattering hot fragments. Matches manufactured in hot countries are particularly susceptible to this problem.

Composition of match heads

Matches are of two distinct types; safety and strike-anywhere. Both types depend upon the reaction between potassium chlorate and a readily oxidised fuel. The heads of strike-anywhere matches consist of a mixture containing potassium chlorate and the so-called phosphorus sesquisulphide (P_4S_3). In addition, siliceous materials such as diatomaceous earths and ground glass are normally present. This type of match composition is almost white in colour, and dyes such as eosin or rhodamine, are added.

THE COMPOSITION OF TYPICAL STRIKE-ANYWHERE MATCHES

28% Potassium chlorate	10% Zinc oxide
13% Phosphorus sesquisulphide	20% Ground glass
15% Ferric oxide	14% Animal glue

Safety match heads have potassium chlorate as a major ingredient and ignition is achieved by abrasion against a friction paint, which contains red phosphorus, on the side of the box or book.

COMPOSITION OF TYPICAL SAFETY MATCH HEADS

51% Potassium chlorate	6% Black iron oxide
15% Flour glass	5% Sulphur
11% Animal glue	4% Manganese dioxide
7% Zinc oxide	1% Potassium dichromate

Typical friction paint applied in strips to safety match books or boxes contains about 50% amorphous red phosphorus, 20% synthetic or natural adhesive and an abrasive such as flour glass.

The composition of match heads varies considerably, particularly with regard to the minor ingredients.

Book matches

For safety reasons no book matches of the strike-anywhere variety are manufactured in either Britain or the USA. Book matches are analogous to wood splint safety matches, the only difference being that they are constructed on a comb of cardboard or wood veneer.

Book matches appear to be more susceptible to misuse than boxed matches, for example, users commonly ignore the instruction to close the flap before striking. This can result in the accidental ignition of the remaining matches in the book. Incidents have also occurred in which books of matches have interleafed allowing the striking surface of one book to come into contact with the match heads of another book.

Vesta matches

These matches, which are popular in Latin countries, are wax impregnated twists of cotton threads or paper. The matches are somewhat fragile but burn steadily and consistently with less tendency to self-extinguish than typical wood splint matches.

Speciality matches

Matches can be manufactured with heads or splints of any colour and long splinted matches with bizarre colour combinations are produced for publicity purposes. Matches are also manufactured which produce perfume, fumigant or dense visible smoke. Matches are manufactured with enlarged bulbs having a very high charcoal content. Such matches can burn without flame but with a strong smouldering glow suitable for the ignition of safety fuses in all weather conditions.

Large bulb matches designed to burn with coloured flames are marketed under the name 'Bengal' and are intended for use as indoor fireworks.

Although it is not unknown for 'Bengal' and other speciality matches to be used for arson, it normally transpires that when such matches have been used, children were the culprits. However, a case has been reported in which a chain of 'Bengal' matches was set up with the intention of forming a delay fuse[1].

Ignition of Matches

Whilst it is intended that matches should ignite when properly struck on a suitable surface, it is a cause for concern to manufacturers that matches should not ignite unintentionally. The major British and US manufacturers produce matches of a high standard which are unlikely to ignite by head to head friction or by being subjected to relatively high temperatures. However, head to head friction in vigorously shaken boxes has been known to ignite matches, particularly those of the strike-anywhere type. Defective matches with abnormally shaped heads are, as has been mentioned previously, more susceptible to such ignition.

While it is well known that strike-anywhere matches can be struck on most hard, dry, rough surfaces, there is a widespread misconception that safety matches can only be struck on the friction paint surfaces applied to the box or book. In fact, although the ignition temperature of a safety match (180°–200°C) is higher than that of a strike-anywhere match (120°–150°C) it is often possible to strike safety matches on smooth surfaces of materials of low thermal conductivity such as glass or cardboard. The successful ignition of a safety match on a sheet of glass normally leaves a characteristic trail of associated fine scratches terminating in flare residues.

Matches have been used in association with hot surfaces in arson attempts. The glass envelope of a round 60 watt incandescent light bulb reaches a temperature of about 185°C and the newer mushroom bulbs can attain temperatures in excess of 250°C. Matches placed in contact with light bulbs can be ignited by the relatively high temperature and may be intended by a criminal to fall and ignite flammable materials beneath. Such attempts may be recognised by the presence of flare residues on the light bulb; confirmation by laboratory analysis is essential, since innocent residues can be confused with these.

Comparison of matches

It may be of considerable value to find evidence to link matches found at the scene of a fire with those taken from the possession of a suspect. Unfortunately matches from the scenes of fires are often well-burnt, wet and dirty. When fires are started by matches

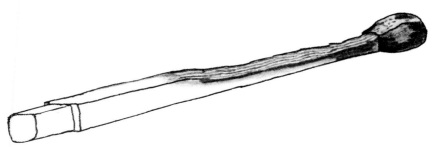

Figure 22.2. The appearance of a match which has burnt whilst lying on a flat horizontal surface. Many matches burnt in this manner may be found in the vicinity of a fire started by children. Figure D. S. Loxley.

struck out of doors, the chances of finding useful matches for comparison purposes increases considerably. Matches struck out of doors are often blown out by the wind or extinguished by the rain. When fires are started by children, evidence may be found that several matches have been ignited and then thrown.

Comparison of the splint
When intact matches are available for comparison, the simplest and most easily measured variable is the splint length. Splint lengths are generally fairly consistent throughout samples from a particular nominal type, but variations of length amongst matches in a single batch may be found.

Other measurements which can be of value are the thickness of the splint in the two directions 'peel' and 'chop'.

The precision with which these two measurements can be made depends to a large extent upon the quality of the wood. Wood with an uneven grain produces matches of irregular shape and inconsistent thickness.

Two other measurements are possible; the length of the insertion mark and of the wax dip.

The insertion mark is easily measured, provided that the match has not suffered prolonged soaking in water, but it is unlikely to provide much evidence to differentiate between different batches made by the same manufacturer.

The wax dip length can be measured by dipping the match stick into a water soluble dye such as rhodamine, washing it and measuring the undyed portion of the match. It is however, by no means always possible to measure this distance accurately.

Other examinations of the splint which may be made include identification of the wood (almost always aspen), dye colour and a study of abnormalities or imperfections.

Dyed boxed match splints are sufficiently unusual to be of good evidential value in themselves, but more exact comparison may be made by extracting the dye with a suitable solvent (e.g. dimethyl formamide) and running the extract on a TLC plate (q.v.).

Abnormalities in matches include a predominance of curved splints, an unusual cross-sectional shape, discolouration, and pronounced striation marks on the peel surface.

Comparison of the head
It is not often that the fire investigator is fortunate enough to find live matches at the scene of a suspected arson but it does happen occasionally. More frequently, matches are found in which most of the head has burned but a ring of unburnt head material remains at the neck of the match.

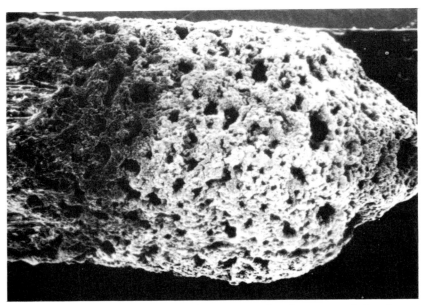

Plate 22B. The microscopical appearance of a burnt match head may help in the identification of the original type of match.

This photograph was taken using a scanning electron microscope operating at a low magnification level. Photograph B. German.

354

The dyes in the unburnt head material can be compared with matches from the suspect by microspectrophotometry and by spectrophotofluorimetry. Both techniques are non-destructive and can produce valuable evidence when applied to very small samples.

Direct comparison of the colour, size, shape and texture of the heads can be carried out, both with naked eye vision and using a microscope. Higher magnification can be achieved by the use of scanning electron microscopy.

Inorganic analysis of the burnt match heads may provide useful discrimination evidence and techniques such as emission spectroscopy, electron microprobe analysis and X-ray fluorescence have been used[2].

Comparison of book matches

Most book matches are made from a thick coarse cardboard which becomes fluffy and irregular when the matches are torn from the book. For this reason it is seldom possible to prove that a cardboard match originated from a particular book by 'jigsaw fit' evidence.

However, imperfections in the cardboard, particularly those caused by the presence of extraneous material may provide a link between the questioned match and the match which had been adjacent to it in the book[3]. Striation marks caused by the cutting tool can also be used to provide evidence linking matches which had been adjacent to one another in the book.

Corresponding imperfections between two book matches may provide conclusive evidence that a match had originated from a particular book. However, even when such imperfections are not found, the diversity of types of book match tends to make them of far higher evidential significance than most boxed matches.

Good 'jigsaw fit' evidence may be found in the case of wooden book matches, but it is important that the comparison of the broken surfaces should be made using a low power microscope.

Match boxes and books

Match boxes and books left at the scene of the fire by the arsonist can provide identifying and implicative evidence.

Fingerprints may be present on the surface of the cardboard particularly if it is glossy. For this reason any books or boxes thought to be significant should not be handled unduly and

Plate 22C. Imperfections and inclusions present in the cardboard used in the manufacture of book matches, can provide links visible even to the naked eye. Two parts of an inclusion correspond between the second and third matches of this book. Photograph B. R. G. Roberts.

should be brought to the attention of a Scenes of Crime Officer.

Since match boxes and books are commonly carried in the pocket, fibres may be found associated with them. These fibres may provide evidence to link the matches with a particular suspect.

The label, advertisements, country of origin and other information may give an indication which may point to a particular suspect. In addition it has happened that a co-operative criminal has used a match box or book to jot down a telephone number or other small piece of information.

Certain information of limited value may be obtained by examination of the striking strip. It is normally possible to establish the direction of abrasion, and regular users of matches are often remarkably consistent in the manner in which they strike a match.

Empty match boxes are discarded so commonly that they may not attract attention at the scene of a fire. However, it sometimes happens that when an arsonist has started a fire, he decides to rid himself of the box of matches which might be regarded as incriminating. The box or book containing a number of live matches is likely therefore to be very much more significant than an empty match box. The place where the box is found can indicate the route taken by the offender after the fire.

Boxes containing live matches are more likely to be discarded by children, young people and non-smokers than by adult smokers who will have a legitimate reason for carrying matches.

References

(1) F. A. S. Lewis. Personal communication.
(2) J. Andrasko. Identification of burnt matches by Scanning Electron Microscopy. J. For. Sci. Soc. 1977 *17*, 637.
(3) H. J. Funk. Comparison of paper matches. J. For. Sci. Soc 1973 *13*, 137.

Chapter 23

Laboratory Analysis

Although a scene examination will often show how a fire could have been caused, confirmation may depend heavily on the results of a laboratory analysis.

In criminal cases, the identification of a fire accelerant, such as petrol or paraffin, may be crucial in establishing arson or in linking a suspect to a particular scene. In other cases, a laboratory examination and analysis may be important to identify materials which have been involved, to explain how a fire spread, to support a story or refute a claim by a witness or a suspect.

It is important to realise, however, that any analysis of fire debris in itself does not prove much, except perhaps to indicate that the material contains a particular substance. Analyses can only be informative in the context from which the materials were recovered. An obvious example of this is that, if the seat of fire has not been determined, random sampling may, on occasions, produce a hoped for 'positive' result. The full significance of such a result cannot be realised because of the lack of knowledge as to what materials should have been legitimately present. It may also lead the investigator into considerable error if the debris which was analysed did not come from the fire seat.

Caution must be exercised in determining whether the materials are representative of the area of interest, and whether or not control or reference samples should be taken for comparison with a questioned sample.

Further, it must be re-emphasised that failure to find fire accelerants in debris does not necessarily disprove that the fire was deliberately started. Sampling techniques may have been inadequate, combustion may have been too complete or, possibly, no accelerant was used. The sensitivity of current laboratory techniques is such that very small (nanogram) quantities of the commonly encountered fire accelerants can be detected and identified. At this level of detection, correct sampling techniques must be scrupulously observed, so that contamination from areas where accelerants exist does not occur via the investigator's boots or trowel.

FUELS AND FIRE ACCELERANTS—HYDROCARBONS

Gas Chromatography

This technique is briefly described in Appendix C1, and is currently the standard method for the detection of volatile fire accelerants. Used with a flame ionisation detector (F.I.D.) it is capable of extremely high sensitivity and reproducibility and can produce excellent discrimination between similar fuels which have a different origin (e.g. different brands of premium paraffin).

In order to analyse debris containing traces of a fire accelerant the material has first to be treated in some way to separate the two. Some of these methods are discussed below.

Headspace Sampling

This technique relies on the fact that volatile fire accelerants in debris in a container will, provided that the debris is warm enough and the surface is exposed, eventually develop a detectable concentration of vapour from the accelerant into the air space above the sample. If a sample of this atmosphere is drawn off and injected into the gas chromatograph, a 'trace' indicative of what substance is present can be produced. Examples of typical traces from petrol, paraffin and diesel fuel can be seen in figures 23.1, 23.2 and 23.3.

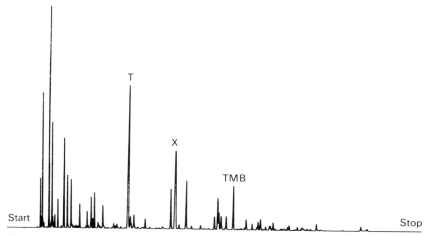

Figure 23.1. Gas Chromatogram of a liquid sample of petrol. The peaks designated T, X, TMB are produced by toluene, the xylenes and the trimethylbenzenes respectively.

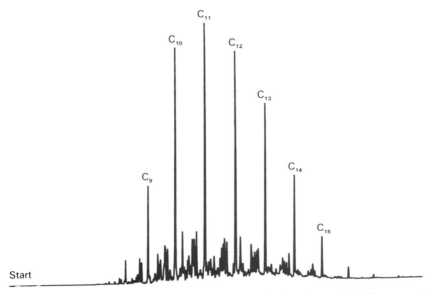

Figure 23.2. Gas chromatogram of a typical, liquid paraffin (kerosene) sample. The peaks designated C_9, C_{10}, C_{11}, C_{12}, etc., are the aliphatic normal alkanes referred to in the text.

This method of analysis is relatively crude and insensitive and has been superseded by more sophisticated techniques.

A current technique which may be of use in screening, is the use of a commercial hydrocarbon 'sniffer', sensitive at parts-per-million levels to screen debris samples on a yes/no basis for suitability for more sophisticated analysis. 'Sniffers' have the disadvantage of giving false positive results to many non-hydrocarbon materials, such as volatile pyrolysates and water vapour, and are less sensitive than many gas chromatography methods. The addition of a 'scrubber' containing an oxidising agent through which the vapour sample must pass before entering the sniffer detector, effectively removes most interfering substances.[1]

Headspace Concentration Methods
There are several methods available; the most successful utilise the principle of adsorption of the hydrocarbon vapour onto a suitable material followed by desorption by heat or solvent. These

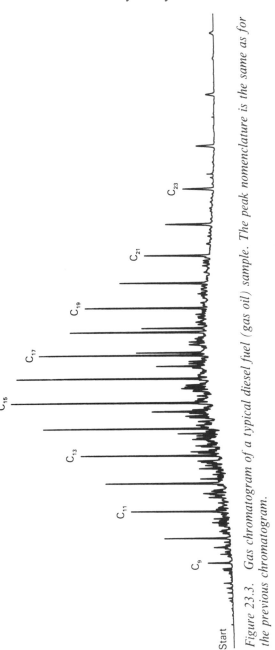

Figure 23.3. Gas chromatogram of a typical diesel fuel (gas oil) sample. The peak nomenclature is the same as for the previous chromatogram.

techniques give results which are several orders more sensitive than simple headspace analysis, and which resemble in peak height ratios, injections of the liquid fuel. Because of their sensitivity they are useful for items such as clothing, which may need to be preserved intact.

(a) *Adsorption onto Carbon.* Specially produced activated carbon granules (generally made from coconut husk), can be used either as a prepared tube (as, for example, N.I.O.S.H. approved tubes) or adhering, to a Curie point wire (see Appendix C2). If the carbon is in a tube, air from the warmed container, preferably a nylon bag which can collapse as the air inside is drawn out, is sucked out through the tube. A variant on this method is to pass warmed nitrogen into the debris container to flush out the hydrocarbon vapours by positive pressure.[2] After a suitable time, the adsorption tube is withdrawn, the carbon removed and extracted with carbon disulphide, and the extract, after some evaporation of the carbon disulphide, is injected onto the gas chromatograph. Results obtained by this method tend to be slightly deficient in low molecular weight hydrocarbons but otherwise show exceptional sensitivity when compared with ordinary headspace analyses.

Carbon coated Curie point wires[3] have the advantage that they can be 'blanked' by a primary heating sequence in the pyrolysis unit which serves to condition the wires for adsorption. The prepared wires are placed in the headspace atmosphere for about forty minutes, after which time they are removed, put into the pyrolysis unit and heated to desorb the hydrocarbons. Again, as is common with other adsorption/desorption methods, excellent results can be obtained, the chromatogram traces resembling more closely true, liquid injections.

(b) *Porous Polymers (Tenax®, Poropak Q®).* These, after conditioning by heating in an inert atmosphere, are capable of adsorbing hydrocarbons in the same manner as activated carbon. Heat desorption[4] is the best method of releasing the hydrocarbons and several methods have been used.

(i) Heated Injection Ports.

The hot injection port of a gas chromatograph is of the right order of temperature (about 270–300°C) for rapid desorption. If the polymer is used in a small glass tube, this may be inserted directly into the injection port and the released vapours passed onto the column. Cryogenic 'focussing' (achieved by cooling with liquid nitrogen or solid carbon dioxide) whereby the released vapours are held on the first stage of the column before the oven temperature is raised to the normal programming rate, may be necessary to give optimum resolution.

(ii) Special Heat Desorbers

These fall into two categories; heating units which pass the hydrocarbons directly onto the G.C. column in the same manner as a heated injection port and units which condense desorped vapours from a polymer into a cold (liquid nitrogen cooled) trap. The former gives problems of chromatogram peak broadening unless the chromatograph column itself can be cooled to sub-ambient temperatures when desorption takes place. The latter allows a condensed, recovered liquid accelerant to be injected directly onto the gas chromatograph.

Liquid Extracts

(a) *Vacuum Distillation.* This method involves drawing air from a nylon bag containing the debris into a cold trap[5][6]. If the bag is placed in an oven, a liquid distillate closely resembling the parent liquid can be obtained. Co-extractants can be a problem, as in any method in which debris containing pyrolysates is involved, and clean-up procedures by aluminium oxide column chromatography may be necessary.

(b) *Steam Distillation.* In order to get liquid extracts, debris which contains moderate quantities of fire accelerants may be distilled. Two steam distillation techniques, the Brackett[7] Method using a modified Dean and Stark condenser and the Macoun Method[8] have been used routinely in forensic science laboratories in the past.

The Brackett Method involves boiling the debris in water and decanting the immiscible hydrocarbons, which are seen as a supernatant layer on the aqueous distillate. This yields distillates which may show deficiencies in the recovery of both the very low and the very high molecular weight hydrocarbons. If the first aqueous distillate drops are removed, water miscible accelerants, such as alcohol, can be found.

The Macoun Method, in which the hydrocarbons are leached from the debris by alcohol and with which they are distilled as an azeotrope, has the disadvantage of a complex recovery process. The distillate must be partly oxidised by a sulphuric acid/potassium dichromate mixture. This makes the hydrocarbons separate out from the alcohol.

This is a technique which requires skill and experience for best results and has the further disadvantage that polar liquids (such as alcohol) will be missed.

The above distillation methods allow a liquid to be recovered which, from an analytical point of view, is more satisfactory to handle both in gas chromatography and in other analytical methods.

Direct Extraction

On occasions, materials soaked with fire accelerants may be directly extracted with a suitable solvent, such as purified n-pentane. This method will invariably extract tarry pyrolysates, so it should be restricted to relatively unburnt items such as fabrics or papers soaked in fuel. Direct extraction methods have the advantage that, if a dyed fuel (premium domestic paraffin) is present, the dye also will be extracted and, under favourable conditions, can be analysed by thin layer chromatography.

Comparison of Fuels by Hydrocarbon Ratio

The preceding techniques provide ways of separating fire accelerant traces or residues from the mass of debris. Analysis of these traces by gas chromatography will give indications of the fuel involved. However, when the fuel is heavily degraded by burning or evaporation, care must be taken in its identification. For example, a domestic paraffin, when evaporated to less than 10% of its original volume, will show hydrocarbons and isomers (typically pristane and phytane at the heptadecane ($C_{17}H_{36}$) to octadecane ($C_{18}H_{38}$) range on the chromatogram) usually only seen in gas oil or diesel fuel (see figure 22.3).

When a fuel is identified as to type, it may be necessary to try to compare it with a control material, that is, a fuel considered to be a possible original source. This is not easily done, as the relative proportions of the component hydrocarbons change during burning or evaporation.

A careful examination of the chromatogram may reveal characteristic patterns of some of the minor peaks, particularly around the dodecane ($C_{12}H_{26}$) area, which are fairly resistant to changes due to evaporation. Similarly with petrols, visual comparison of component petroleum hydrocarbons may be possible. A headspace sample must never be compared with a liquid sample and, because of the inherently unstable nature of a headspace analysis, dependent as it is on temperature and concentration, comparison of two samples by this method is not meaningful unless strict matching of analytical conditions can be employed.

Provided that two liquid samples are to be compared, paraffin and gas oils (including diesel fuels) can yield useful results from the ratios of their straight chain hydrocarbons (n-alkanes).

In gas chromatograms of these substances the straight chain n-alkanes stand out as dominant peaks (see fig. 22.3), which increase to a maximum at about dodecane ($C_{12}H_{26}$) for paraffins (kerosenes) and at about pentadecane ($C_{15}H_{32}$) for gas oils or diesel fuels. When matched sample-to-sample analytical conditions are used, the chromatograms to be compared can have each of their relevant n-alkanes measured as a proportion, by

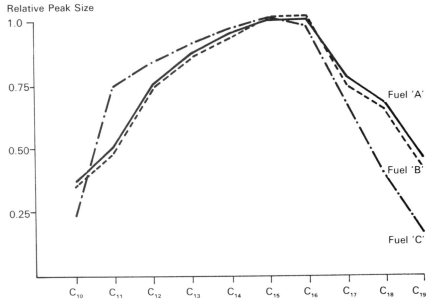

Figure 23.4. Matching of Liquid Fuels by Hydrocarbons Comparison (n-Alkanes). The relative chromatogram peak size for each n-alkane is plotted for fuel 'A' and similarly for fuels 'B' and 'C'. C_{10} is n-decane ($C_{10}H_{22}$) and so on. In this example fuels 'A' and 'B' match each other. Fuel 'C' does not match and probably comes from a different origin.

which the size of a particular peak is ratioed against a reference peak (generally the largest and which, in a gas-oil, would be pentadecane). This gives a set of so called 'normalised' n-alkane peak size ratios. If access to a recording integrator or a computerised data station linked to the chromatograph is available these calculations can be automatically made. Plotting the normalised peaks as a ratio against the respective hydrocarbons, a stylised representation of the n-alkane 'envelope' is obtained. Matching samples will show superimposed graphs (See Figure 23.4).

A further development of this is to take the ratio of each specific pair of between-sample n-alkanes. Thus, for example, the normalised peak size of dodecane in Sample 'A' is compared with the normalised peak size of dodecane for sample 'B'. This procedure is repeated for each hydrocarbon. If sample 'A' and sample 'B' are identical, a value of unity would be obtained for each ratioed pair. Plotting the sample-to-sample ratio will produce a straight line at unity across the hydrocarbon range. (See Figure 23.5). If both samples are from the same origin but one has evaporated, the line will be essentially straight but tilted. The direction of tilt will depend on whether the evaporated sample is taken as the numerator or denominator when the ratios are calculated.

FUELS AND FIRE ACCELERANTS—
NON-HYDROCARBONS

Components or Residues of Hydrocarbon Mixtures

(a) *Leaded Petrol.* Lead is being gradually phased out as a petrol additive in Western countries. Lead alkyls (lead tetramethyl or lead tetraethyl) may be present as anti-knock agents in petrol at levels of about 0.4 grammes per litre for 'four star' (98 octane) petrol, together with ethylene dibromide which acts as a scavenger. During the burning process the two chemicals react together to produce lead dibromide, $Pb Br_2$. Lead, then, can be looked for as a diagnostic feature of petrol in two ways; as the organic lead alkyl or as the inorganic lead bromide. Lead alkyls are easily degraded by adverse storage conditions; water and light can make them decompose. It is consequently dangerous practice to use quantitative methods on recovered samples to try to match them with control materials.

366

Laboratory Analysis

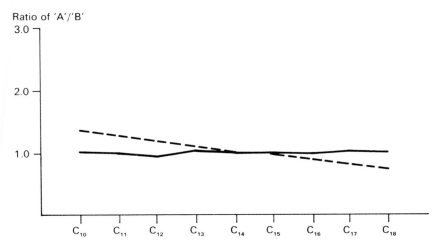

Fuels 'A' and 'B' have very closely matching n-alkane proportions and dividing the proportions of C_{10} (n-decane) for 'A' by that of C_{10} for 'B' gives a value of 1.0. This process is repeated for each n-alkane and values of approximately 1.0 are found on each occasion. The dotted line shows the result which could be expected if fuel 'B' was slightly more evaporated than fuel 'A'.

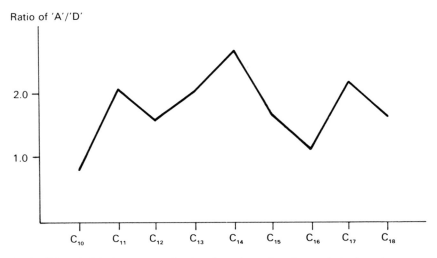

Fuels 'A' and 'D' do not match, therefore the ratios for each hydrocarbon vary considerably.

Figure 23.5.   Matching of Liquid Fuels by Sample-to-Sample Ratio.

(i) Lead Alkyls.

Mass spectrometers are capable of detecting the ions of masses characteristic of lead compounds. An example of the use of this technique is where a degraded liquid extract, which is heavily contaminated with other volatile materials, needs to be analysed.

(ii) Lead Bromide

Flames from burning petrol impinging onto a surface can deposit small quantities of lead bromide[9]. This can be detected with suitable techniques, for example, X-ray fluorescence or scanning electron microscopy with microprobe analysis.

Care must be exercised in interpreting the results of this analysis. Lead bromide is present in car exhaust gases (the reason for the addition of ethylene dibromide) and many plastics contain brominated fire retardants. Painted surfaces may also contain significant quantities of lead. Questioned samples must, therefore, always be checked against a control material.

(b) *Sulphur Compounds.* Most crude oils contain sulphur compounds. On refining, some pass into the fuel where, by suitable analysis (gas chromatography using a sulphur sensitive, flame photometric detector), they can be analysed. There is good reason to believe that fuels can be characterised by their sulphur compounds[10]. As the gas chromatographic analysis of sulphur compounds shows them to be relatively less volatile than many of the component hydrocarbons in the fuel, they are relatively insensitive to evaporation.

(c) *Ketones and Esters in Paint Thinners.* Cellulose paint thinners typically contain, a ketone (such as acetone or methyl ethyl ketone), an ester (such as n-butyl acetate), and an aromatic hydrocarbon mixture, (such as toluene and the xylenes).

Gas chromatography of the liquid or headspace vapour will, under suitable operating conditions, resolve all these components but headspace analysis will probably show over-rich proportions of the more volatile ketones and esters.

If debris is steam-distilled to separate an accelerant or when one of the headspace concentration methods (e.g. adsorption onto charcoal) is used, problems will arise due to non-detection of the ketones and esters.

With steam distillation, the aqueous phase will contain these compounds so that if the first few drops of a Brackett distillation are reserved, they may be analysed for them. It should be noted, however, that many cellulosic materials, when burnt, produce alcohols and ketones naturally, so that significant results can only be assessed when there are clearly dominant substances present.

Non-Hydrocarbon Substances
Obviously there are many combustible materials which could act as fire initiators or accelerants each of which would require a special analytical procedure. Two main groups will be considered here, drying oils, and mixtures containing oxidising agents. These latter may be the results of incompatible chemical mixtures or may be purpose made incendiary devices.

(a) *Drying Oils.* These contain unsaturated fatty acid esters which can combine exothermically with atmospheric oxygen. There are two broad analytical approaches which can be made, either a test to show their heating properties or an analysis of their fatty acid content.

(i) Self Heating Tests
The classic test is the Mackey Test[11] in which 14 gm of oil is dispersed onto 7 gm of cotton wool. The doped cotton wool is packed into a ventilated chamber maintained at 100°C for one hour. If the temperature in the middle of the sample rises to more than 100°C after this time it shows that self heating properties exist. Oils such as linseed oil (well known for spontaneous combustion hazards) can actually catch fire in this test.

A preferred method of demonstrating self heating is by the use of cubes of impregnated material, tested isothermally in progressively increasing sizes as described in Chapter 17, (Physical Processes in Fire).

(ii) Oil Analysis
Methyl esters of fatty acids can be prepared by various methods (boron trifluoride/methanol is in current use). The resultant mixture of methyl esters is analysed by gas chromatography using a stationary phase which is made from a polar material such as diethylene glycol succinate (D.E.G.S.). Methyl esters are considerably more volatile than the free fatty acids (e.g. stearic, oleic and linoleic acids) or their naturally occurring glycerol esters.

(b) *Oxidising Agents and Mixtures.* These will mostly be solid materials containing inorganic nitrates, chlorates, perchlorates, permanganates, etc.

A general test for oxidising agents is diphenylamine in concentrated sulphuric acid. This turns a dark blue in their

369

presence. Tests for individual oxidising agents can be found in any general test book on inorganic analysis. Many of these tests are, however, not specific for a particular substance. As fires initiated by oxidising agents usually involve an organic reducing agent (often an alcohol or a sugar) it is of advantage to analyse both materials simultaneously.

The following scheme is a method whereby oxidising agents and organic reducing agents can be analysed by thin layer chromatography (T.L.C.).

The suspect residue is dissolved in the minimum quantity of water and a micro-drop of the solution is applied to a silica gel coated T.L.C. plate. The chromatogram is developed in a mixture which consists of n-butanol (50 parts), glacial acetic acid (45 parts) and water (5 parts). The solvent is allowed to run about 4 cm up the plate. The spots are visualised by spraying with a mixture of diphenylamine (1 gm), aniline (1 ml) and phosphoric acid (10 ml) dissolved in acetone (100 ml). The plate is then heated to 80°C for 5 minutes.

Substance	Initial colour developed	Rf
Lactose	Blue	0.25
Sucrose	Brown	0.35
Maltose	Blue	0.35
Galactose	Purple	0.45
Fructose	Pink	0.50
Glucose	Blue	0.50
Chlorate	Green	0.60
Chromate	Pale green*	0.20
Dichromate	Pale green*	0.20
Iodate	Pale green*	Streaks
Nitrate	None	
Perchlorate	None	—
Periodate	Pale green*	Streaks
Permanganate	Pale green*	Streaks
Persulphate	Green*	Streaks

(i) * A blue colour develops immediately after the initial spraying with the diphenylamine, aniline, orthophosphoric acid reagent; this colour intensifies to a dark green on heating.

(ii) On treatment of the plate with sulphuric acid, the organic sugars turn brown and the oxidising agents turn blue. Nitrate shows as a blue spot, Rf = 0.55.

TOXIC COMBUSTION PRODUCTS

The analysis of body fluids for these substances is of direct interest to the fire investigator. Carbon monoxide is by far the most important of these, followed by certain intermediate combustion products (e.g. cyanides from modern urethane plastics or proteinaceous materials).

Carbon Monoxide in Blood
Most of the laboratory methods use measurement of the carboxyhaemoglobin (Hb.CO) as compared with the residual oxyhaemoglobin (Hb.O$_2$) content. These are basically optical methods which operate by measurement of the shift in wavelength of the peak absorption of carboxyhaemoglobin compared with oxyhaemoglobin alone.

For example, if one were to plot the absorption spectrum of oxyhaemoglobin and compare this with that of carboxyhaemo-globin the following graphs would be obtained.

In the spectra in Figure 23.6 oxyhaemoglobin has two peaks at 542 nm. and 579 nm. Carboxyhaemoglobin has peaks at 540 nm. and 568 nm. A sample of diluted blood viewed through a spectroscope would show these peaks as dark absorbing bands.

This is the basis of the Hartridge Reversion Spectroscopic method in which the peak absorptions are visible as dark bands in an eyepiece to which a scale is attached. As the shift in band position from 579 nm. to 568 nm. is linear with increasing concentration of carbon monoxide, observation of the degree of the shift against known standards will indicate the amount of carboxyhaemoglobin in the specimen blood sample.

This method is relatively imprecise and insensitive to small changes in concentration. The instrument is, however, robust and requires little scientific sophistication in its application. The blood sample is diluted 1 : 50 with water or 0.1 molar ammonium hydroxide solution and viewed directly in the special cells through an eyepiece.

Alternative spectroscopic methods which are inherently more accurate are performed by measuring the absorbance of the blood sample at two points, one where the absorbance between zero and one hundred per cent saturation is greatest and one where it is the least[12]. Typical wavelengths would be 540 nm. for maximum difference and about 578 nm. where the absorptions are roughly the same. The ratio of absorbances for the questioned blood sample is compared with those for blank blood and fully (100%) saturated blood to calculate the percentage saturation.

Carboxyhaemoglobin can be measured concurrently with

371

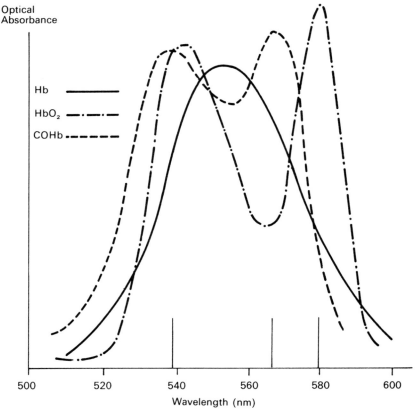

Figure 23.6. Absorption Spectra of Haemoglobin (Hb), Oxyhaemoglobin (HbO₂) and Carboxyhaemoglobin (COHb).

oxyhaemoglobin and haemoglobin in the CO-Oximeter[13].

This is an automatic instrument which performs the above comparisons by micro-processor and is capable of extremely accurate determinations. The simultaneous measurement of oxyhaemoglobin is of particular value when studies of carbon monoxide poisoning and anoxia are made on fire victims.

Cyanide

Normal post-mortem blood can contain cyanide because of protein breakdown. Concern has been felt about the contribution that inhaled cyanides may make to fatalities in fires involving polyurethane foams or wool. Laboratory analysis for inhaled cyanide generally involves analysis of blood. This will only contain very small amounts, possibly only 1.0 mg per litre of cyanide calculated as CN.

The Conway diffusion method has been used for analysis of levels of this order. It utilises the fact that acidified blood will evolve any cyanide present as HCN. This is absorbed into a test solution containing barbitone in pyridine[14]. Cyanide concentration is calculated by changes in optical absorption of this solution.

An alternative method is to pass the released HCN gas onto alkaline iron (II) hydroxide impregnated paper. On treating this with sulphuric acid iron (III) ferrocyanide (Prussian blue) is formed. The intensity of stain is proportional to the quantity of cyanide present.

A potentially more sensitive and accurate method of cyanide detection is by using a 'specific ion electrode' which can measure the quantity of CN ion present in blood serum[16].

References

(1) Twibell, J. B., Sanger, D. G., Silvester, A. M. B. 1982. Home Office C.R.E. Report.
(2) Christowsky, J. E., Holmes, R. N. 1979. Arson Analysis Newsletter. Vol. 3.
(3) Twibell, J. D., Home, J. M. 1977. Nature. Vol. 268, 711.
(4) Russell, L. W. 1981. J. Forens. Sc. Soc. Vol. 21, (4), 317.
(5) Andrasko, J. 1982. Centrum for Forensisk Vetenskap. Rep. No. 9.
(6) Hrynchuk, R., Cameron, R., Rodgers, P. G. 1977. Can. Soc. Forens. Sc. J. Vol. 10(2).
(7) Brackett, J. W. 1955. J. Crim, Crim Law and Pol. Sc. (46) 554.
(8) Macoun, J. M. 1952. Analyst (77) 381.
(9) Vispaa, A., Heinonen, K. 1977. Criminology 10. (38) 22.
(10) Fergusson, D. A., Luke, L. A. 1979. Chromatograph (12) No. 4.
(11) Garner, W., Leach, W. 1936. Analyst (61) 337.
(12) Van Kampen, E. J., Klouwen, H. 1954. Rev. Trav. Chim. Pays Bas (73) 119.
(13) Maas, A. H. J., Hamelink, M. L., De Leeuw, R. J. M. 1970. Clin Chem Acta 29. 303.
(14) Gettler, A. O., Goldbaum, L. 1947. Anal. Chem. (19) 270.
(15) Baselt, R. C. 1980. Analytical Procedures for Therapeutic Drug Monitoring and Emergency Toxicology 94–97 Biomedical.
(16) Basalt, R. C. 1980. Ibid.

Chapter 24

The Expert Witness

The end product of any fire investigation is the report. Where the fire brigade investigating officer is concerned this may be, in the United Kingdom, the standard 'F.D.R.1' report form, a research report for submission to the brigade or Home Office or, possibly, the preparation of written evidence to be given to a civil or criminal court. For investigators, such as Home Office forensic scientists reporting on criminal matters, the report will frequently be made in formal statement form conforming to the Magistrates Courts Act (1981) requirements (previously the Criminal Justice Act, 1967), for eventual use in the criminal courts.

Variations in reporting requirements can be found in Scotland where a legal system more akin to that found in European courts operates. Statements made to a Sheriff's Court or to the Procurator Fiscal need to be corroborated by a second person, normally a working colleague.

These formal statements may be accepted by both parties in a criminal action without any need for the investigator to go to court when the case is heard. Where argument may exist over a fact or an opinion, either side can call for the witness who will then be examined and cross-examined on what he has written.

Private forensic scientists may submit reports to their clients to demonstrate the liability of an insurer or a plaintiff without the necessity of statutory restrictions. Additionally their requirements may be to instruct counsel in the possible alternative explanations of the cause of a fire or of the responsibility for it, together with a demonstration of flaws in the logic of an opposing expert.

It can be seen, therefore, that considerable differences exist between the various responsibilities of investigators, but once the report is written, it is there to be used and there is an obvious possibility that it will be used in a court of law.

Thus, the reporting officer may well find himself in either a civil court or tribunal, or a criminal court, producing his report and using it to give evidence. At this point he becomes a witness as well as a reporting officer and will become subject to legal restraints. These may affect what he may say as well as how he may say it.

Lay witnesses

In most legal systems, witnesses can be divided into two types, lay and expert witnesses. Lay witnesses give evidence of fact only and are not allowed to give opinions about those facts. Strict legal rulings exist which prevent such witnesses from enlarging upon the bare facts of what they saw, what they heard or what they found. Evidence which goes beyond this, for example when a witness tries to tell what someone else saw or found, is termed 'hearsay evidence'. The rule against hearsay evidence disallows a witness from relaying reported speech or acts except in very exceptional circumstances[1, 2, 3].

This rule breaks down somewhat in Civil Law. For instance, where documents prepared by a person contain admissible evidence, these may be accepted on their own if the person who had compiled them cannot be found[4, 5]. This probably does not apply to computer records.

In Criminal Law, the rule is more strictly applied[6]. A recent case[7] showed that the acceptance of Home Office documents in the form of a computer record was not admissible, because it was not compiled 'by way of trade or business' and the person who compiled the particular item involved was not identifiable. Computer records compiled so that an expert opinion can be made on the relevance of results have been allowed, however[8, 9].

Expert witnesses

The functions of an expert witness mark him out for special attention by the court, because his status allows him to offer opinions about his own findings, and also about them when viewed in the light of other evidence already adduced in court. This freedom to form an opinion is also a freedom to have one's opinions attacked, for, if the expert can be made to change his mind, the outcome of the case may well be altered by it.

It is the expert witness' duty to supply the court with such knowledge and opinions of science, etc., of which the court itself has no knowledge and requires guidance[9]. This, obviously, places a serious responsibility upon him, because the court relies on his integrity in these matters. It is for the court to decide whether or not a person has 'expert' status[10] but, perhaps strangely, the court is not bound to believe him even though they accept him[11]. This last ruling probably makes more sense when one considers that, if the opposing sides each have an expert witness who disagree in their findings and opinions, if one *must* be believed, the trial becomes trial by expert and not trial by jury[12].

In the adversary systems prevalent in the English and United States legal systems it is inevitable that opposing sides will seek the most skilful help they can find. In practice it is a frequent occurrence for experts to agree on most factual points.

As to who can become an expert in the court's eyes, it has been held for some considerable time[13, 14] that there need not be any recognised course of study. It has been said that 'experience provides the tools for judgement' and 'study without practice is insufficient'[15]. Certainly the witness' own profession need not recognise him as an 'expert'. The court may take notice of his qualifications and background but may question him by oral examination as to his acceptability.

Having dealt broadly with the status and background of the expert witness, particular aspects of the fire examiner as an expert witness must now be considered.

Evidence
Evidence is divided into functional parts where its operation in court is concerned.

Real evidence is to a large extent self explanatory. It is the material which can be examined, handled, seen and labelled in court, (i.e. the 'exhibit'). Examples of this can be, for example, the remains of a petrol bomb, the fragments of glass removed from an accused's clothing, etc. Its existence is obvious but, from the lawyer's point of view, its origins or its relevance may be questioned. Thus, its history must be authenticated, usually in the Criminal Court by verbal introduction or by statement.

This can involve questions of admissibility, for if the materials were illegally seized, the court may decide that evidence concerning them or evidence resulting from them cannot be used in court.

In Great Britain, and countries which follow the same common law system, legal precedent[16] has established that, provided the police had powers of entry by, for instance, a search warrant or notional permission to enter, then any materials which appeared to be incriminating (even though they may not have been related to the originally suspected offence) can be legitimately taken. During and immediately after a fire it would appear that the collection of exhibits poses no problems. In United Kingdom law, even beyond that period, a fire scene can be revisited if it is suspected that a crime may have been committed, provided no objections to entry are made by the occupier.

In the USA the situation is somewhat different. Supreme Court rulings[17] make it apparent that a properly constituted search warrant is necessary at any time after the initial post-fire search if materials are to be taken and evidence (even arising from scene observations) is to be used. This is apparently enforceable even if no material objections have been made by the occupier and even if the premises are badly damaged and unusable after the fire.

There is little benefit in using exhibits or relying on them if their continuity from the alleged offence to the trial cannot be demonstrated. This is particularly important where the object has passed through several hands before it is examined and reported on. It is essential, therefore, that any item which may be discovered during the course of an investigation and which has evidential value, should be noted and entered in an exhibits 'log-book' and that a statement concerning its transfer of possession is made according to, in criminal proceedings in the United Kingdom, the Magistrates Courts Act (1981) rules. To police officers and Home Office forensic scientists, this continuity procedure is standard practice but to the fire officer or other investigators, who may not normally be involved in such matters, care must be taken not to omit these essential steps.

For example, if during the early stages of an investigation, any item such as a petrol can is discovered and thought to be of possible evidential value, the wrong procedure is merely to put it on one side and leave it (possibly in a place where contamination or confusion as to its identity can occur) and then expect someone else to retrieve it for further examination. The correct procedure is to mark or label it so that it can be identified, and to keep it in your secure possession prior to handing it over with documentary evidence of that handing over. One only has to ponder the answer that one must give on oath to the question 'How can you be certain that this is the item?' to realise the necessity of this approach.

Articles tendered as real evidence tend to speak for themselves in court but a badly damaged item may need some interpretation (for example, what it is or the manner in which the damage occurred). We are now in the area of evidence of testimony and evidence of opinion.

Evidence of testimony is straightforward in that this is what all witnesses provide on oath. However, words spoken in court achieve a formalism that does not exist in conversation. The witness must state his facts in unambiguous terms, eliminating jargon as much as possible. The greatest difficulty with testimony of a scientific or technical nature is to achieve lucidity and simplicity, without sacrificing accuracy. The expert should seek a pre-trial conference with counsel so that important points are not missed or misunderstood.

Evidence of opinion. It is important that the fire investigator correctly separates what is fact from what is opinion in his evidence. Evidence about fire scene damage may mix the two to an alarming extent. A statement that, for example, the seat of fire was in the corner of the room may sound factual to a layman, but is probably an opinion. Likewise, an estimate of the duration of the fire will, almost certainly be pure opinion.

Having given evidence about the facts as he found them, the expert will be asked his opinion on them either, as they stand alone or in conjunction with other evidence previously adduced in court. This will probably be by means of hypothetical questions put to him.

In the UK he can draw upon several sources to support his opinion apart from those facts he has personally proved.

(a) *Personal knowledge.* If he is accepted as an expert, then it is implicit that he must have knowledge of the subject. The court may enquire as to how he has gained knowledge about the specific item in issue; he could well have gained it by personal experiment or by experience. There is little problem in getting this accepted, apart from the fact that experiments in the fire field, with the inherently large number of variables, may not yield the same results for different experimenters. Unless exhaustive experimentation is conducted, a result may mean only that an event is possible rather than probable. One must beware of dogmatism in this field as an opposing expert may well possess different and equally valid results.

So far as experimentation, analysis and direct observation at the scene of fire is concerned, the expert will have taken notes either at the time or some time later. The notes themselves may be required to be admitted as evidence—in the Civil Courts they could be required by the process known as 'discovery of documents', whereas in the Criminal Courts they may be examined by the court if they are referred to when giving evidence.

A question frequently arises as to how soon afterwards should notes be made after an observation. The requirement is, basically, that they must be made as soon as possible because, while conditions at the scene may not be good for coherent noting, the legal requirement for notes which are referred to in court to refresh the witness' memory, is that they must be 'contemporaneous' with the examination they refer to.

The definition of 'contemporaneous' is somewhat elastic and is generally accepted to mean the earliest opportunity, but not necessarily immediately, after the event. The case law covering this subject rests upon some extreme conditions and it would be unwise for the expert to test the legal precedent which held that a delay of two weeks before the notes of the event were written up was acceptable[18].

Situations have arisen where the original notes may have been lost and the witness' memory over details may be faint if a long period has elapsed between the examination and the subsequent hearing. In these circumstances it is possible to use one's previous statement (e.g. one made at committal proceedings) to refresh one's memory even though that statement does not contain all the details[19]. It appears possible also that, if a colleague is giving evidence and notes were made at the same time and in collaboration with him, those notes may be referred to [20].

(b) *Reference books.* This knowledge is used frequently and may be unchallenged. The fact that, for instance, water has a boiling point of 100°C at 1 Bar atmospheric pressure is one that few people have ascertained by experiment but treat as fact merely by having read it. In more uncertain fields, reference books may need to be used as a basis for opinion and at one time could only be used if the author had died. This was because he may have changed his mind in a subsequent edition had he lived! Nowadays a published work is admitted as evidence and can be accepted, but also can be challenged as a relevant fact[21, 22].

Counsel may, on occasion, quote from a textbook which has divergent views from those given by the expert. If the witness can show that his views are the results of more up-to-date research, then no problems will exist. It is quite possible, however, that the different opinions are perfectly legitimate, and depend largely on the individual circumstances of the case. The witness is then in a position to use his expertise to help to guide the court.

(c) *Knowledge of work done by, and consultation with colleagues.* This is an area where direct testimony and hearsay blend. Until recently, work done and facts found from that work, could not be accepted as evidence unless the work had been personally done by the witness who was testifying. This was essentially the rule which applied in Myers v the Director of Public Prosecutions[23]. The obvious injustice in this case, where documentary evidence is concerned, has been remedied by subsequent legislation[5,6] and case-law[8] (mentioned earlier in this chapter). However, these cases where evidence of a documentary nature which has been prepared by another (e.g. identification of the origin of articles by their serial numbers) is admitted as evidence and used by the expert to form an opinion, are different from the situation where a person in his own statement uses information given to him by another. This, strictly speaking, is hearsay evidence, and has been a stumbling block in the presentation of evidence where the expert witness has headed a team of assistants in the examination and analysis of materials. Thus, applying this rule, each worker in the team should present a statement about the work done by him and him alone. This is of obvious disadvantage to the team leading 'expert' as it tends to dilute his evidence unless he can knit together the sum of their findings. Recent cases[24,25] suggest that, provided it can be demonstrated that the expert witness, has exercised full control and supervision over the work done, the results of that work can be assimilated into his own testimony. Both of these cases involve Home Office forensic scientists but it is probable that other expert witnesses may be included in these decisions. The courts now recognise[8] that expertise in any subject is not gained in isolation but is the sum total of experience which includes consultation with colleagues.

What these cases do *not* do, is to make it unnecessary for assistants or colleagues to be called to give evidence of the factual parts of the evidence going to make the expert's statement. Most statements made by expert witnesses are in two parts, in that facts are presented together with an opinion as to their worth. An assistant's help in the fact-finding stage may, even if these cases can be applied successfully, still cause elements of hearsay to be present.

The situation appears to be that, provided the opposing party agrees on the assistant's evidence, then the expert can use the assistant's work together with his own even if the assistant did not actually give evidence. Otherwise the assistant must give evidence on his own work.

References

(1) R. v. Gibson. 1887. 18 QBD 537.
(2) Ratten v. R. 1972. AC 378.
(3) Sparks v. R. 1964. AC 964.
(4) Civil Evidence Act. 1968. Secs. 2(i), 2(iii), 4(i), 4(iii).
(5) Civil Evidence Act. 1972. Sec. 1.
(6) Criminal Evidence Act. 1965. Sec. 1.
(7) R. v. Patel. 1981. Court of Appeal. 73 Cr. App. R. 117, 120.
(8) R. v. Abadom. 1982. Court of Appeal. CLR 1983. 254.
(9) R. v. Wood. 1982. Times Law Report.
(10) Folkes v. Chadd. 1782. 3 Doug. 197.
(11) R. v. Silverlock. 1894. 2 Q.B. 766.
(12) R. v. Silverlock. Ibid.
(13) R. v. Silverlock. Ibid.
(14) R. v. Summers. 1963.
(15) Bristowe v. Sequeville. 1850. 5 Exch. 275.
(16) Chic Fashions (West Wales) Ltd. v. Jones. 1968. 2 Q.B. 299.
(17) Michigan v. Tyler. 1978. US Supreme Court. 56 L.Ed.2d 486.
(18) R. v. Langton. 1876. 2 Q.B. 296.
(19) R. v. Cheng. 1976. CLR 379.
(20) R. v. MacLean. 1968. 52 Crim. App. Rep., 80.
(21) Re Ripon Housing Order. 1938. 3 All ER 548.
(22) Thornton v. Fisher and Ludlow Ltd. 1968. 2 All ER 241.
(23) Myers v. DPP. 1965. AC 1001.
(24) R. v. Tate. 1978. (Court of Appeal). Road Traffic Reports.
(25) R. v. Kirshberg. 1978. (Court of Appeal). Road Traffic Reports.

Further Reading
Law of Evidence. Cross.
Phipson on Evidence.

These books provide more than is necessary for the understanding of giving testimony.

Law of Evidence. Curzon. M. & E. Handbooks 1978.
Fire and the Law. Everton A. R. 1972. Butterworth.
Everton's 'Law as a Liberal Study'. Everton A. E. 1969. Butterworth.

Appendix A

Estimation of Temperature Attained

Pure substances melt at specific temperatures which are normally relatively unaffected by variables such as atmospheric pressure and humidity. It would appear therefore, that temperature would be the one property of a fire scene which could be estimated with considerable accuracy and certainty. However, there are practical difficulties and limitations which must be borne in mind when making such estimates. Temperatures alone are rather meaningless: it is possible for example, to melt fine copper wire (melting point 1087°C) in the flame of a match. What is of significance is the amount of heat which has been produced. The amount of heat involved can be estimated in a general way by taking into account the mass of material which has been melted. Clearly a great deal more heat is needed to melt, for example, the glass of a window than to melt a hair-fine filament of copper wire.

The position in the burning building of the melted object also affects the significance of the observation. A considerable vertical temperature gradient exists in most fires, and objects situated at a high level are likely to be subjected to considerably higher temperatures than those at floor level.

Impurities in substances, whether deliberately or accidentally introduced, often have the effect of depressing the melting point, and for this reason alloys tend to melt at temperatures lower than those of their major component.

Other materials such as glass and many plastics, do not melt at one specific temperature but progressively soften as the temperature rises (Table 1).

Glass used in buildings and for the glazing of vehicles is normally soda glass. Borosilicate glass which includes that sold under the trade name 'Pyrex' is used in applications in which its good thermal properties, (particularly its low coefficient of thermal expansion), are needed. These applications include cooking utensils, vehicle headlights, and laboratory glassware.

The final appearance of fused glass depends not only upon its composition and the temperature to which it has been raised, but also the time for which it has been subjected to the elevated temperature. The softening properties of glass are therefore said to

Table 1   BEHAVIOUR OF GLASS AT ELEVATED TEMPERATURES

	Soda glass	Borosilicate
Very slight distortion	700°C	750°C
Slight distortion	750°C	800°C
Considerable distortion and rounding of corners	800°C	850°C
Flows retaining only slight evidence of original form	850°C	900°C
Flows forming a liquid-like pool	900°C	950°C

be time/temperature dependent. The descriptions in Table 1 refer to glass samples that had been heated in a furnace for periods of 30 minutes. Glass is seldom found in totally amorphous liquid pools at actual fire scenes because as it becomes less viscous it falls to a lower and normally cooler position.

Temperature indications from plastics

Plastics can give useful indications of temperatures attained in parts of the building not directly involved in the fire. Like glass, plastics do not have sharply defined melting points but soften over a temperature range. The compositions of samples of plastic of nominally the same type may vary considerably, and the degree of cross linking, and the amount and types of plasticisers present, can all influence the softening temperatures. Table 2 should only therefore be regarded as an approximate guide.

Table 2   SOFTENING RANGES OF PLASTICS

	Degrees Celsius
Cellulose acetate	40–120
PVC rigid	60–100
Poly-(methyl methacrylate) (perspex)	60–120
PVC flexible	65– 80
Celluloid	70– 90
Polystyrene	80–110
Polyethylene low density	100–120
Polypropylene, isotactic	160–170
Polycarbonate (lexan)	200–240
Polytetrafluoroethylene (PTFE)	300–350

The softening points of samples of particular plastic objects can be tested using a hot stage microscope of the type used by Forensic Science Laboratories for the measurement of the refractive index of glass.

Temperature indications from metals
Metals and alloys melt at precise specific temperatures. It is
however, common to find half-melted objects, and this effect may
sometimes be a result of the vertical temperature gradient.
However, more commonly part of the object is either shielded
from the heat, or is in contact with another body which acts as a
heat sink.

Table 3 lists the melting points of a number of metals and
alloys. The list includes metals such as bismuth, antimony and
manganese which are unlikely to be encountered at normal fire
scenes, or to be recognised even if they were present. They are
however, included for completeness.

Table 3   MELTING POINTS OF METALS AND ALLOYS

Material	°Celsius	Comments
Tin	232	
Bismuth	268	
Lead	327	
Zinc	419	
Aluminium alloy	c.600	Depends upon composition
Antimony	632	
Magnesium	651	May ignite at its melting point
Aluminium	657	
Brass	c.900	Depends upon composition
Silver	955	In oxidising atmosphere
Silver	962	In reducing atmosphere
Bronze	c.1000	Depends upon composition
Gold	1064	
Copper	1062	In oxidising atmosphere
Copper	1087	In reducing atmosphere
Cast iron	1200–1350	Depends upon composition
Manganese	1260	
Nickel	1462	
Cobalt	1480	
Iron	1530	
Platinum	1769	
Titanium	1800	
Chromium	1830	
Tungsten	3380	Sublimes

Metal artifacts encountered in buildings are seldom constructed
of pure metal and even gold and silver are normally encountered
as alloys. One effect of the presence of an impurity in a metal is
that the melting point is lowered. If it is important to establish a
melting point exactly, a sample of the metal should be heated in
an appropriate (normally oxidising) atmosphere in a muffle

furnace. In the case of materials which do not show a time/temperature effect, such as metals, it is sufficient to simply heat the sample until it melts. In the case of materials such as glass which show time/temperature effects the sample should be heated for a period of time appropriate to the fire in question.

For most fire investigations, approximate temperature estimates to within 50°C or 100°C are normally sufficiently accurate.

Temperature estimates from tempering colours
Some metals when heated in air, form oxide layers which, under certain conditions are of an appropriate thickness to interfere with light, producing colour effects. The principle is the same as that which causes the irridescent colours observed when a thin film of oil floats on the surface of water.

The exact colour observed depends upon the thickness of oxide film, which in its turn depends upon the nature of the metal and the temperature to which it has been subjected.

Table 4 lists the temperature corresponding with observed colours for both ordinary carbon steel and a typical stainless steel.

Table 4   TEMPERING COLOURS

| Colour | Temperature °Celsius | |
	Ordinary carbon steel	Stainless steel
Yellow	230	300
Brown	260	400
Purple	280	450
Blue	310	600

Experimental verification will be required if it is necessary for the exact temperature attained to be established, because variations in the conditions will affect the final colour attained. Details of tempering colours which draw distinctions between subtle colour changes such as very pale yellow, light yellow, straw yellow and deep straw yellow involve unwarranted delusions of precision and accuracy, and should not be relied upon.

Temperature estimates from concrete and stone
Most sands, sandstones, concretes and mortars show a marked colour change from yellow to pink or reddish brown at about 300°C. The effect is probably the result of the dehydration of hydrated iron oxides present as a yellow impurity in the sand and

was first studied in detail by Bessey[1]. Other colour changes and alterations in physical properties occur with time and temperature.

Quartz undergoes a change at 573°C, the inversion temperature of the two forms α and β, and at this temperature considerable expansion occurs. This expansion causes grains of sand to rupture, weakening sandstones and making them friable.

Changes in appearance and physical properties of cements, stones and related materials are listed in Table 5.

Table 5

Changes in appearance and physical properties	°Celsius
Cements and sandstone change from grey or yellow to pink	300
Flint undergoes some shattering	500
Inversion temperature of quartz; sandstone becomes friable	573
Cement cracks and becomes friable at the higher end of the range	500–600
Many cements become grey	600+
Limestone calcines	850–900
Cement changes from grey to buff	1000
Cement sinters forming a cracked yellow surface with brown spots	1200+
The density of flint drops from 2.55–2.65 to about 2.22 due to the formation of cristobalite	1200+

It is questionable whether colour changes in concrete are of any great value in fire seat location because concrete at fire scenes is normally soot-stained, wet and of unknown composition or homogeneity.

References
(1) G. E. Bessey. The visible changes in concrete or mortar exposed to high temperatures. National Building Studies Technical Paper No. 4, Part II HMSO.

387

Appendix B(1)

Flash Points of Commonly Occurring Substances

The flash point (the lowest temperature at which an ignitable concentration of vapour is given off from a substance) may be determined by the 'open' or 'closed' cup method. Flash point has nothing to do with spontaneous ignition—a spark or small flame is required before ignition of the accumulated vapours can take place. The values most usually quoted are those found by the closed cup method, these are generally significantly lower temperatures than open cup flash points. This is because flammable vapour concentrations can build up more easily in the closed cup. The more hazardous situation where flammable solvents are concerned, exists when they reach the 'fire point' temperature at which, not just the vapour flashes but the liquid sustains burning over its surface.

Few reliable fire point values are available. All are higher than the flash points of their respective substances. The following flash points, therefore, represent the approximate minimum temperatures at which an ignition hazard exists. It must be remembered that commercial substances are seldom pure and, for accurate determination in any particular case, a sample of the suspect material should be tested.

Substance	Flash point °C	Remarks
Acetone	−20 to −9	Depending on grade
Dichloroethylene	2–4	Industrial solvent
Benzene	25.9	
Butane (LPG)	Below −30	Contains other C_4 hydrocarbons
n-Butanol	29	
n-Butyl acetate	39	Found in cellulose thinners
n-Butyl phthalate	175	Used as a plasticiser
Ethylene glycol	115	Anti freeze
Ethyl alcohol	18.9	
Di-ethyl ether	−40	Anaesthetic ether
Iso-propyl alcohol	13.9	
Methyl alcohol	18	Anti freeze additive
Methyl ethyl ketone	2	Industrial solvent
Styrene	31–37	Depends on degree of polymerisation
Toluene	4	
Petrol (motor spirit)	−45 ⎫	Approximate values only
Premium paraffin	35 ⎬	which depend on the
Gas oil	43–75 ⎭	distillation range involved

Appendix B(2)

Calorific Values of Materials

It is frequently of use to know how much heat energy is produced when a material burns or the relative amount of heat which is produced when compared with, say, wood. Such values are needed for the calculations of the expected fire resistances of rooms. Knowledge of the calorific values of materials will also help to explain fire damage patterns at a scene. From the investigators point of view, however, the rate at which the material burns has equal importance. Such values cannot be quoted with any accuracy as the physical form in which the material is encountered needs to be known. For example, coal dust suspended in air can ignite with explosive force whereas lumps of coal burn comparatively slowly.

The values quoted in the table below must be regarded as somewhat approximate in view of the variability in the test methods and the purity of the materials.

Substance	Calorific Value (MJ/Kg)
LNG (methane)	51
LPG (propane)	50
LPG (butane)	49
Petroleum motor spirit	47
Kerosene/paraffin	46
Gas oil/diesel fuel	44
Crude oil	42–45
Paraffin wax	46
Coal	23–34
Rubber	40
Timber	17–18
Ethanol	27
Dynamite (75% NG)	5
Gun powder	3
PVC	19
Polystyrene	40
Polypropylene	44
Polyethylene	46
Polyurethane	28
Polymethyl methacrylate (PMMA)	26
ABS	35

Appendix C(1)

Gas Chromatography
This technique is capable of sensitive and precise detection of materials, such as hydrocarbons, which can be vaporised or which already exist in their vaporised state.

The instrument basically comprises a tube (termed a column), either packed with a suitable finely divided absorbent material, on which a high boiling liquid (termed the stationary phase) is deposited or in which the wall of the tube itself is coated with the stationary phase. In the first case the column is termed a 'packed' column and the stationary phase would, for hydrocarbons analysis, usually be a silicone gum or heavy grease. In the second case the column would be a fine capillary column 15 m long and the same stationary phase is used. Capillary columns, which have a far higher resolution, are now used for most gas chromatography.

A continuous and closely controlled stream of gas (usually nitrogen, helium or hydrogen) passes through the column which is mounted inside an oven capable of precise temperature control over a suitably pre-programmed range and rate. Most gas chromatography is performed at temperatures up to about $200/250°C$.

The column is arranged so that one end contains an injection port into which very small liquid samples (typically about 0.1 to 0.5 µl) or, possibly, vapour or air samples (typically 1 ml) can be injected. The other end passes into a detecting chamber.

When a sample of a hydrocarbon mixture, say petrol or paraffin, is injected onto the column the sample vaporises and passes along towards the detection chamber. During its passage the component hydrocarbons separate out with smaller molecular weight substances or those having a lower boiling point (e.g. butane, pentane or hexane) moving more swiftly than those which have a larger molecular weight or a higher boiling point. As a rough guide, the larger the molecule, the more it is retarded and the separation can be likened to a miniature form of a very efficient fractional distillation plant.

As the compounds pass into the detecting chamber an electronic signal is generated which is amplified and converted into

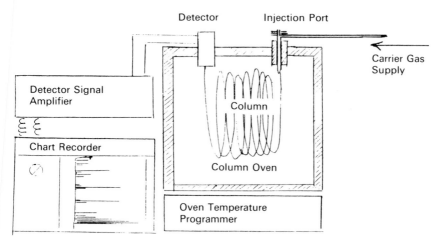

Detector   Injection Port

Carrier Gas Supply

Detector Signal Amplifier

Chart Recorder

Column

Column Oven

Oven Temperature Programmer

Figure C.1.1. Schematic Representation of Gas Chromatography.

a trace on a continuously moving chart. The trace takes the form of a series of peaks, each peak registering the presence of a compound as it enters the detector. Thus a 'fingerprint' of the mixture is shown in which the peak heights and their positions (termed the peak retention times) together characterise the substance (see Figures 23.1, 23.2, 23.3).

The detectors can be of various types depending on the type of substance to be analysed. These can be for example:—

(i) *F.I.D. (Flame ionisation detector).* In this type, an electrical potential across two electrodes placed on either side of a hydrogen flame allows a very small standing current to flow. This is due to the very small quantity of ions present in a hydrogen/oxygen flame. When a substance which contains carbon emerges from the column into the flame it burns and produces more free ions. These cause more current to flow and, therefore, an increased signal to pass from the detector, via the amplifier, to the chart. The more substance present, the greater the signal peak. This detector is one of the most frequently used for general analysis involving organic compounds.

(ii) *E.C.D. (Electron capture detector).* This detector has an electron emitting substance such as the radioactive isotope of nickel (Ni^{63}) or tritium (H^3) which allows a standing

391

current to flow across the ionised air between two electrodes. Some substances are capable of capturing free electrons; these include lead alkyls, used as anti-knock additives in petrols, or halogenated hydrocarbons, also found in fuels as scavengers in combination with the lead compounds.

When these materials pass between the electrodes they reduce the current flow and consequently reduce the detector signal. (This is the same principle as that utilised in an ionising chamber smoke detector). The change in response is amplified and fed to a chart recorder.

(iii) *F.P.D. (Flame photometric detector).* This is an ultra-violet wavelength detector which is capable of responding to the characteristic wavelengths which are emitted when sulphur or phosphorus containing substances are burnt in a hydrogen flame. Sulphur compounds are found in most fuels and provide an alternative method of comparisons between fuels to hydrocarbons analysis.

(iv) *P.I.D. (Photo-ionising detector).* This utilises the principle that many substances will ionise and thus allow an electrical current to flow when they are irradiated by ultra-violet light. Photo-ionising detectors have a response similar in sensitivity to flame ionising detectors but with the advantage of not needing hydrogen and air supplies for a flame and that the substances are not burnt and destroyed when they pass through the detector. This last is of great use if further analytical techniques are required after detection.

Portable Gas Chromatographs have been used from time to time in scene investigations. P.I.D. models obviously possess some advantages over F.I.D. models in the lack of any need for hydrogen to be carried with the equipment.

All of the above detectors are capable of response of at least nanogram (10^{-9} gm) levels and so will give results of high sensitivity.

Appendix C(2)

Curie Point Pyrolysis Wires

These wires are made from a nickel and iron alloy which is ferro-magnetic. If placed in a strong radio-frequency electro-magnetic field they will heat up to the temperature at which their ferro-magnetism changes to para-magnetism. The composition of the wire determines the temperature at which this happens; this is termed the 'Curie Point temperature' after the discoverer of the physical laws involved, Pierre Curie.

When para-magnetism is achieved no further heating takes place and the temperature drops back to the point at which ferro-magnetism is restored. Thus, an almost constant temperature predetermined by the composition of the alloy, can be achieved within a few milliseconds.

This phenomenon is utilised in a compact 'Curie Point pyrolysis' unit which fits onto the injection port of a gas chromatograph. Materials placed on a wire made out of the alloy—a 'Curie Point wire'—can be vaporised or selectively decomposed (pyrolysed) in a reproducible manner. The products pass into the chromatography column and are analysed in the manner previously described in Appendix C(1).

Activated charcoal can be stuck onto a suitable Curie Point wire and used to adsorb hydrocarbons which could be present in arson debris (see Chapter 23). By heating the wire in the Curie Point pyrolysis unit the hydrocarbons are driven off and pass onto the chromatograph column.

Appendix C(3)

Gas Chromatography/Mass Spectrometry (GC–MS)

The gas chromatographic analysis of a hydrocarbon mixture gives a 'finger-print' of a specific fuel. The pattern of peaks with their characteristic spacing and relative peak heights does not really analyse the substance, however. When there is plenty of hydrocarbon present the results may be unequivocal enough for

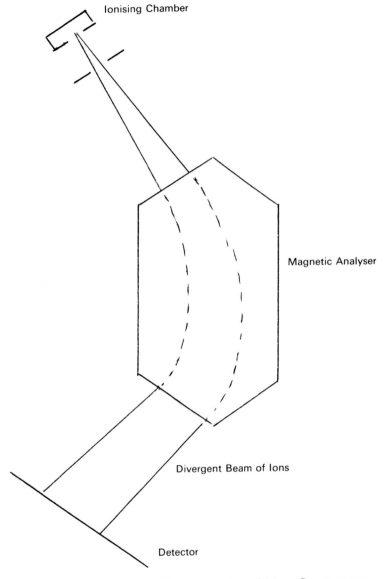

Figure C.3.1.   Schematic Representation of Mass Spectrometry.

the analyst to conclude by comparison with reference samples that, say, petrol is really present. There are occasions though when the amount of fuel is small, very degraded by evaporation or masked by unwanted background from other volatile materials. A true identification of a particular series of hydrocarbons which can be performed by a mass spectrometer will then be necessary.

Mass spectrometry is a technique whereby a molecule (which is electrically neutral) is split up either by a high electrical charge or by chemical means. The fragments of the molecule which result have an electric charge and are thus ions. Ions have mass as well as charge and can be made to travel in a curved path by the application of very high intensity electromagnetic and electrostatic fields. A detector which registers where a series of ions hits it is put into the pathway of the charged particles. Ions which have high mass are deflected by the magnetic field less than those with low mass provided that the charge is the same. In this way a 'spectrogram' which shows the separation of particles of varying mass can be built up. (See Figure C3.1). To a large extent different substances will give different and precisely calculable 'mass spectrograms' which enables the analyst to determine the original substance which was present. Tables and computerised data are available to identify specific substances by the range of particles of particular masses which are diagnostic of that substance. For instance, most straight-chain hydrocarbons break down to produce a series of ions which include those of mass 57. Aromatic hydrocarbons, such as toluene and the xylenes are also broken down to produce ions including, for toluene, mass 92 and, for xylene, mass 106. Lead alkyls (from leaded petrol) yield ions of masses 206, 207 and 208.

A gas chromatograph can be attached to a mass spectrograph and the system arranged so that as a gas chromatography peak emerges into the detector the mass spectrometer analyses it. The power of this technique is that the mass spectrometer can be tuned to look for particles of a specific mass as, for instance, those mentioned above. In this way the mass spectrometer is used as a special sensitivity detector for the gas chromatograph and unwanted background peaks can be eliminated.

Appendix C(4)

Thin Layer Chromatography

This analytical technique is very simple to do and suits non-volatile substances, such as dyes or fuel additives. It is comparatively difficult to reproduce results in subsequent analyses because of the lack of control over temperature and vapour saturation in the system. However, several analyses, can be performed simultaneously, unlike other chromatography methods.

The apparatus consists of a rigid or semi-rigid plate (usually glass or acetate film) one face of which is coated with an even layer of absorbent substance, usually silica (SiO_2) or cellulose.

The substance to be analysed is dissolved in a suitable solvent and is deposited as a small spot on a line drawn about 1 or 2 cm from the end of the plate. A line of such spots can be made, one spot for each substance to be analysed. The plate is then placed vertically in a 'developing solvent' in a sealed tank with the 'spotted' end down, taking care not to submerge the spots in the solvent. The developing solvent is usually a mixture in which the substances to be analysed are slightly soluble. If the developing solvent has been correctly chosen this now seeps by capillary action up the plate carrying the substance with it but behind the solvent front.

Mixtures of several substances will resolve into separate spots along the line of run because different compounds will move up the plate at different rates. Their final position is measured and compared with the distance that the solvent front has travelled. This ratio is expressed as the term Rf. Thus, a substance with Rf = 0.5 has run half way between the origin and the solvent front.

If coloured compounds, such as dyes, are involved the spots can be seen without further treatment, otherwise treatment by a visualising agent, which is usually sprayed on, is needed. This is a suitable chemical mixture which will react with the compound in the spot to form a coloured substance. Other visualising treatments are possible, such as ultra-violet light or heat.

An example of thin-layer chromatography can be found at the end of Chapter 23 (Laboratory Analyses). Another example is in

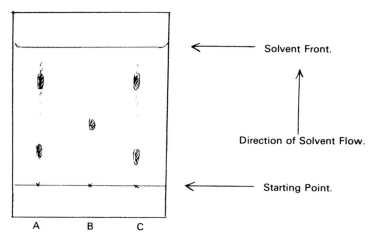

Figure C.4.1. *Thin-Layer Chromatography. Substances 'A' and 'C' have resolved into two matching spots each. Substance 'B' is different from 'A' and 'C' and produces only one spot.*

the examination of dye stuffs which are added to premium paraffins (kerosenes) in the United Kingdom. Different brands contain different dyes and thus it may be possible to determine the brand by this method independently of any hydrocarbons analysis.

Appendix D

Reasons for Suspecting Deliberate Ignition

The following list is a condensed form of the reasons discussed in Chapter 15, (Arson). They must be regarded as reasons for suspicion only and do not in themselves provide absolute proof of deliberate action.

(1) There were several seats of fire.
(2) There had been previous fires in the same building.
(3) There had been several fires in the area.
(4) The same person has been involved in several fires.
(5) The fire had spread in an unnatural way.
(6) Fire spread trailers were found.
(7) The fire was unduly fierce.
(8) A suspicious smell was detected.
(9) The seat of the fire was near to expensive equipment.
(10) Extraneous items, such as incendiary devices or containers, were found.
(11) The seat of fire was in an unusual place.
(12) There is no plausible cause for the fire.
(13) The fire occurred at an improbable time.
(14) There had been unexpected difficulties in fire fighting.
(15) Alarms or fire prevention systems were inactivated before the fire.
(16) The company had been in financial difficulties.
(17) Company records had been destroyed in an otherwise small fire.
(18) The contents of the building had been removed or substituted prior to the fire.
(19) The insurance on the premises or contents had been recently increased.
(20) No insurance claim was made following police interest in the fire.
(21) The tenant of the property has been evicted.
(22) The fire had occurred immediately before a stock taking or audit.
(23) The owner had been trying to sell or move from the property.

(24) The fire had developed shortly after the occupants had left the building.
(25) Evidence was destroyed after the fire by an interested party.
(26) The owner objects to an investigation.
(27) The person involved had been incorrectly dressed for the time of day.
(28) An interested party arrived at the scene in an unexpectedly short time.
(29) The owner behaves abnormally e.g. he was particularly calm.
(30) The owner was well prepared and unexpectedly knows details of his insurance, etc.
(31) Animals, or objects of sentimental or other value were removed prior to the fire.
(32) An interested party shows unique knowledge relating to the time or seat of the fire.
(33) There is evidence of forced entry to the building.
(34) Items have been displaced and there is evidence of a search.
(35) There is evidence of criminal damage in or near the building.
(36) There is evidence that there had been a struggle.
(37) The deceased shows no evidence of having been alive at the time of the fire.
(38) The deceased shows evidence of having been drugged or tied.
(39) The deceased shows evidence of injuries inconsistent with the fire.
(40) The building had been a particular target for vandals or political activists.
(41) The fire coincided with an important meeting or visit.
(42) Threats or warnings were received before the fire.
(43) Accusations were made after the fire.
(44) The accounts of eye witnesses were not reconcilable either with known events or with each other.

Appendix E.1

United Kingdom Sprinkler Colour Codes
The following temperatures are the nominal minimum temperatures at which a sprinkler will operate. The actual operating temperatures at a scene may vary from the quoted values because of paint, dirt or other ageing factors.

Minimum operating temperature °C	Fusible strut	Bulb
57	—	Orange
68	Uncoloured	Red
79	—	Yellow
95	White	Green
141	Blue	Blue
182	Yellow	Mauve
204	—	Black
227	Red	—

Appendix E.2

Fusing Currents for Copper Wires
As the fusing of a copper conductor by excess current depends on many factors, including time, insulation, ambient temperature, etc., the following values must be considered to be only approximate.

Diameter (mm)	Fusing current (amp)
0.05	1
0.09	2
0.115	3
0.14	4
0.160	5
0.25	10
0.4	20
0.76	50
1.14	100
1.8	200

Index

Polyurethane foams, burning
  characteristics 5, 228
  chemistry of 320–323
  smoke hazards 154
  smouldering 6, 7
Polyvinyl chloride 316
Prefire events 115
Premixed flames 298
Preternatural burning of bodies 152
Professional fire setters 249
Propane (see also L.P.G.) 305
Protective clothing 54
Proteins 327
Psychotics 259
Pyromaniacs 259
Pyrotechnics 172
P.V.C.—see polyvinyl chloride

Radiation, causing apparent fire
  seats 103
  effects of 271
  focusing of heat 230, 272
  heat transfer by 269
Radius of error 72, 77, 116
Rapid fire spread, conditions for
  226
Reconstruction of room geometry
  113
Refractive index 341
Resistance, heating effects in
  circuits 278
Revenge in arson 238
Rubber 324

Safety, collapse of building 47
  electricity 51
  explosions 52, 186, 187
  floors and stairs 49–51
  precautions 53–55
  roofs 49
  walls 47
Scenes of Crimes Officers 44
School fires 25, 252, 256, 257
Scorch marks 339
Self-heating—see Spontaneous
  ignition
Sexual abnormalities 259, 262
Ship fires 26

Smoke, effects on photographs 63
  effects of temperature 267
  estimating type of fire by 82
  fire victim's behaviour in 159
  locating seat of fire by 81
  records 138
  smouldering 225
Smouldering combustion 4, 23, 299
  effect of draughts 224, 225, 232
  recognition of 224
  urethane foams 6, 7
Sniffers, for fire accelerants 98
Soot, deposition 138
Spark ignition, energies 281
Spontaneous combustion—see
  spontaneous ignition
Spontaneous ignition 23, 232, 272,
  299, 301, 302
  by heat 232, 272
  in hay 300, 301
  tests for 274, 369
  urethane foams 322, 323
Spontaneous ignition temperature
  (SIT) 301
Sprinklers 16, 22, 37
  interference with 237
Starter canisters 206
Static electricity, fire hazards 280
  lightning 281
  spark energies 283
Stefans constant 270
Stoichiometric mixtures 296
Suicide, by fire 164
  fire following 165

Tape recorders 61
Temperature estimation 383
Tempering colours 386
Thermal conductivity, causing
  apparent fire seat 103
  coefficients of 268
Thermal expansion, coefficients of
  266
  gases 266
  liquids 266
  solids 83, 265
Thin-layer chromatography 396
Timber char, depth measurements
  93

Index